INTRODUCTION TO
THE THEORY OF PLASTICITY
FOR ENGINEERS

INTRODUCTION TO
THE THEORY OF PLASTICITY
FOR ENGINEERS

OSCAR HOFFMAN

Professor, Department of Civil Engineering
and Engineering Mechanics, Case Institute of Technology

GEORGE SACHS

Director of Metallurgical Research Institute of
Industrial Research, Syracuse University,
Syracuse, N. Y.

New York   Toronto   London
McGRAW-HILL BOOK COMPANY, INC.
1953

THE MAPLE PRESS COMPANY, YORK, PA.

PREFACE

This book is intended to be an introduction to the fundamentals as well as to the most important engineering applications of the theory of plasticity. This branch of the mechanics of continua, which is concerned with the behavior of ductile metals beyond the elastic range, has a comparatively recent history. The theory of elasticity, which deals with the behavior in the elastic range, was already in a highly advanced stage regarding its fundamental principles and applications when H. Tresca, B. de Saint-Venant, and M. Lévy, in the years between 1868 and 1875, made the first attempt to formulate an acceptable theory of plastic deformations. A period of stagnation of about 40 years followed this first significant step, until T. von Kármán and A. Haar in 1909 and R. von Mises in 1913 reopened the field and thus gave stimulus to a period of intense developments in the years following the First World War.

A few years ago the authors recognized the need for taking stock of the status of the theory of plasticity resulting from the work done during the last three decades, and for presenting its principles and significant technological applications in an easily readable and logically organized fashion. They were encouraged in their efforts by the Office of Naval Research, which sponsored part of the work leading to the present publication. The authors are grateful for the help thus received.

The fundamentals of the mechanics of continua are presented in Part I, together with the basic theories of postelastic behavior, in such detail as is necessary for a full understanding of the subsequent parts of the book. In the presentation of applications, emphasis is placed on fields in which working solutions of engineering problems are obtainable which are susceptible to comparisons with experimental results. Several classical problems involving small plastic strains, *i.e.*, of the same order as the elastic strains, are included in Parts II and III. The last chapter of Part III and all of Part IV are devoted to problems characterized by large plastic strains, and Part IV specifically to technologically important metal-forming processes.

Since this book was planned as a text for advanced engineering students as well as a reference book for practicing engineers, the authors, after many years of experience of teaching the subject, gave preference to methods of presentation that appear to be best adapted to the needs of engineers. The mathematical tools employed were chosen on the assump-

v

tion that the reader has a working knowledge of the calculus, which is nowadays an integral part of the training of engineers. The tensor concept, which is usually outside the scope of such training, is developed from the physical concepts of stress state and strain state; tensors are represented by the matrix of their nine components, and such matrices are referred to, for brevity, by boldface capital letters (*e.g.*, **S**) in analogy to the widely used boldface lower-case letter notation for vectors (*e.g.*, **s**). This symbolic notation permits condensing into a single relation a number of linear relations (nine of them in the general case) between corresponding tensor components and affords a concise formulation of stress-strain relations.

The authors are indebted to Dr. S. K. Clark of the Department of Civil Engineering and Engineering Mechanics of Case Institute of Technology for valuable assistance in the proofreading of the manuscript.

Oscar Hoffman
George Sachs

Cleveland, Ohio
Syracuse, N.Y.
January, 1953

CONTENTS

PART III.   PROBLEMS IN PLASTIC FLOW OF STRAIN-HARDENING MATERIALS

PART IV.   THEORY OF METAL-FORMING PROCESSES

NOTATION

a inner radius

b outer radius; width of beam

e base of natural logarithms

$\mathbf{e}$ irrotational relative displacement vector

f coefficient of friction

$\mathbf{f}$ force vector

h depth of beam; thickness of strip

k constant in stress-strain relations

$\mathbf{l}$ position vector

m strain-hardening exponent

$\mathbf{n}$ unit normal vector

r radial distance

$\mathbf{s}$ stress vector

t time

u_x, u_y, u_z components of displacement

w parameter in theory of rolling

x, y, z cartesian coordinates

A area; constant in stress-strain relations; constant in theory of rolling

B constant in stress-strain relations; constant in theory of wire drawing

C integration constant

D density; diameter of wire or rod

E Young's modulus

$\mathbf{E}$ strain tensor

F stress function; draw force

G shear modulus

I_1, I_2, I_3 invariants of stress tensor

J_1, J_2, J_3 invariants of strain tensor

K bulk modulus

L length of plate

M bending moment

P axial load on column

R radius; reduction in area

S die spacing in tandem drawing

$\mathbf{S}$ stress tensor

T torque

U elastic strain energy per unit volume

W plastic work of deformation per unit volume

γ (conventional) shearing strain

$\bar{\gamma}$ logarithmic shearing strain

$\gamma_{xy}, \gamma_{yz}, \gamma_{zx}$ shearing-strain components in rectangular coordinates

γ_{oct} octahedral shearing strain

ϵ (conventional) linear strain

$\bar{\epsilon}$ logarithmic linear strain

xiii

$\epsilon_x, \epsilon_y, \epsilon_z$ linear strains in rectangular coordinates

$\epsilon_1, \epsilon_2, \epsilon_3$ principal strains

$\epsilon_I, \epsilon_{II}, \epsilon_{III}$ major, intermediate, minor principal strain

ϵ_m mean strain

ϵ_{oct} octahedral linear strain

ϑ angle of twist per unit length

λ coefficient in Saint-Venant's law of plastic flow

μ coefficient of viscosity; Lode's stress parameter

ν Poisson's ratio; Lode's strain parameter

ρ radius of plastic front

$\sigma_x, \sigma_y, \sigma_z$ normal stresses in rectangular coordinates

$\sigma_1, \sigma_2, \sigma_3$ principal stresses

$\sigma_I, \sigma_{II}, \sigma_{III}$ major, intermediate, minor principal stress

σ_m mean stress

σ_{oct} octahedral normal stress

σ_0 yield stress in tension

$\tau_{xy}, \tau_{yz}, \tau_{zz}$ shearing stress components in rectangular coordinates

τ_{oct} octahedral shearing stress

φ angle of friction ($\tan^{-1} f$)

ω angular velocity

Δ (conventional) volume strain

$\overline{\Delta}$ logarithmic volume strain

Part I

BASIC LAWS AND THEORIES

CHAPTER 1

STATE OF STRESS

The relationships presented in this chapter characterize the equilibrium of continuous media; they are developed and represented with a view toward their later application to the mechanics of plastic bodies, but their validity is general and by no means limited by the specific mechanical properties of the medium.

1.1. Stress at a Point

In consistency with engineering usage, the term "stress" will be used here to signify the intensity of internal forces acting between particles of a body across imaginary internal surfaces.

Consider a point in the interior of the body and imagine it surrounded by a very small closed surface; each plane element of this surface, dA, is acted upon by a force $d\mathbf{f}$ or by a stress, *i.e.*, force per unit area, of the amount $d\mathbf{f}/dA$.

A homogeneous state of stress will be assumed hereafter, defined by the property that the stress is independent of the shape and actual size of the plane element dA and of its assumedly small distance from the given point; but it depends upon the orientation of the plane element, defined by the unit vector $\mathbf{n}$ normal to it and pointing away from the closed surface that surrounds the point. The state of stress at a point is known when for any given unit vector $\mathbf{n}$ the corresponding stress vector

$$\mathbf{s}_n = \frac{d\mathbf{f}}{dA}$$

is also known. The subscript n indicates the dependence of the stress upon the direction of $\mathbf{n}$.

In a system of cartesian coordinate axes x, y, z, the components of $\mathbf{n}$ are

$$n_x = \cos(n,x)$$
$$n_y = \cos(n,y)$$
$$n_z = \cos(n,z)$$

where (n,x) is the angle between the vector $\mathbf{n}$ and the x axis, etc.; and the components of $\mathbf{s}_n$ are

$$s_{nx}$$
$$s_{ny}$$
$$s_{nz}$$

3

According to the system of notation used here, symbols of cartesian stress components have two subscripts: the first of them indicates the direction normal to the plane element acted upon by the stress; the second identifies the direction of the component. In addition, specialized notations are used whenever the unit vector **n** coincides with one of the three cartesian axes; then, the normal components of stress are indicated with the letter σ and the subscript is used only once; the tangential components are indicated with the letter τ. Figure 1.1 shows a small rectangular parallelepiped, with the faces perpendicular to the x, y, z axes, and the stress components acting on the near faces. Homogeneity of the state of stress requires that the far faces be acted upon by stress components equal and opposite to those acting on the corresponding near faces.

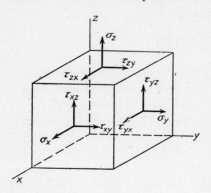

FIG. 1.1. Components of stresses on a volume element.

The following table shows the correspondence between the two systems of notation:

Direction of **n**:	x	y	z
x components:	$s_{xx} \equiv \sigma_x$	$s_{yx} \equiv \tau_{yx}$	$s_{zx} \equiv \tau_{zx}$
y components:	$s_{xy} \equiv \tau_{xy}$	$s_{yy} \equiv \sigma_y$	$s_{zy} \equiv \tau_{zy}$
z components:	$s_{xz} \equiv \tau_{xz}$	$s_{yz} \equiv \tau_{yz}$	$s_{zz} \equiv \sigma_z$

The above-tabulated nine components represent the least number of data which describe the stress on a closed surface surrounding a point. It will be shown next that, given the values of such nine components, the stress s_n can be calculated for any orientation of the surface, $i.e.$, for any unit vector **n**. For this purpose consider a very small volume element, surrounding the point in question and having the shape of a tetrahedron with three faces perpendicular to the coordinate axes and the fourth normal to the given unit vector **n** (see Fig. 1.2). The laws of statics applied to the equilibrium of this volume element furnish three equations expressing the equilibrium of the x, y, z components, respectively,

$$s_{nx}A_{ABC} - \sigma_x A_{OBC} - \tau_{yx}A_{OAC} - \tau_{zx}A_{OAB} = 0$$
$$s_{ny}A_{ABC} - \tau_{xy}A_{OBC} - \sigma_y A_{OAC} - \tau_{zy}A_{OAB} = 0 \qquad (1.1)$$
$$s_{nz}A_{ABC} - \tau_{xz}A_{OBC} - \tau_{yz}A_{OAC} - \sigma_z A_{OAB} = 0$$

where A_{ABC} = area of triangle ABC

A_{OBC} = area of triangle OBC = $A_{ABC} \cos (n,x)$

A_{OAC} = area of triangle OAC = $A_{ABC} \cos (n,y)$

A_{OAB} = area of triangle OAB = $A_{ABC} \cos (n,z)$

By substituting these expressions for A_{OBC}, A_{OAC}, and A_{OAB} and simplifying, Eqs. (1.1) furnish the components of the stress acting on the plane element normal to **n**:

$$s_{nx} = \sigma_x \cos (n,x) + \tau_{yx} \cos (n,y) + \tau_{zx} \cos (n,z)$$
$$s_{ny} = \tau_{xy} \cos (n,x) + \sigma_y \cos (n,y) + \tau_{zy} \cos (n,z) \qquad (1.2)$$
$$s_{nz} = \tau_{xz} \cos (n,x) + \tau_{yz} \cos (n,y) + \sigma_z \cos (n,z)$$

Three additional equilibrium equations can be written for the stresses acting on the volume element shown in Fig. 1.1, expressing that the

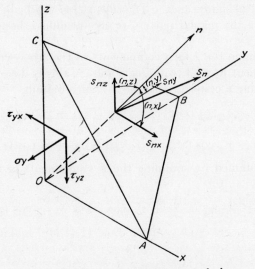

FIG. 1.2. Stresses on an elementary tetrahedron.

moment of all forces about the three coordinate axes vanishes. Thus the following three known relations are obtained:

$$\tau_{xy} = \tau_{yx}$$
$$\tau_{yz} = \tau_{zy} \qquad (1.3)$$
$$\tau_{zx} = \tau_{xz}$$

In conclusion, the state of stress at a point is defined when the six quantities σ_x, σ_y, σ_z, τ_{xy}, τ_{yz}, τ_{zx} are known.

1.2. Stress Tensor

The three linear equations (1.2) represent a transformation that furnishes for any given vector **n** another vector, s_n; the nine coefficients of

Eqs. (1.2) form a mathematical entity called a tensor, and in this case, by virtue of Eqs. (1.3), a symmetric tensor. The coefficients σ_x . . . τ_{xy} . . . are the so-called components of the stress tensor, the values of which depend on the selection of the reference frame.

It is convenient to represent tensors by a single (bold-faced) letter symbol or, more explicitly, by the matrix of the components; accordingly, any one of the following notations will be adopted for the stress tensor:

$$\mathbf{S} = \begin{pmatrix} \sigma_x & \tau_{xy} & \tau_{zx} \\ \tau_{xy} & \sigma_y & \tau_{yz} \\ \tau_{zx} & \tau_{yz} & \sigma_z \end{pmatrix}$$

Changing from a system of axes x, y, z to another, x', y', z', the components assume new values that can be calculated in two steps, by recalling their physical significance. The calculation will be limited to $\sigma_{x'}$ and $\tau_{x'y'}$; in view of the regular pattern of the formulas, these two examples should suffice.

First, determine the x, y, z components of the stress vector acting on the plane element normal to the new axis x'; this is done by using Eqs. (1.2) and making $\mathbf{n}$ coincide with the x' axis, obtaining

$$s_{x'x} = \sigma_x \cos (x',x) + \tau_{xy} \cos (x',y) + \tau_{zx} \cos (x',z)$$
$$s_{x'y} = \tau_{xy} \cos (x',x) + \sigma_y \cos (x',y) + \tau_{yz} \cos (x',z) \qquad (1.4)$$
$$s_{x'z} = \tau_{zx} \cos (x',x) + \tau_{yz} \cos (x',y) + \sigma_z \cos (x',z)$$

$\sigma_{x'} \equiv s_{x'x'}$ is obtained by summing the x' components of $s_{x'x}$, $s_{x'y}$, $s_{x'z}$ as follows:

$$\sigma_{x'} = s_{x'x} \cos (x',x) + s_{x'y} \cos (x',y) + s_{x'z} \cos (x',z)$$

Substituting $s_{x'x}$, $s_{x'y}$, and $s_{x'z}$ from Eqs. (1.4) and making use of Eqs. (1.3), one obtains

$$\sigma_{x'} = \sigma_x \cos^2 (x',x) + \sigma_y \cos^2 (x',y) + \sigma_z \cos^2 (x',z)$$
$$+ 2\tau_{xy} \cos (x',x) \cos (x',y) + 2\tau_{yz} \cos (x',y) \cos (x',z)$$
$$+ 2\tau_{zx} \cos (x',z) \cos (x',x) \quad (1.5)$$

$\tau_{x'y'}$ is obtained similarly by summing the y' components of $s_{x'x}$, $s_{x'y}$, $s_{x'z}$ as follows:

$$\tau_{x'y'} = \sigma_x \cos (x',x) \cos (y',x) + \sigma_y \cos (x',y) \cos (y',y)$$
$$+ \sigma_z \cos (x',z) \cos (y',z) + \tau_{xy}[\cos (x',x) \cos (y',y) + \cos (x',y) \cos (y',x)]$$
$$+ \tau_{yz}[\cos (x',y) \cos (y',z) + \cos (x',z) \cos (y',y)]$$
$$+ \tau_{zx}[\cos (x',z) \cos (y',x) + \cos (x',x) \cos (y',z)] \quad (1.6)$$

The transformation equations for the other components of the stress tensor follow an entirely analogous pattern and need not be shown here.

1.3. Principal Stresses

In order to visualize certain important features of the state of stress, the variation of the normal component σ_n of the stress vector $\mathbf{s}_n$ will be represented graphically as a function for the variable direction of $\mathbf{n}$.

From Eq. (1.5) the expression for σ_n is obtained by replacing x' by n.

$$\sigma_n = \sigma_x \cos^2 (n,x) + \sigma_y \cos^2 (n,y) + \sigma_z \cos^2 (n,z)$$
$$+ 2\tau_{xy} \cos (n,x) \cos (n,y) + 2\tau_{yz} \cos (n,y) \cos (n,z)$$
$$+ 2\tau_{zx} \cos (n,z) \cos (n,x) \quad (1.7)$$

For each vector $\mathbf{n}$ define another vector having the same direction but the length equal to $1/\sqrt{|\sigma_n|}$; the end point of such a vector has the cartesian coordinates

$$x = \frac{\cos (n,x)}{\sqrt{|\sigma_n|}}$$

$$y = \frac{\cos (n,y)}{\sqrt{|\sigma_n|}} \quad (1.8)$$

$$z = \frac{\cos (n,z)}{\sqrt{|\sigma_n|}}$$

and it lies on a surface the equation of which is obtained from (1.7) by dividing both sides by $|\sigma_n|$ and substituting the values $\cos (n,x)/\sqrt{|\sigma_n|}$ etc., from Eqs. (1.8).

$$\pm 1 = \sigma_x x^2 + \sigma_y y^2 + \sigma_z z^2 + 2\tau_{xy} xy + 2\tau_{yz} yz + 2\tau_{zx} zx \quad (1.9)$$

This is the equation of a surface of second degree, the so-called "stress-quadric." From the rules given above for its construction it follows that Eq. (1.9) defines the same surface regardless of the orientation of the x, y, z axes, while the coefficients σ_x . . . etc., depend upon such orientation. It is known from the theory of quadrics that there is always an orthogonal system of axes such that the coefficients of the bilinear terms on the right side of Eq. (1.9) vanish. These are the so-called principal axes of stress; the plane elements normal to them, the principal planes of stress, are acted upon only by normal stresses, the so-called "principal stresses," henceforth denoted by σ_i ($i = 1, 2, 3$). The fact that the principal stresses are normal stresses permits writing a set of three equations for each principal stress, stating that the cartesian components s_{ix}, s_{iy}, and s_{iz}, expressed by Eqs. (1.2), are equal to the respective cartesian components of σ_i:

$$\sigma_x \cos (i,x) + \tau_{xy} \cos (i,y) + \tau_{zx} \cos (i,z) = \sigma_i \cos (i, x)$$
$$\tau_{xy} \cos (i,x) + \sigma_y \cos (i,y) + \tau_{yz} \cos (i,z) = \sigma_i \cos (i,y)$$
$$\tau_{zx} \cos (i,x) + \tau_{yz} \cos (i,y) + \sigma_z \cos (i,z) = \sigma_i \cos (i,z)$$

or, transposing and rearranging terms,

$$(\sigma_x - \sigma_i) \cos(i,x) + \tau_{xy} \cos(i,y) + \tau_{zx} \cos(i,z) = 0$$
$$\tau_{xy} \cos(i,x) + (\sigma_y - \sigma_i) \cos(i,y) + \tau_{yz} \cos(i,z) = 0 \quad (1.10)$$
$$\tau_{zx} \cos(i,x) + \tau_{yz} \cos(i,y) + (\sigma_z - \sigma_i) \cos(i,z) = 0$$

This is a system of homogeneous linear equations that combined with the known relation

$$\cos^2(i,x) + \cos^2(i,y) + \cos^2(i,z) = 1 \quad (1.11)$$

can be solved for the unknown direction cosines. The trivial solution of Eqs. (1.10), $\cos(i,x) = \cos(i,y) = \cos(i,z) = 0$ would violate Eq. (1.11); hence, it can be ruled out. Other than trivial solutions can exist only if the determinant of the coefficients of Eqs. (1.10) vanishes, or

$$\begin{vmatrix} \sigma_x - \sigma_i & \tau_{xy} & \tau_{zx} \\ \tau_{xy} & \sigma_y - \sigma_i & \tau_{yz} \\ \tau_{zx} & \tau_{yz} & \sigma_z - \sigma_i \end{vmatrix} = \sigma_i^3 - (\sigma_x + \sigma_y + \sigma_z)\sigma_i^2$$
$$+ (\sigma_x\sigma_y + \sigma_y\sigma_z + \sigma_z\sigma_x - \tau_{xy}^2 - \tau_{yz}^2 - \tau_{zx}^2)\sigma_i - \sigma_x\sigma_y\sigma_z$$
$$- 2\tau_{xy}\tau_{yz}\tau_{zx} + \sigma_x\tau_{yz}^2 + \sigma_y\tau_{zx}^2 + \sigma_z\tau_{xy}^2 = 0 \quad (1.12)$$

This is a cubic equation the three roots of which are the three principal stresses.

By using the principal directions as reference axes, the matrix of the stress tensor will be written as

$$S = \begin{pmatrix} \sigma_1 & 0 & 0 \\ 0 & \sigma_2 & 0 \\ 0 & 0 & \sigma_3 \end{pmatrix}$$

and Eqs. (1.2) become

$$s_{n1} = \sigma_1 \cos(n,1)$$
$$s_{n2} = \sigma_2 \cos(n,2) \quad (1.13)$$
$$s_{n3} = \sigma_3 \cos(n,3)$$

Heretofore, the subscripts 1, 2, 3 were assigned arbitrarily to the three principal stresses. Sometimes the subscripts are selected to indicate their relative magnitudes; roman numerals will be used for this purpose, as follows:

$$\sigma_{\mathrm{I}} \geq \sigma_{\mathrm{II}} \geq \sigma_{\mathrm{III}}$$

Recalling known properties of the stress quadric, it can be seen that σ_{I} is the largest normal stress, σ_{III} the smallest normal stress for all possible orientations of the plane element.

Furthermore, if two principal stresses are equal, for example, $\sigma_1 = \sigma_2$, the stress quadric becomes a surface of revolution, with the third principal direction, in this example the direction "3," being the axis of revolution.

Hence, all directions normal to direction "3" are principal directions, and the corresponding principal stresses are all equal to $\sigma_1 = \sigma_2$ ("cylindrical" state of stress).

Finally, if all three principal stresses are equal, $\sigma_1 = \sigma_2 = \sigma_3$, the stress quadric becomes a sphere, and all directions in the space are principal directions with identical principal stress values ("spherical" or "hydrostatic" state of stress).

Figure 1.3 illustrates that the general state of stress ($\sigma_1 \neq \sigma_2 \neq \sigma_3$) can be represented by normal stresses acting on an infinitesimal rectan-

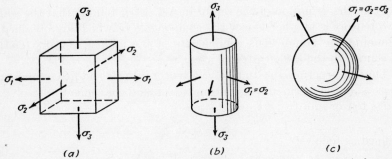

(a)   (b)   (c)

FIG. 1.3. (a) Triaxial state of stress; (b) cylindrical state of stress; (c) spherical state of stress.

gular parallelepiped; the "cylindrical" state of stress by normal stresses on an infinitesimal circular cylinder; the "spherical" state of stress by normal stresses on an infinitesimal sphere.

1.4. Invariants of the Stress Tensor

For a given state of stress, the cubic equation (1.12) furnishes the same principal stresses, regardless of the assumed cartesian reference frame; this requires that the coefficients of the second, first, and zero degree terms be independent of the selection of such a reference frame. The three coefficients are the so-called invariants of the stress tensor and are denoted as follows:

$$
\begin{aligned}
I_1 &= \sigma_x + \sigma_y + \sigma_z \\
I_2 &= \sigma_x\sigma_y + \sigma_y\sigma_z + \sigma_z\sigma_x - \tau_{xy}{}^2 - \tau_{yz}{}^2 - \tau_{zx}{}^2 \\
I_3 &= \sigma_x\sigma_y\sigma_z + 2\tau_{xy}\tau_{yz}\tau_{zx} - \sigma_x\tau_{yz}{}^2 - \sigma_y\tau_{zx}{}^2 - \sigma_z\tau_{xy}{}^2
\end{aligned} \tag{1.14}
$$

The same values can be obtained by using the principal axes as a reference frame.

$$
\begin{aligned}
I_1 &= \sigma_1 + \sigma_2 + \sigma_3 \\
I_2 &= \sigma_1\sigma_2 + \sigma_2\sigma_3 + \sigma_3\sigma_1 \\
I_3 &= \sigma_1\sigma_2\sigma_3
\end{aligned} \tag{1.15}
$$

Thus, Eq. (1.12) can be written as follows:

$$\sigma_i{}^3 - I_1\sigma_i{}^2 + I_2\sigma_i - I_3 = 0 \tag{1.16}$$

Introducing the "mean stress" σ_m, defined by the expressions

$$\sigma_m = \frac{\sigma_x + \sigma_y + \sigma_z}{3} = \frac{\sigma_1 + \sigma_2 + \sigma_3}{3} \tag{1.17}$$

the first invariant becomes

$$I_1 = 3\sigma_m \tag{1.18}$$

1.5. Spherical and Deviator Stress Tensors

From the definition of the tensor in Art. 1.2 it follows that the sum of two tensors is another tensor the components of which are obtained by summing the homologous components of the addend tensors referred, of course, to the same cartesian axes.

Thus, it is permissible to resolve a tensor into two additive component tensors; in the mechanics of continua it is found convenient to resolve the stress tensor into two component tensors:

$$\mathbf{S} = \mathbf{S}' + \mathbf{S}''$$

defined as follows:

$$\mathbf{S}'' = \begin{pmatrix} \sigma_m & 0 & 0 \\ 0 & \sigma_m & 0 \\ 0 & 0 & \sigma_m \end{pmatrix} \tag{1.19}$$

is the "spherical stress tensor" that represents a spherical state of stress with the principal stress σ_m;

$$\mathbf{S}' = \mathbf{S} - \mathbf{S}''$$

is the "deviator stress tensor" the matrix of which, with reference to arbitrary axes, is

$$\mathbf{S}' = \begin{pmatrix} \dfrac{2\sigma_x - \sigma_y - \sigma_z}{3} & \tau_{xy} & \tau_{zx} \\[2ex] \tau_{xy} & \dfrac{2\sigma_y - \sigma_z - \sigma_x}{3} & \tau_{yz} \\[2ex] \tau_{zx} & \tau_{yz} & \dfrac{2\sigma_z - \sigma_x - \sigma_y}{3} \end{pmatrix} \tag{1.20}$$

or, with reference to the three principal axes,

$$\mathbf{S}' = \begin{pmatrix} \dfrac{2\sigma_1 - \sigma_2 - \sigma_3}{3} & 0 & 0 \\[2ex] 0 & \dfrac{2\sigma_2 - \sigma_3 - \sigma_1}{3} & 0 \\[2ex] 0 & 0 & \dfrac{2\sigma_3 - \sigma_1 - \sigma_2}{3} \end{pmatrix} \tag{1.21}$$

By applying the general equations (1.15), the invariants of the spherical stress tensor are obtained as follows:

$$I_1'' = I_1 = 3\sigma_m$$

$$I_2'' = \frac{I_1^2}{3} = 3\sigma_m{}^2 \qquad (1.22)$$

$$I_3'' = \frac{I_1^3}{27} = \sigma_m{}^3$$

and the invariants of the deviator stress tensor are

$$I_1' = 0$$

$$I_2' = I_2 - \frac{I_1^2}{3} = -\frac{1}{6}\left[(\sigma_1 - \sigma_2)^2 + (\sigma_2 - \sigma_3)^2 + (\sigma_3 - \sigma_1)^2\right]$$

$$I_3' = I_3 - \frac{I_1 I_2}{3} + \frac{2}{27} I_1^3 \qquad (1.23)$$

$$= \frac{1}{27}\left[(2\sigma_1 - \sigma_2 - \sigma_3)(2\sigma_2 - \sigma_3 - \sigma_1)(2\sigma_3 - \sigma_1 - \sigma_2)\right]$$

1.6. Mohr's Representation of the State of Stress

In the preceding articles, cartesian components were used to define the stress vector. In the study of the mechanical behavior of materials beyond the elastic range, an alternate approach becomes significant, in which the stress vector is resolved into a normal component σ_n in the direction of the unit vector **n**, normal to the plane element, and into a so-called tangential (or shearing) component τ_n lying in the plane element itself.

The relation

$$s_n{}^2 = \sigma_n{}^2 + \tau_n{}^2 \qquad (1.24)$$

exists between the two components and s_n, a scalar, the magnitude of the stress vector $\mathbf{s}_n$ (see Fig. 1.4).

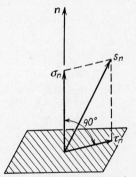

FIG. 1.4. Normal and shearing component of stress.

The Mohr diagram proposes to represent the totality of stress vectors pertaining to all possible plane-element orientations by considering σ_n and τ_n as coordinates of points in the so-called "stress plane" and plotting loci of such points for various assumptions concerning the orientation of the plane element.

Assume that the state of stress is given by the three principal stresses σ_1, σ_2, σ_3 and by the known orientation of the principal axes. Equation

(1.5) furnishes σ_n by making coincide the x, y, z axes with the "1," "2," "3" principal axes and the x' axis with the direction of n as follows:

$$\sigma_n = \sigma_1 \cos^2 (n,1) + \sigma_2 \cos^2 (n,2) + \sigma_3 \cos^2 (n,3) \qquad (1.25)$$

The cartesian components of the stress vector $\mathbf{s}_n$ are, according to Eqs. (1.13),

$$s_{n1} = \sigma_1 \cos (n,1)$$
$$s_{n2} = \sigma_2 \cos (n,2)$$
$$s_{n3} = \sigma_3 \cos (n,3)$$

hence,

$$
\begin{aligned}
s_n{}^2 &= s_{n1}{}^2 + s_{n2}{}^2 + s_{n3}{}^2 \\
&= \sigma_1{}^2 \cos^2 (n,1) + \sigma_2{}^2 \cos^2 (n,2) + \sigma_3{}^2 \cos^2 (n,3) \quad (1.26)
\end{aligned}
$$

and, recalling Eq. (1.24),

$$\sigma_n{}^2 + \tau_n{}^2 = \sigma_1{}^2 \cos^2 (n,1) + \sigma_2{}^2 \cos^2 (n,2) + \sigma_3{}^2 \cos^2 (n,3) \quad (1.27)$$

Equations (1.25) and (1.27) together with Eq. (1.11) form a linear non-homogeneous system in terms of $\cos^2 (n,1)$, $\cos^2 (n,2)$, and $\cos^2 (n,3)$, the solution of which gives

$$
\begin{aligned}
\cos^2 (n,1) &= \frac{\sigma_n{}^2 + \tau_n{}^2 - \sigma_n(\sigma_2 + \sigma_3) + \sigma_2\sigma_3}{(\sigma_2 - \sigma_1)(\sigma_3 - \sigma_1)} \\
\cos^2 (n,2) &= \frac{\sigma_n{}^2 + \tau_n{}^2 - \sigma_n(\sigma_3 + \sigma_1) + \sigma_3\sigma_1}{(\sigma_3 - \sigma_2)(\sigma_1 - \sigma_2)} \\
\cos^2 (n,3) &= \frac{\sigma_n{}^2 + \tau_n{}^2 - \sigma_n(\sigma_1 + \sigma_2) + \sigma_1\sigma_2}{(\sigma_1 - \sigma_3)(\sigma_2 - \sigma_3)}
\end{aligned}
\qquad (1.28)
$$

These equations can be rearranged and written as follows:

$$\left(\frac{\sigma_2 + \sigma_3}{2}\right)^2 + (\sigma_2 - \sigma_1)(\sigma_3 - \sigma_1) \cos^2 (n,1) - \sigma_2\sigma_3$$
$$= \tau_n{}^2 + \left(\sigma_n - \frac{\sigma_2 + \sigma_3}{2}\right)^2$$

$$\left(\frac{\sigma_3 + \sigma_1}{2}\right)^2 + (\sigma_3 - \sigma_2)(\sigma_1 - \sigma_2) \cos^2 (n,2) - \sigma_3\sigma_1$$
$$= \tau_n{}^2 + \left(\sigma_n - \frac{\sigma_3 + \sigma_1}{2}\right)^2 \qquad (1.29)$$

$$\left(\frac{\sigma_1 + \sigma_2}{2}\right)^2 + (\sigma_1 - \sigma_3)(\sigma_2 - \sigma_3) \cos^2 (n,3) - \sigma_1\sigma_2$$
$$= \tau_n{}^2 + \left(\sigma_n - \frac{\sigma_1 + \sigma_2}{2}\right)^2$$

The first of these equations defines a circle as the locus of the (σ_n, τ_n) points for a given value of $(n,1)$; and similarly the other two equations define circles for constant values of $(n,2)$ and $(n,3)$, respectively.

Given a plane element by means of the three angles $(n,1)$, $(n,2)$, $(n,3)$, the corresponding σ_n and τ_n components are obtained graphically as coordinates of the common point of intersection of the three circles represented by Eqs. (1.29). Assuming, for instance, a value for the angle $(n,1)$, one obtains the equation of a circle with its center on

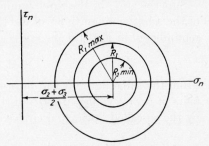

Fig. 1.5. Graphical representation of states of stress corresponding to constant $(n,1)$ angles.

the σ_n axis at distance $(\sigma_2 + \sigma_3)/2$ from the origin and with the radius (see Fig. 1.5)

$$R_1 = \sqrt{\left(\frac{\sigma_2 + \sigma_3}{2}\right)^2 + (\sigma_2 - \sigma_1)(\sigma_3 - \sigma_1)\cos^2(n,1) - \sigma_2\sigma_3}$$

By varying the angle $(n,1)$, one obtains concentric circles of various radii; to $(n,1) = 0$ corresponds the largest radius:

$$R_{1\,\text{max}} = \sigma_1 - \frac{\sigma_2 + \sigma_3}{2}$$

and to $(n,1) = \pi/2$ corresponds the smallest radius:

$$R_{1\,\text{min}} = \frac{\sigma_2 - \sigma_3}{2}$$

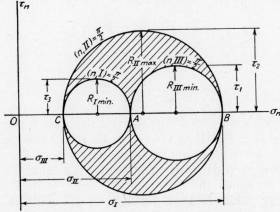

Fig. 1.6. Mohr's diagram for the state of stress.

Analogous relations apply to circles corresponding to constant $(n,2)$ and $(n,3)$ angles.

Superposition of the three families of circles requires the consideration of the relative magnitudes of the three principal stresses; hence, they are renumbered in Fig. 1.6 according to the ordering rule

$$\sigma_{\mathrm{I}} \geq \sigma_{\mathrm{II}} \geq \sigma_{\mathrm{III}}$$

From the same figure it can be seen that all points representing possible pairs of (σ_n, τ_n) values are within the shaded curvilinear triangle bounded by the so-called "principal circles."

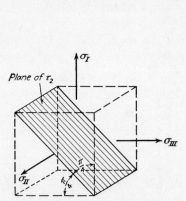

FIG. 1.7. Plane of maximum shearing stress.

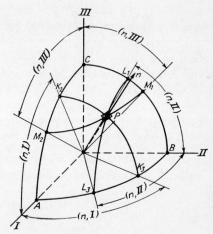

FIG. 1.8. Circles of constant (n,I), (n,II), and (n,III) on spherical volume element.

The tangential stress τ_n reaches three relative maxima, the so-called "principal shearing stresses"

$$\tau_1 = \frac{\sigma_{\mathrm{II}} - \sigma_{\mathrm{III}}}{2}$$

$$\tau_2 = \frac{\sigma_{\mathrm{I}} - \sigma_{\mathrm{III}}}{2} \qquad (1.30)$$

$$\tau_3 = \frac{\sigma_{\mathrm{I}} - \sigma_{\mathrm{II}}}{2}$$

$\tau_2 = \tau_{\max}$ is the absolute maximum shearing stress and is acting on a plane defined by $(n,\mathrm{I}) = (n,\mathrm{III}) = \pi/4$ and $(n,\mathrm{II}) = \pi/2$ (see Fig. 1.7).

Figure 1.8 shows an octant of a spherical volume element with the circles of constant (n,I), (n,II), and (n,III) through a given plane element; Fig. 1.9 shows the corresponding circles in the Mohr diagram. Corresponding points in Figs. 1.8 and 1.9 are given the same letter symbols.

The spherical stress tensor is represented in the Mohr diagram by a point (a circle with zero radius) on the σ_n axis at distance σ_m from the origin. The representation of the deviator stress tensor is obtained

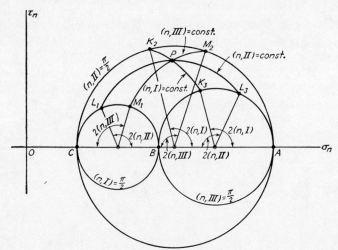

FIG. 1.9. Circles of constant (n,I), (n,II), and (n,III) in Mohr's diagram.

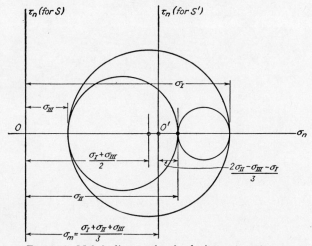

FIG. 1.10. Mohr's diagram for the deviator stress tensor.

from that of the given stress tensor by shifting the τ_n axis by σ_m (see Fig. 1.10).

1.7. Octahedral Stresses

The use of the invariants of the stress tensor can offer advantages by providing the possibility of reducing the number of significant parameters necessary to represent the state of stress in the study of plastic phenomena. The same purpose is served by the introduction of the octahedral stresses which, as it will be shown, are in close relationship with the invariants of the stress tensor.

Consider an octahedral volume element formed by eight plane elements, the normal vector **n** of which makes the same angles with the three principal directions:

$$(n,1) = (n,2) = (n,3) = 54°44'$$

so that

$$\cos (n,1) = \cos (n,2) = \cos (n,3) = \frac{1}{\sqrt{3}}$$

The so-called "octahedral normal stress" acting on each face of the octa-

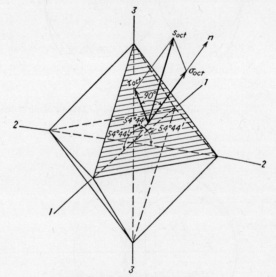

FIG. 1.11. Octahedral stresses.

hedron is then, from Eq. (1.25),

$$\sigma_{oct} = \sigma_1 \cos^2 (n,1) + \sigma_2 \cos^2 (n,2) + \sigma_3 \cos^2 (n,3) = \frac{\sigma_1 + \sigma_2 + \sigma_3}{3} = \sigma_m$$

$$(1.31)$$

while the "octahedral shearing stress" is to be calculated from the relation (see Fig. 1.11)

$$s_{oct}^2 = \sigma_{oct}^2 + \tau_{oct}^2 \tag{1.32}$$

where s_{oct} is the magnitude of the octahedral stress vector. From Eq. (1.26) one obtains

$$s_{oct}^2 = \sigma_1^2 \cos^2 (n,1) + \sigma_2^2 \cos^2 (n,2) + \sigma_3^2 \cos^2 (n,3) = \frac{\sigma_1^2 + \sigma_2^2 + \sigma_3^2}{3}$$

hence,

$$\tau_{oct} = \sqrt{s_{oct}^2 - \sigma_{oct}^2} = \frac{1}{3}\sqrt{(\sigma_1 - \sigma_2)^2 + (\sigma_2 - \sigma_3)^2 + (\sigma_3 - \sigma_1)^2}$$

$$= \sqrt{\frac{2}{3}}\sqrt{\frac{I_1^2}{3} - I_2} = \sqrt{-\frac{2}{3}I_2'} \qquad (1.33)$$

Another invariantive parameter of the state of stress is occasionally used with advantage, the so-called "effective stress" defined by

$$\sigma_{eff} = \frac{3}{\sqrt{2}}\tau_{oct} = \frac{\sqrt{2}}{2}\sqrt{(\sigma_1 - \sigma_2)^2 + (\sigma_2 - \sigma_3)^2 + (\sigma_3 - \sigma_1)^2}$$

$$= \sqrt{I_1^2 - 3I_2} \qquad (1.34)$$

While the "effective stress" cannot be visualized as acting on a specified plane element, as can the octahedral stresses, it has the advantage that in case of a uniaxial state of stress $\sigma_1 \neq 0$, $\sigma_2 = \sigma_3 = 0$, as occurs, for example, in simple tension, it becomes equal to the nonvanishing principal stress σ_1.

1.8. First Special Case: The Uniaxial State of Stress

The uniaxial state of stress exists when two principal stresses are zero, for example, σ_2 and σ_3, and the remaining principal stress σ_1 represents the intensity of a state of pure tension or pure compression. The matrices of the stress tensor, its deviatorial and spherical components then become

$$S = \begin{pmatrix} \sigma_1 & 0 & 0 \\ 0 & 0 & 0 \\ 0 & 0 & 0 \end{pmatrix}$$

$$S' = \begin{pmatrix} \frac{2}{3}\sigma_1 & 0 & 0 \\ 0 & -\frac{\sigma_1}{3} & 0 \\ 0 & 0 & -\frac{\sigma_1}{3} \end{pmatrix} \qquad (1.35)$$

$$S'' = \begin{pmatrix} \frac{\sigma_1}{3} & 0 & 0 \\ 0 & \frac{\sigma_1}{3} & 0 \\ 0 & 0 & \frac{\sigma_1}{3} \end{pmatrix}$$

The invariants of the stress tensor have the values

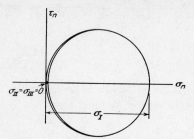

$$I_1 = \sigma_1, \qquad I_2 = I_3 = 0 \quad (1.36)$$

and the octahedral stresses are

$$\sigma_{oct} = \frac{\sigma_1}{3}$$

$$\tau_{oct} = \frac{\sqrt{2}}{3}\sigma_1$$

$$(1.37)$$

FIG. 1.12. Mohr's diagram for uni-axial state of stress.

Figure 1.12 shows the Mohr diagram representing a uniaxial state of stress for a positive $\sigma_1 = \sigma_I$.

1.9. Second Special Case: The State of Plane Stress

The "state of plane stress" occurs when one of the principal stresses, for example, σ_3, is zero.

Assume an x, y, z reference frame so that the z axis coincides with the principal direction "3." Then

$$\sigma_z = \tau_{yz} = \tau_{zx} = 0 \quad (1.38)$$

and the matrices of the stress

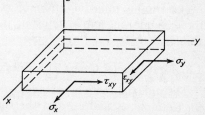

FIG. 1.13. Plane stress.

tensor, its deviator and spherical components become (see Fig. 1.13)

$$\mathbf{S} = \begin{pmatrix} \sigma_x & \tau_{xy} & 0 \\ \tau_{xy} & \sigma_y & 0 \\ 0 & 0 & 0 \end{pmatrix}$$

$$\mathbf{S'} = \begin{pmatrix} \dfrac{2\sigma_x - \sigma_y}{3} & \tau_{xy} & 0 \\ \tau_{xy} & \dfrac{2\sigma_y - \sigma_x}{3} & 0 \\ 0 & 0 & -\dfrac{\sigma_x + \sigma_y}{3} \end{pmatrix} \quad (1.39)$$

$$\mathbf{S''} = \begin{pmatrix} \dfrac{\sigma_x + \sigma_y}{3} & 0 & 0 \\ 0 & \dfrac{\sigma_x + \sigma_y}{3} & 0 \\ 0 & 0 & \dfrac{\sigma_x + \sigma_y}{3} \end{pmatrix}$$

In order to determine the principal stresses σ_1 and σ_2, the directions of which are contained in the xy plane, the invariants of the stress tensors are calculated from Eqs. (1.14) as follows:

$$\begin{aligned}
I_1 &= \sigma_x + \sigma_y \\
I_2 &= \sigma_x\sigma_y - \tau_{xy}^2 \\
I_3 &= 0
\end{aligned} \tag{1.40}$$

With these values the cubic equation (1.16) becomes

$$\sigma_i^3 - (\sigma_x + \sigma_y)\sigma_i^2 + (\sigma_x\sigma_y - \tau_{xy}^2)\sigma_i = 0 \tag{1.41}$$

and this, by dividing both sides by σ_i, reduces to the quadratic equation

$$\sigma_i^2 - (\sigma_x + \sigma_y)\sigma_i + \sigma_x\sigma_y - \tau_{xy}^2 = 0 \tag{1.42}$$

The solution furnishes the principal stresses as follows:

$$\left.\begin{aligned}\sigma_1 \\ \sigma_2\end{aligned}\right\} = \frac{\sigma_x + \sigma_y}{2} \pm \sqrt{\left(\frac{\sigma_x - \sigma_y}{2}\right)^2 + \tau_{xy}^2} \tag{1.43}$$

where the subscripts "1" and "2" are assigned so that $\sigma_1 \geq \sigma_2$. The expressions for the octahedral stresses are

$$\begin{aligned}
\sigma_{oct} &= \frac{\sigma_1 + \sigma_2}{3} = \frac{\sigma_x + \sigma_y}{3} \\
\tau_{oct} &= \frac{\sqrt{2}}{3}\sqrt{\sigma_1^2 - \sigma_1\sigma_2 + \sigma_2^2} = \frac{\sqrt{2}}{3}\sqrt{\sigma_x^2 - \sigma_x\sigma_y + \sigma_y^2 + 3\tau_{xy}^2}
\end{aligned} \tag{1.44}$$

In plotting the Mohr diagram, several distinct possibilities arise, according to the relative magnitudes of the three principal stresses. An inspection of Eq. (1.43) shows that the following cases can exist:

Case (a): If $\sigma_x\sigma_y > \tau_{xy}^2$, both principal stresses have the same sign.

Case (b): If $\sigma_x\sigma_y < \tau_{xy}^2$, the two principal stresses have opposite signs.

Case (c): If $\sigma_x\sigma_y = \tau_{xy}^2$, the state of stress degenerates into a uniaxial state of stress.

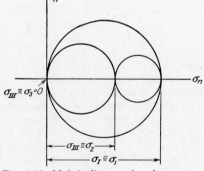

Fig. 1.14. Mohr's diagram for plane stress, case (a).

Figure 1.14 shows the Mohr diagram plotted for case (a), assuming that both σ_1 and σ_2 are positive. The three principal stresses, labeled consistently with the ordering rule given in Art. 1.3, are in this case

$$\sigma_I \equiv \sigma_1 \geq \sigma_{II} \equiv \sigma_2 \geq \sigma_{III} = 0$$

Hence, the maximum shearing stress results as

$$\tau_{max} = \frac{\sigma_I - \sigma_{III}}{2} = \frac{\sigma_1}{2} = \frac{1}{2}\left[\frac{\sigma_x + \sigma_y}{2} + \sqrt{\left(\frac{\sigma_x - \sigma_y}{2}\right)^2 + \tau_{xy}^2} \right] \quad (1.45)$$

The Mohr diagram for case (b) is shown in Fig. 1.15; here the following

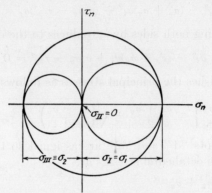

FIG. 1.15. Mohr's diagram for plane stress, case (b).

values are assigned to the principal stresses ordered according to their magnitudes:

$$\sigma_I \equiv \sigma_1 \geq \sigma_{II} = 0 \geq \sigma_{III} \equiv \sigma_2$$

and consequently the maximum shearing stress becomes

$$\tau_{max} = \frac{\sigma_I - \sigma_{III}}{2} = \frac{\sigma_1 - \sigma_2}{2} = \sqrt{\left(\frac{\sigma_x - \sigma_y}{2}\right)^2 + \tau_{xy}^2} \quad (1.46)$$

REFERENCES

LOVE, A. E. H., "A Treatise on the Mathematical Theory of Elasticity," 4th ed., pp. 74–83, Dover Publications, New York, 1944.

MOHR, O., "Abhandlungen aus dem Gebiete der technischen Mechanik," 2d ed., pp. 192–203, Wilhelm Ernst & Sohn, Berlin, 1914.

NÁDAI, A., "Theory of Flow and Fracture of Solids," Vol. I, pp. 88–108, McGraw-Hill Book Company, Inc., New York, 1950.

TIMOSHENKO, S., "Theory of Elasticity," pp. 182–188, McGraw-Hill Book Company, Inc., New York, 1934.

CHAPTER 2

STATE OF STRAIN

This chapter presents relationships of general validity governing the deformations of continuous media. These relationships are the counterpart of those for the stresses discussed in the preceding chapter; the similarity of the mathematical developments will be apparent, and this will permit stating a number of results based on the analogy with previous developments.

2.1. Infinitesimal Strain at a Point. Strain Tensor

Consider a point P in the neighborhood of a given point O; the relative position of the two points is defined by the position vector $\mathbf{l}$, pointing from O to P. With reference to a cartesian system having its origin at O, the coordinates of P are (see Fig. 2.1)

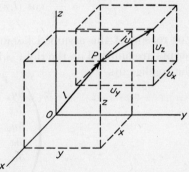

$$x = l \cos (l,x)$$
$$y = l \cos (l,y) \qquad (2.1)$$
$$z = l \cos (l,z)$$

where l is the magnitude of the vector $\mathbf{l}$. During deformation, point P undergoes a small displacement $\mathbf{u}$, the cartesian components of which, u_x, u_y, u_z, are continuous single-valued

Fig. 2.1. Components of displacement at a point.

functions of the coordinates of the point, this being the mathematical criterion of the conservation of continuity of the medium. It follows that u_x, u_y, and u_z can be expanded in Taylor's series, obtaining

$$u_x = (u_x)_0 + \left(\frac{\partial u_x}{\partial x}\right)_0 x + \left(\frac{\partial u_x}{\partial y}\right)_0 y + \left(\frac{\partial u_x}{\partial z}\right)_0 z + \cdots$$

$$u_y = (u_y)_0 + \left(\frac{\partial u_y}{\partial x}\right)_0 x + \left(\frac{\partial u_y}{\partial y}\right)_0 y + \left(\frac{\partial u_y}{\partial z}\right)_0 z + \cdots \qquad (2.2)$$

$$u_z = (u_z)_0 + \left(\frac{\partial u_z}{\partial x}\right)_0 x + \left(\frac{\partial u_z}{\partial y}\right)_0 y + \left(\frac{\partial u_z}{\partial z}\right)_0 z + \cdots$$

The subscript 0 indicates values assumed at $(x = 0,\ y = 0,\ z = 0)$. The dots indicate terms containing higher powers of x, y, z; if point P is within an infinitesimal neighborhood of O, such terms are negligible and the deformation components are linear functions of the coordinates. Such a state of deformation is called "homogeneous," and when it exists the vector defined by the ratio

$$\frac{\mathbf{u} - (\mathbf{u})_0}{l}$$

or the "unit relative displacement," is independent of the magnitude of l and depends only on its direction.

The cartesian components of the unit relative displacement vector are obtained from Eqs. (2.2) by substituting the expressions of x, y, z from Eqs. (2.1) and dividing both sides by l, as follows:

$$\frac{u_x - (u_x)_0}{l} = \frac{\partial u_x}{\partial x} \cos (l,x) + \frac{\partial u_x}{\partial y} \cos (l,y) + \frac{\partial u_x}{\partial z} \cos (l,z)$$

$$\frac{u_y - (u_y)_0}{l} = \frac{\partial u_y}{\partial x} \cos (l,x) + \frac{\partial u_y}{\partial y} \cos (l,y) + \frac{\partial u_y}{\partial z} \cos (l,z) \qquad (2.3)$$

$$\frac{u_z - (u_z)_0}{l} = \frac{\partial u_z}{\partial x} \cos (l,x) + \frac{\partial u_z}{\partial y} \cos (l,y) + \frac{\partial u_z}{\partial z} \cos (l,z)$$

For reason of the assumed homogeneity of the deformation, the 0 subscripts are omitted on the right sides of the above equations; the matrix of the coefficients

$$\begin{pmatrix} \dfrac{\partial u_x}{\partial x} & \dfrac{\partial u_x}{\partial y} & \dfrac{\partial u_x}{\partial z} \\[2mm] \dfrac{\partial u_y}{\partial x} & \dfrac{\partial u_y}{\partial y} & \dfrac{\partial u_y}{\partial z} \\[2mm] \dfrac{\partial u_z}{\partial x} & \dfrac{\partial u_z}{\partial y} & \dfrac{\partial u_z}{\partial z} \end{pmatrix} \qquad (2.4)$$

defines the tensor of "unit relative displacements." Generally, this matrix is not symmetrical about its main diagonal, *i.e.*, it contains effects of a rigid rotational motion about an axis passing through O.

A small rotation, represented in the well-known manner by a vector with the cartesian components ω_x, ω_y, ω_z, produces a relative displacement tensor

$$\begin{pmatrix} 0 & -\omega_z & \omega_y \\ \omega_z & 0 & -\omega_x \\ -\omega_y & \omega_x & 0 \end{pmatrix} \qquad (2.5)$$

which is skew-symmetric about its main diagonal. Hence, subtracting from the tensor represented by the matrix (2.4) its skew-symmetric component

$$\begin{pmatrix} 0 & \dfrac{1}{2}\left(\dfrac{\partial u_x}{\partial y} - \dfrac{\partial u_y}{\partial x}\right) & \dfrac{1}{2}\left(\dfrac{\partial u_x}{\partial z} - \dfrac{\partial u_z}{\partial x}\right) \\[2ex] \dfrac{1}{2}\left(\dfrac{\partial u_y}{\partial x} - \dfrac{\partial u_x}{\partial y}\right) & 0 & \dfrac{1}{2}\left(\dfrac{\partial u_y}{\partial z} - \dfrac{\partial u_z}{\partial y}\right) \\[2ex] \dfrac{1}{2}\left(\dfrac{\partial u_z}{\partial x} - \dfrac{\partial u_x}{\partial z}\right) & \dfrac{1}{2}\left(\dfrac{\partial u_z}{\partial y} - \dfrac{\partial u_y}{\partial z}\right) & 0 \end{pmatrix} \tag{2.6}$$

one obtains the symmetrical component, the so-called "irrotational" or "pure" strain tensor

$$\mathbf{E} = \begin{pmatrix} \dfrac{\partial u_x}{\partial x} & \dfrac{1}{2}\left(\dfrac{\partial u_x}{\partial y} + \dfrac{\partial u_y}{\partial x}\right) & \dfrac{1}{2}\left(\dfrac{\partial u_x}{\partial z} + \dfrac{\partial u_z}{\partial x}\right) \\[2ex] \dfrac{1}{2}\left(\dfrac{\partial u_x}{\partial y} + \dfrac{\partial u_y}{\partial x}\right) & \dfrac{\partial u_y}{\partial y} & \dfrac{1}{2}\left(\dfrac{\partial u_y}{\partial z} + \dfrac{\partial u_z}{\partial y}\right) \\[2ex] \dfrac{1}{2}\left(\dfrac{\partial u_x}{\partial z} + \dfrac{\partial u_z}{\partial x}\right) & \dfrac{1}{2}\left(\dfrac{\partial u_y}{\partial z} + \dfrac{\partial u_z}{\partial y}\right) & \dfrac{\partial u_z}{\partial z} \end{pmatrix} \tag{2.7}$$

Thus, the equations expressing the components of the irrotational relative displacement vector $\mathbf{e}_l$ as functions of the vector $\mathbf{1}$ can be written as follows:

$$e_{lx} = \frac{\partial u_x}{\partial x}\cos(l,x) + \frac{1}{2}\left(\frac{\partial u_x}{\partial y} + \frac{\partial u_y}{\partial x}\right)\cos(l,y) + \frac{1}{2}\left(\frac{\partial u_x}{\partial z} + \frac{\partial u_z}{\partial x}\right)\cos(l,z)$$

$$e_{ly} = \frac{1}{2}\left(\frac{\partial u_x}{\partial y} + \frac{\partial u_y}{\partial x}\right)\cos(l,x) + \frac{\partial u_y}{\partial y}\cos(l,y) + \frac{1}{2}\left(\frac{\partial u_y}{\partial z} + \frac{\partial u_z}{\partial y}\right)\cos(l,z)$$

$$e_{lz} = \frac{1}{2}\left(\frac{\partial u_x}{\partial z} + \frac{\partial u_z}{\partial x}\right)\cos(l,x) + \frac{1}{2}\left(\frac{\partial u_y}{\partial z} + \frac{\partial u_z}{\partial y}\right)\cos(l,y) + \frac{\partial u_z}{\partial z}\cos(l,z)$$

$$\tag{2.8}$$

or also

$$e_{lx} = \epsilon_x \cos(l,x) + \frac{\gamma_{yx}}{2}\cos(l,y) + \frac{\gamma_{zx}}{2}\cos(l,z)$$

$$e_{ly} = \frac{\gamma_{xy}}{2}\cos(l,x) + \epsilon_y \cos(l,y) + \frac{\gamma_{zy}}{2}\cos(l,z) \tag{2.9}$$

$$e_{lz} = \frac{\gamma_{zx}}{2}\cos(l,x) + \frac{\gamma_{yz}}{2}\cos(l,y) + \epsilon_z \cos(l,z)$$

where

$$\begin{aligned} \epsilon_x &= \frac{\partial u_x}{\partial x} & \gamma_{xy} = \gamma_{yx} &= \frac{\partial u_x}{\partial y} + \frac{\partial u_y}{\partial x} \\[1ex] \epsilon_y &= \frac{\partial u_y}{\partial y} & \gamma_{yz} = \gamma_{zy} &= \frac{\partial u_y}{\partial z} + \frac{\partial u_z}{\partial y} \\[1ex] \epsilon_z &= \frac{\partial u_z}{\partial z} & \gamma_{zx} = \gamma_{xz} &= \frac{\partial u_z}{\partial x} + \frac{\partial u_x}{\partial z} \end{aligned} \tag{2.10}$$

The physical significance of ϵ_x, for example, is recognized by considering a point P_1 situated on the x axis at distance x from the origin (see Fig. 2.2); after deformation, the x coordinate of P_1 has changed into $x + \epsilon_x x = (1 + \epsilon_x)x$. Therefore, by neglecting small quantities of higher order, ϵ_x represents the unit change of length of a line element in the x direction; accordingly, the terms of cartesian "linear strain components" are used for ϵ_x, ϵ_y, ϵ_z.

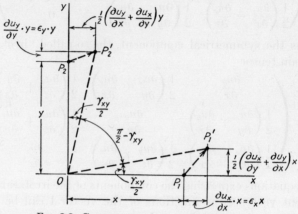

FIG. 2.2. Components of strain in the xy plane.

From Fig. 2.2 it can be seen also that γ_{xy} represents, in first approximation, the change in the originally right angle between the x and y axes; hence, γ_{xy}, γ_{yz}, γ_{zx}, are called the cartesian shearing strains; half their values are cartesian components of the strain tensor which is written, with the above notations, as follows:

$$\mathbf{E} = \begin{pmatrix} \epsilon_x & \dfrac{\gamma_{xy}}{2} & \dfrac{\gamma_{zx}}{2} \\[2mm] \dfrac{\gamma_{xy}}{2} & \epsilon_y & \dfrac{\gamma_{yz}}{2} \\[2mm] \dfrac{\gamma_{zx}}{2} & \dfrac{\gamma_{yz}}{2} & \epsilon_z \end{pmatrix} \qquad (2.11)$$

The transformation equations for the strain tensor components are patterned after those derived in Art. 2 for the stress tensor components; the following two equations are given as typical examples:

$$\epsilon_{x'} = \epsilon_x \cos^2 (x',x) + \epsilon_y \cos^2 (x',y) + \epsilon_z \cos^2 (x',z)$$
$$+ \gamma_{xy} \cos (x',x) \cos (x',y) + \gamma_{yz} \cos (x',y) \cos (x',z)$$
$$+ \gamma_{zx} \cos (x',z) \cos (x',x) \quad (2.12)$$

$$\gamma_{x'y'} = 2[\epsilon_x \cos (x',x) \cos (y',x) + \epsilon_y \cos (x',y) \cos (y',y)$$
$$+ \epsilon_z \cos (x',z) \cos (y',z)] + \gamma_{xy}[\cos (x',x) \cos (y',y)$$
$$+ \cos (x',y) \cos (y',x)] + \gamma_{yz}[\cos (x',y) \cos (y',z)$$
$$+ \cos (x',z) \cos (y',y)] + \gamma_{zx}[\cos (x',z) \cos (y',x)$$
$$+ \cos (x',x) \cos (y',z)] \quad (2.13)$$

2.2. Principal Strains

The expression for the normal strain ϵ_l in the direction of a line element vector $\mathbf{l}$ is, from Eq. (2.12),

$$\epsilon_l = \epsilon_x \cos^2 (l,x) + \epsilon_y \cos^2 (l,y) + \epsilon_z \cos^2 (l,z) + \gamma_{xy} \cos (l,x) \cos (l,y)$$
$$+ \gamma_{yz} \cos (l,y) \cos (l,z) + \gamma_{zx} \cos (l,z) \cos (l,x) \quad (2.14)$$

The end point of a vector having the direction of $\mathbf{l}$ and the magnitude $1/\sqrt{|\epsilon_l|}$ has the coordinates

$$x = \frac{\cos (l,x)}{\sqrt{|\epsilon_l|}}$$
$$y = \frac{\cos (l,y)}{\sqrt{|\epsilon_l|}} \quad (2.15)$$
$$z = \frac{\cos (l,z)}{\sqrt{|\epsilon_l|}}$$

and lies on the "strain quadric," a surface with the equation

$$\pm 1 = \epsilon_x x^2 + \epsilon_y y^2 + \epsilon_z z^2 + \gamma_{xy} xy + \gamma_{yz} yz + \gamma_{zx} zx \quad (2.16)$$

The system of axes for which the coefficients of the bilinear terms in this equation vanish form the system of principal axes of strain. Line elements oriented along such axes before deformation remain mutually perpendicular during deformation. The "principal strains" $\epsilon_i (i = 1, 2, 3)$ are determined from the cubic equation

$$\epsilon_i^3 - (\epsilon_x + \epsilon_y + \epsilon_z)\epsilon_i^2 + [\epsilon_x \epsilon_y + \epsilon_y \epsilon_z + \epsilon_z \epsilon_x - \tfrac{1}{4}(\gamma_{xy}^2 + \gamma_{yz}^2 + \gamma_{zx}^2)]\epsilon_i$$
$$- \epsilon_x \epsilon_y \epsilon_z - \tfrac{1}{4}[\gamma_{xy}\gamma_{yz}\gamma_{zx} - \epsilon_x \gamma_{yz}^2 - \epsilon_y \gamma_{zx}^2 - \epsilon_z \gamma_{xy}^2] = 0 \quad (2.17)$$

The matrix of the strain tensor with reference to the principal axes is written as

$$\mathbf{E} = \begin{pmatrix} \epsilon_1 & 0 & 0 \\ 0 & \epsilon_2 & 0 \\ 0 & 0 & \epsilon_3 \end{pmatrix} \quad (2.18)$$

and Eqs. (2.8) become

$$e_{l1} = \epsilon_1 \cos (l,1)$$
$$e_{l2} = \epsilon_2 \cos (l,2) \quad (2.19)$$
$$e_{l3} = \epsilon_2 \cos (l,3)$$

2.3. Invariants of the Strain Tensor

The coefficients of the cubic equation (2.17) are the invariants of the strain tensor, denoted as follows:

$$J_1 = \epsilon_x + \epsilon_y + \epsilon_z$$
$$J_2 = \epsilon_x \epsilon_y + \epsilon_y \epsilon_z + \epsilon_z \epsilon_x - \tfrac{1}{4}(\gamma_{xy}^2 + \gamma_{yz}^2 + \gamma_{zx}^2) \quad (2.20)$$
$$J_3 = \epsilon_x \epsilon_y \epsilon_z + \tfrac{1}{4}(\gamma_{xy}\gamma_{yz}\gamma_{zx} - \epsilon_x \gamma_{yz}^2 - \epsilon_y \gamma_{zx}^2 - \epsilon_z \gamma_{xy}^2)$$

or, in terms of the principal strains,

$$J_1 = \epsilon_1 + \epsilon_2 + \epsilon_3$$
$$J_2 = \epsilon_1\epsilon_2 + \epsilon_2\epsilon_3 + \epsilon_3\epsilon_1 \qquad (2.21)$$
$$J_3 = \epsilon_1\epsilon_2\epsilon_3$$

With such notations, Eq. (2.17) can be written as

$$\epsilon_i^3 - J_1\epsilon_i^2 + J_2\epsilon_i - J_3 = 0 \qquad (2.22)$$

The "mean normal strain" is defined by

$$\epsilon_m = \frac{\epsilon_x + \epsilon_y + \epsilon_z}{3} = \frac{\epsilon_1 + \epsilon_2 + \epsilon_3}{3} \qquad (2.23)$$

and the first invariant of strain can be expressed as

$$J_1 = 3\epsilon_m \qquad (2.24)$$

2.4. Spherical and Deviator Strain Tensors

In analogy with the procedure followed for the stress tensor in Art. 1.4, the strain tensor is resolved in two component tensors:

$$\mathbf{E} = \mathbf{E}' + \mathbf{E}''$$

where

$$\mathbf{E}'' = \begin{pmatrix} \epsilon_m & 0 & 0 \\ 0 & \epsilon_m & 0 \\ 0 & 0 & \epsilon_m \end{pmatrix} \qquad (2.25)$$

is the spherical strain tensor and

$$\mathbf{E}' = \begin{pmatrix} \dfrac{2\epsilon_x - \epsilon_y - \epsilon_z}{3} & \dfrac{\gamma_{xy}}{2} & \dfrac{\gamma_{zx}}{2} \\[2ex] \dfrac{\gamma_{xy}}{2} & \dfrac{2\epsilon_y - \epsilon_z - \epsilon_x}{3} & \dfrac{\gamma_{yz}}{2} \\[2ex] \dfrac{\gamma_{zx}}{2} & \dfrac{\gamma_{yz}}{2} & \dfrac{2\epsilon_z - \epsilon_x - \epsilon_y}{3} \end{pmatrix} \qquad (2.26)$$

is the matrix of the deviator strain tensor with reference to arbitrary x, y, z axes. With respect to the principal axes of strain it becomes

$$\mathbf{E}' = \begin{pmatrix} \dfrac{2\epsilon_1 - \epsilon_2 - \epsilon_3}{3} & 0 & 0 \\[2ex] 0 & \dfrac{2\epsilon_2 - \epsilon_3 - \epsilon_1}{3} & 0 \\[2ex] 0 & 0 & \dfrac{2\epsilon_3 - \epsilon_1 - \epsilon_2}{3} \end{pmatrix} \qquad (2.27)$$

The invariants of the spherical strain tensor are

$$J_1'' = J_1$$
$$J_2'' = \frac{J_1{}^2}{3}$$
$$J_3'' = \frac{J_1{}^3}{27}$$

(2.28)

and the invariants of the deviator strain tensor are

$$J_1' = 0$$
$$J_2' = J_2 - \frac{J_1{}^2}{3}$$
$$J_3' = J_3 - \frac{J_1 J_2}{3} + \frac{2}{27} J_1{}^3$$

(2.29)

The physical significance of the spherical strain tensor becomes apparent by calculating the volume strain, *i.e.*, the change in volume per unit original volume. By referring to an elementary rectangular parallelepiped with its edges l_1, l_2, l_3 parallel to the principal axes of strain, the volume strain becomes

$$\Delta = \frac{l_1(1 + \epsilon_1)l_2(1 + \epsilon_2)l_3(1 + \epsilon_3) - l_1 l_2 l_3}{l_1 l_2 l_3} = (1 + \epsilon_1)(1 + \epsilon_2)(1 + \epsilon_3) - 1$$

which for small strains becomes, neglecting products of ϵ's,

$$\Delta = \epsilon_1 + \epsilon_2 + \epsilon_3 = J_1$$

(2.30)

Hence, the deviator strain tensor, for which

$$J_1' = 0$$

represents a pure distortional deformation, with no volume change. Conversely, the spherical strain tensor represents a pure volumetric deformation.

2.5. Mohr's Diagram for the State of Strain

The analogy between the stress and strain tensor permits the extension of Mohr's graphical representation to the latter. The coordinates of a point are, in consistence with the notations heretofore used,

ϵ_l = linear component of strain, *i.e.*, component of vector $\mathbf{e}_l$ in direction of vector l.

$\dfrac{\gamma_l}{2}$ = half the shearing strain in the common plane of l and $\mathbf{e}_l$.

Points corresponding with constant $(l,1)$, $(l,2)$, $(l,3)$ angles are represented by circles with centers on the ϵ_l axis. All significant points are within the curvilinear triangle formed by the principal circles of strain (see Fig. 2.3).

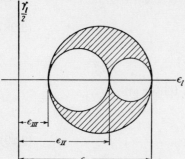

Introducing roman-numeral subscripts and the ordering rule

$$\epsilon_I \geq \epsilon_{II} \geq \epsilon_{III}$$

the relative maxima of the shearing strain, the so-called "principal shearing strains," are

$$\gamma_1 = \epsilon_{II} - \epsilon_{III}$$
$$\gamma_2 = \epsilon_I - \epsilon_{III} \qquad (2.31)$$
$$\gamma_3 = \epsilon_I - \epsilon_{II}$$

FIG. 2.3. Mohr's diagram for the state of strain.

and $\gamma_2 = \max \gamma_l$ is the absolute maximum shearing strain at the given point.

The Mohr diagram for the deviator strain tensor is obtained from that of the total strain tensor by shifting the $\gamma_l/2$ axis by the distance ϵ_m.

2.6. Octahedral Strains

By orienting the vector 1 in a direction normal to one of the octahedral planes defined in Art. 1.7, *i.e.*, so that it includes the angle of 54°44′ with the principal axes, one obtains the following expressions for the octahedral strains:

$$\epsilon_{oct} = \frac{\epsilon_1 + \epsilon_2 + \epsilon_3}{3} = \frac{J_1}{3}$$
$$\gamma_{oct} = \tfrac{2}{3}\sqrt{(\epsilon_1 - \epsilon_2)^2 + (\epsilon_2 - \epsilon_3)^2 + (\epsilon_3 - \epsilon_1)^2} \qquad (2.32)$$

where ϵ_{oct} is the octahedral linear strain, *i.e.*, the unit change in length in direction of 1_{oct}; and γ_{oct} is the octahedral shearing strain, *i.e.*, the change in the originally right angle between 1_{oct} and the octahedral plane.

The term "effective strain," often used in the literature, is arbitrarily defined by the expression

$$\epsilon_{eff} = \frac{\sqrt{2}}{2}\,\gamma_{oct} = \frac{\sqrt{2}}{3}\sqrt{(\epsilon_1 - \epsilon_2)^2 + (\epsilon_2 - \epsilon_3)^2 + (\epsilon_3 - \epsilon_1)^2} \qquad (2.33)$$

and it has the property that in the case of a state of strain defined by

$$\epsilon_2 = \epsilon_3 = -\frac{\epsilon_1}{2}$$

one obtains $\epsilon_{eff} = \epsilon_1$.

2.7. Finite Deformations

As the strain components become larger, their products cannot be neglected with respect to the strains themselves, and the relationships heretofore developed for infinitesimal strains become increasingly inaccurate. More rigorous relationships, applicable to finite strains, will be developed herein for the special case when the principal directions of the infinitesimal strain maintain their orientation with respect to the given particle of the medium during the finite deformation.

Assume that the principal strains ϵ_1, ϵ_2, ϵ_3, that is, the unit elongations in the principal directions, are known finite quantities and determine the unit elongation ϵ_l in direction of a line element, represented by the vector 1. The original length l of the line element becomes $(1 + \epsilon_l)l$ in the deformed state, and its orthogonal projections on the principal axes are calculated from the original components of 1 and the respective principal strains as

$$(1 + \epsilon_1)l \cos (l,1)$$
$$(1 + \epsilon_2)l \cos (l,2)$$
$$(1 + \epsilon_3)l \cos (l,3)$$

where $(l,1)$, $(l,2)$, $(l,3)$ are the angles between 1 and the principal axes in the initial unstrained state. The length of the line element in the strained state satisfies the relation

$$(1 + \epsilon_l)^2 l^2 = (1 + \epsilon_1)^2 l^2 \cos^2 (l,1) + (1 + \epsilon_2)^2 l^2 \cos^2 (l,2) + (1 + \epsilon_3)^2 l^2 \cos^2 (l,3) \quad (2.34)$$

from which the unit elongation of the line element results as

$$\epsilon_l = \sqrt{(1 + \epsilon_1)^2 \cos^2 (l,1) + (1 + \epsilon_2)^2 \cos^2 (l,2) + (1 + \epsilon_3)^2 \cos^2 (l,3)} - 1 \quad (2.35)$$

For infinitesimal strains, this equation reduces to

$$\epsilon_l = \epsilon_1 \cos^2 (l,1) + \epsilon_2 \cos^2 (l,2) + \epsilon_3 \cos^2 (l,3) \quad (2.36)$$

which follows from Eq. (2.12) or from Eq. (2.14).

The direction cosines of the line element after deformation are

$$\frac{1 + \epsilon_1}{1 + \epsilon_l} \cos (l,1), \qquad \frac{1 + \epsilon_2}{1 + \epsilon_l} \cos (l,2), \qquad \frac{1 + \epsilon_3}{1 + \epsilon_l} \cos (l,3)$$

Consider the second line element **k**, perpendicular to 1 in the unstrained state; by analogy, its projections on the principal axes in the strained state are

$$(1 + \epsilon_1)k \cos (k,1)$$
$$(1 + \epsilon_2)k \cos (k,2)$$
$$(1 + \epsilon_3)k \cos (k,3)$$

and its direction cosines after deformation

$$\frac{1 + \epsilon_1}{1 + \epsilon_k} \cos (k,1), \qquad \frac{1 + \epsilon_2}{1 + \epsilon_k} \cos (k,2), \qquad \frac{1 + \epsilon_3}{1 + \epsilon_k} \cos (k,3)$$

The cosine of the angle θ between the line elements l and $\mathbf{k}$ after deformation results from a known relationship of analytical geometry.

$$\cos\theta = \frac{\left\{\begin{matrix}(1+\epsilon_1)^2\cos(l,1)\cos(k,1)+(1+\epsilon_2)^2\cos(l,2)\cos(k,2)\\+(1+\epsilon_3)^2\cos(l,3)\cos(k,3)\end{matrix}\right\}}{(1+\epsilon_l)(1+\epsilon_k)} \quad (2.37)$$

According to the previously used notations, γ_{lk} is the change in the originally right angle between l and $\mathbf{k}$, so that

$$\gamma_{lk} = \frac{\pi}{2} - \theta, \qquad \sin\gamma_{lk} = \cos\theta$$

hence,

$$\gamma_{lk} = \sin^{-1}\frac{\left\{\begin{matrix}(1+\epsilon_1)^2\cos(l,1)\cos(k,1)+(1+\epsilon_2)^2\cos(l,2)\cos(k,2)\\+(1+\epsilon_3)^2\cos(l,3)\cos(k,3)\end{matrix}\right\}}{(1+\epsilon_l)(1+\epsilon_k)} \quad (2.38)$$

For infinitesimal strains, this equation reduces to

$$\gamma_{lk} = 2[\epsilon_1\cos(l,1)\cos(k,1) + \epsilon_2\cos(l,2)\cos(k,2) \\ + \epsilon_3\cos(l,3)\cos(k,3)]$$

consistently with Eq. (2.13).

The volume strain is

$$\begin{aligned}\Delta &= (1+\epsilon_1)(1+\epsilon_2)(1+\epsilon_3) - 1\\ &= \epsilon_1 + \epsilon_2 + \epsilon_3 + \epsilon_1\epsilon_2 + \epsilon_2\epsilon_3 + \epsilon_3\epsilon_1 + \epsilon_1\epsilon_2\epsilon_3\\ &= J_1 + J_2 + J_3\end{aligned} \quad (2.39)$$

where J_1, J_2, J_3 are the invariants of the strain tensor [see Eqs. (2.20) and (2.21)].

The fact expressed by this equation, that for large strains the first invariant of the strain tensor does not represent rigorously the volume strain, makes it desirable to use a different measure of the strain, not affected by such a discrepancy. In 1909 Ludwik suggested introducing the so-called "logarithmic" or "natural" strain $\bar{\epsilon}$, related to the heretofore-used "conventional" strain ϵ by the expression

$$\bar{\epsilon} = \ln(1+\epsilon) \quad (2.40)$$

The significance of the difference between the two measures of strain becomes apparent by considering the deformed state and calculating the increment of strain according to the two definitions. Denoting the initial length of the line element with l_0, its deformed length with l, the conventional strain is

$$\epsilon = \frac{l-l_0}{l_0} = \frac{l}{l_0} - 1 \quad (2.41)$$

and the logarithmic strain, by its definition,

$$\bar{\epsilon} = \ln \frac{l}{l_0} = \ln (1 + \epsilon) \tag{2.42}$$

An increment dl in the deformed length gives rise to the conventional strain increment

$$d\epsilon = \frac{dl}{l_0} \tag{2.43}$$

and to the logarithmic strain increment

$$d\bar{\epsilon} = \frac{dl}{l_0} \frac{l_0}{l} = \frac{dl}{l} = \frac{d\epsilon}{1 + \epsilon} \tag{2.44}$$

Thus, an infinitesimal increment of the conventional strain expresses the change in length with reference to the original length l_0 of the line

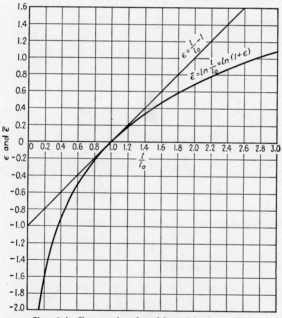

Fig. 2.4. Conventional and logarithmic strain.

element, while increments of the logarithmic strain are calculated in terms of the instantaneous length l. For very small strains the two definitions of strain (and strain increment) yield identical values (see Fig. 2.4).

Neither the transformation formulas for infinitesimal strains nor Eqs. (2.35), (2.38), and (2.39) for finite strains apply directly to logarithmic strains. Given the logarithmic principal strains, first, they are converted into the conventional principal strains

$$\epsilon_1 = e^{\bar{\epsilon}_1} - 1$$
$$\epsilon_2 = e^{\bar{\epsilon}_2} - 1 \qquad (2.45)$$
$$\epsilon_3 = e^{\bar{\epsilon}_3} - 1$$

Substitution of these expressions in Eq. (2.36) yields

$$\epsilon_l = \sqrt{e^{2\bar{\epsilon}_1} \cos^2 (l,1) + e^{2\bar{\epsilon}_2} \cos^2 (l,2) + e^{2\bar{\epsilon}_3} \cos^2 (l,3)} - 1$$

from which the logarithmic linear strain is obtained as

$$\bar{\epsilon}_l = \ln (1 + \epsilon_l) = \ln \sqrt{e^{2\bar{\epsilon}_1} \cos^2 (l,1) + e^{2\bar{\epsilon}_2} \cos^2 (l,2) + e^{2\bar{\epsilon}_3} \cos^2 (l,3)}$$
$$(2.46)$$

Similarly, substituting expressions (2.46) into Eq. (2.38), one obtains for the conventional shearing strain

$$\gamma_{lk} = \sin^{-1} \frac{\left\{ \begin{matrix} e^{2\bar{\epsilon}_1} \cos (l,1) \cos (k,1) + e^{2\bar{\epsilon}_2} \cos (l,2) \cos (k,2) \\ + e^{2\bar{\epsilon}_3} \cos (l,3) \cos (k,3) \end{matrix} \right\}}{\left\{ \begin{matrix} \sqrt{[e^{2\bar{\epsilon}_1} \cos^2 (l,1) + e^{2\bar{\epsilon}_2} \cos^2 (l,2) + e^{2\bar{\epsilon}_3} \cos^2 (l,3)]} \\ \overline{[e^{2\bar{\epsilon}_1} \cos^2 (k,1) + e^{2\bar{\epsilon}_2} \cos^2 (k,2) + e^{2\bar{\epsilon}_3} \cos^2 (k,3)]} \end{matrix} \right\}}$$

from which one has the expression for the logarithmic shearing strain

$$\bar{\gamma}_{lk} = \ln (1 + \gamma_{lk}) =$$

$$\ln \left[1 + \sin^{-1} \frac{\left\{ \begin{matrix} e^{2\bar{\epsilon}_1} \cos (l,1) \cos (k,1) + e^{2\bar{\epsilon}_2} \cos (l,2) \cos (k,2) \\ + e^{2\bar{\epsilon}_3} \cos (l,3) \cos (k,3) \end{matrix} \right\}}{\left\{ \begin{matrix} \sqrt{[e^{2\bar{\epsilon}_1} \cos^2 (l,1) + e^{2\bar{\epsilon}_2} \cos^2 (l,2) + e^{2\bar{\epsilon}_3} \cos^2 (l,3)]} \\ \overline{[e^{2\bar{\epsilon}_1} \cos^2 (k,1) + e^{2\bar{\epsilon}_2} \cos^2 (k,2) + e^{2\bar{\epsilon}_3} \cos^2 (k,3)]} \end{matrix} \right\}} \right]$$
$$(2.47)$$

Finally the conventional volume strain becomes

$$\Delta = e^{\bar{\epsilon}_1} e^{\bar{\epsilon}_2} e^{\bar{\epsilon}_3} - 1 = e^{\bar{\epsilon}_1 + \bar{\epsilon}_2 + \bar{\epsilon}_3} - 1$$

and the logarithmic volume strain

$$\bar{\Delta} = \ln (1 + \Delta) = \bar{\epsilon}_1 + \bar{\epsilon}_2 + \bar{\epsilon}_3 \qquad (2.48)$$

REFERENCES

LOVE, A. E. H., "A Treatise on the Mathematical Theory of Elasticity," 4th ed., pp. 32–73, Dover Publications, New York, 1944.

LUDWIK, P., "Elemente der technologischen Mechanik," Springer-Verlag, Berlin, 1909.

NÁDAI, A., "Theory of Flow and Fracture of Solids," Vol. I, pp. 109–150, McGraw-Hill Book Company, Inc., New York, 1950.

SOKOLNIKOFF, I. S., "Mathematical Theory of Elasticity," pp. 1–34, McGraw-Hill Book Company, Inc., New York, 1946.

CHAPTER 3

ELASTIC BEHAVIOR OF MATERIALS

The preceding chapters presented analyses of the states of stress and strain at a point. Such analyses have general validity; specialization begins when relationships between the two physical entities are examined. The stress-strain relationships governing the behavior of an isotropic elastic body are the first and simplest example to be discussed. The importance of this example is due to the fact that most of the engineering materials present a more or less extended elastic range for sufficiently low values of the stresses; hence, the study of the gradual developing of plastic regions must be preceded by an analysis of the stresses in the elastic state.

3.1. Elastic Stress-Strain Relations

The relations between the instantaneous states of stress and strain at a point of a solid body within the elastic range are expressed by the "generalized Hooke's law ." With the tensor notations heretofore used, this law can be condensed into the two equations:

$$\mathbf{S}' = 2G\mathbf{E}' \tag{3.1}$$

and

$$\mathbf{S}'' = 3K\mathbf{E}'' \tag{3.2}$$

where G, the shear modulus, and K, the bulk modulus, are two constants which define the elastic behavior of an isotropic material. In terms of Young's modulus E and Poisson's ratio ν, these constants have the well-known expressions

$$G = \frac{E}{2(1 + \nu)}, \qquad K = \frac{E}{3(1 - 2\nu)}$$

If the tensors $\mathbf{S}$ and $\mathbf{E}$ are given with respect to an arbitrary cartesian reference frame, Eq. (3.1) can be written as

33

$$\begin{pmatrix} \dfrac{2\sigma_x - \sigma_y - \sigma_z}{3} & \tau_{xy} & \tau_{zx} \\[3mm] \tau_{xy} & \dfrac{2\sigma_y - \sigma_z - \sigma_x}{3} & \tau_{yz} \\[3mm] \tau_{zx} & \tau_{yz} & \dfrac{2\sigma_z - \sigma_x - \sigma_y}{3} \end{pmatrix}$$

$$= 2G \begin{pmatrix} \dfrac{2\epsilon_x - \epsilon_y - \epsilon_z}{3} & \dfrac{\gamma_{xy}}{2} & \dfrac{\gamma_{zx}}{2} \\[3mm] \dfrac{\gamma_{xy}}{2} & \dfrac{2\epsilon_y - \epsilon_z - \epsilon_x}{3} & \dfrac{\gamma_{yz}}{2} \\[3mm] \dfrac{\gamma_{zx}}{2} & \dfrac{\gamma_{yz}}{2} & \dfrac{2\epsilon_z - \epsilon_x - \epsilon_y}{3} \end{pmatrix} \tag{3.3}$$

Such a tensor equation has the meaning that each element on the left side equals $2G$ times the corresponding element on the right side. Thus, owing to the symmetry of the two tensors, Eq. (3.3) yields the following six equations:

$$\begin{aligned} 2\sigma_x - \sigma_y - \sigma_z &= 2G(2\epsilon_x - \epsilon_y - \epsilon_z) \\ 2\sigma_y - \sigma_z - \sigma_x &= 2G(2\epsilon_y - \epsilon_z - \epsilon_x) \\ 2\sigma_z - \sigma_x - \sigma_y &= 2G(2\epsilon_z - \epsilon_x - \epsilon_y) \\ \tau_{xy} &= G\gamma_{xy} \\ \tau_{yz} &= G\gamma_{yz} \\ \tau_{zx} &= G\gamma_{zx} \end{aligned} \tag{3.4}$$

Selecting the principal deviator strain axes as a reference frame, it can be seen that both the principal stress axes and the principal deviator stress axes coincide with the principal deviator strain axes. Equations (3.4) then reduce to the following three equations:

$$\begin{aligned} 2\sigma_1 - \sigma_2 - \sigma_3 &= 2G(2\epsilon_1 - \epsilon_2 - \epsilon_3) \\ 2\sigma_2 - \sigma_3 - \sigma_1 &= 2G(2\epsilon_2 - \epsilon_3 - \epsilon_1) \\ 2\sigma_3 - \sigma_1 - \sigma_2 &= 2G(2\epsilon_3 - \epsilon_1 - \epsilon_2) \end{aligned} \tag{3.5}$$

Equation (3.2) is essentially a relationship between two scalar quantities which can be written as

$$\sigma_m = 3K\epsilon_m \tag{3.6}$$

or also

$$I_1 = 3KJ_1 \tag{3.7}$$

From Eqs. (3.5) and (3.6) the principal strains can be expressed as follows:

$$\epsilon_1 = \frac{2\sigma_1 - \sigma_2 - \sigma_3}{6G} + \frac{\sigma_1 + \sigma_2 + \sigma_3}{9K}$$

$$\epsilon_2 = \frac{2\sigma_2 - \sigma_3 - \sigma_1}{6G} + \frac{\sigma_1 + \sigma_2 + \sigma_3}{9K} \qquad (3.8)$$

$$\epsilon_3 = \frac{2\sigma_3 - \sigma_1 - \sigma_2}{6G} + \frac{\sigma_1 + \sigma_2 + \sigma_3}{9K}$$

3.2. Elastic Strain Energy

The well-known expression for the strain energy per unit volume of an elastic body is, in terms of the principal stresses σ_1, σ_2, σ_3 and the principal strains ϵ_1, ϵ_2, ϵ_3,

$$U = \tfrac{1}{2}(\sigma_1\epsilon_1 + \sigma_2\epsilon_2 + \sigma_3\epsilon_3) \qquad (3.9)$$

Substituting the expressions for the principal strains in terms of the principal stresses [see Eqs. (3.8)], the strain energy is obtained in terms of the principal stresses and the material constants G and K:

$$U = \frac{(\sigma_1 - \sigma_2)^2 + (\sigma_2 - \sigma_3)^2 + (\sigma_3 - \sigma_1)^2}{12G} + \frac{(\sigma_1 + \sigma_2 + \sigma_3)^2}{18K} \qquad (3.10)$$

The same procedure applied to the deviator stress tensor and to the corresponding deviator strain tensor yields the following expression for the so-called "strain energy of distortion":

$$U' = \frac{1}{2}\left[\frac{(2\sigma_1 - \sigma_2 - \sigma_3)^2}{18G} + \frac{(2\sigma_2 - \sigma_3 - \sigma_1)^2}{18G} + \frac{(2\sigma_3 - \sigma_1 - \sigma_2)^2}{18G} \right]$$

$$= \frac{(\sigma_1 - \sigma_2)^2 + (\sigma_2 - \sigma_3)^2 + (\sigma_3 - \sigma_1)^2}{12G} = -\frac{I_2'}{2G} = \frac{3}{4G}\tau_{oct}^2 \qquad (3.11)$$

Finally, the strain energy corresponding to the spherical stress tensor, the so-called "strain energy of dilatation," is found to be

$$U'' = \frac{(\sigma_1 + \sigma_2 + \sigma_3)^2}{18K} = \frac{\sigma_m^2}{2K} = \frac{I_1^2}{18K} \qquad (3.12)$$

While in general the strain energies of two arbitrary superimposed states of stress are not additive, in this case it can be seen that

$$U = U' + U'' \qquad (3.13)$$

CHAPTER 4

THEORIES OF STRENGTH

The purpose of this chapter is to survey the theories and methods of representation widely used to describe the "failure" of a material or the limits of elastic strength, *i.e.*, the conditions under which the elastic relations outlined in the preceding chapter cease to be valid. The problem has two ramifications according to the phenomena occurring after the limit of elastic strength has been reached. In the case of so-called "brittle failure" or "fracture," separation of material particles takes place while the strains are still essentially in the elastic range. The term "plastic yielding" is used when large permanent deformations follow the elastic behavior with a more or less noticeable transition phase. Older theories often do not distinguish between the two types of failure. A third type of failure, fracture after extended plastic strains, is sometimes represented by similar methods, but will not be treated in this book.

4.1. Older Failure Theories

The common philosophy of all theories of strength is to predict the behavior of a material for generally complex stress states on the basis of experimental observations under particularly simple and well-duplicated conditions, *e.g.*, uniaxial states of stress. For isotropic materials the orientation of the principal axes is immaterial, and the values of the three principal stresses suffice to describe the state of stress uniquely.

A theory of failure consists essentially in a relationship of the type

$$F(\sigma_1, \sigma_2, \sigma_3, k_1, k_2 \ldots) = 0$$

(where k_1, k_2, . . . are material constants to be determined experimentally) so constructed that a stress state, defined by principal stresses that satisfy it, produces failure. To illustrate the development of engineering thinking on this subject, several approaches, mostly of historical interest, may be mentioned.

(*a*) *The Lamé-Navier Theory.* According to this theory, two strength values, the ultimate tensile strength σ_{tu} and the ultimate compressive strength σ_{cu}, are to be known in order to predict the behavior of a material. Failure is assumed to occur when either the largest principal stress is equal to σ_{tu}:

$$\sigma_I = \sigma_{tu}$$

or the smallest principal stress is equal to $-\sigma_{cu}$:

$$\sigma_{III} = -\sigma_{cu}$$

This theory disregards entirely the influence of two out of three principal stresses and conflicts with the most fundamental experimental facts.

(b) *Maximum-normal-strain Theory (Saint-Venant)*. This theory states that (brittle) failure occurs when the maximum elastic normal strain ϵ_I reaches a critical value to be determined experimentally. As it was shown in Art. 3.1, the expression for ϵ_I is

$$\epsilon_I = \frac{2\sigma_I - \sigma_{II} - \sigma_{III}}{6G} + \frac{\sigma_I + \sigma_{II} + \sigma_{III}}{9K} = \frac{1}{E}[\sigma_I - \nu(\sigma_{II} + \sigma_{III})]$$

It can be seen that the same critical value of ϵ_I is obtained at failure in uniaxial tension ($\epsilon_I = \sigma_{tu}/E$) and at failure in uniaxial compression $[\epsilon_I = (\sigma_{cu}/E)\nu]$ only if

$$\frac{\sigma_{tu}}{\sigma_{cu}} = \nu$$

This relationship also conflicts with experimental evidence.

(c) *Beltrami's Energy Theory*. This theory considers the total elastic strain energy U [see Eq. (18.2)] as the measure of impending failure. An examination of the expression for U shows that, for any given critical value of U, failure can be produced by a sufficiently high hydrostatic pressure ($\sigma_1 = \sigma_2 = \sigma_3$), a conclusion that conflicts with well-known experimental facts.

(d) *Maximum-shearing-stress Theory*. The concept of the maximum shearing stress as a measure of impending failure originated with Coulomb and was later proposed by Tresca and Saint-Venant as a yield condition. This theory predicts failure to occur when

$$\tau_{max} = \frac{\sigma_I - \sigma_{III}}{2}$$

reaches a critical value to be determined from a single experiment. As a theory of fracture, it implies the existence of the same value for ultimate tensile strength, $\tau_{max} = \sigma_{tu}/2$, and for ultimate compressive strength, $\tau_{max} = \sigma_{cu}/2$, and consequently $\sigma_{tu} = \sigma_{cu}$, a condition that is not verified for brittle materials. The theory has an important role as a yield condition, and it will be discussed in that connection in the next article.

(e) *Mohr's Theory*. This theory may be considered as a generalized version of the maximum-shearing-stress theory. Both theories are based on the implicit assumption that only the largest and smallest principal stresses σ_I and σ_{III} have influence on the impending failure, while the intermediate stress σ_{II} has no influence whatsoever. In terms of Mohr's graphical representation of the state of stress (see Art. 1.6) this means that the largest principal circle with the radius

$$\tau_{max} = \frac{\sigma_I - \sigma_{III}}{2}$$

is the only decisive measure of impending failure. But while the maximum-shearing-stress theory assigns a constant radius to the largest principal circles which represent critical conditions, Mohr's theory of failure admits that the radius be a function of the coordinate of the center $(\sigma_I + \sigma_{III})/2$, so that circles which represent critical states of stress have a common envelope, to be determined experimentally for a given material in order to define its behavior (see Fig. 4.1).

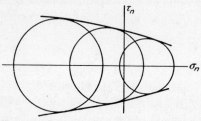

FIG. 4.1. Graphical representation of critical states of stress according to Mohr's theory of strength.

Mohr's theory is notable in that it allows for an effect of the mean stress σ_m. Experimental evidence indicates that both fracture and yielding of any material are affected by the mean stress, to an extent that depends upon the material. The yield conditions, to be discussed below, neglect this effect which appears to be small in the range of stresses occurring in practical applications. In regard to fracturing, however, Mohr's theory predicts that the largest principal stress σ_I at the moment of fracture increases with increasing mean stress σ_m, and this prediction has been confirmed by recent tests on metals. Thus, Mohr's theory appears at present to be the best-adapted device to describe the behavior of nonmetallic brittle materials and of some brittle metals. The additional claim by Mohr connected with this theory, that the point of tangency of the critical stress circle with the envelope represents the stress in the plane of fracture, however is not borne out by experimental results. A more detailed discussion of this theory, as related to fracture, is outside the scope of this book.

4.2. Yield Conditions or "Plasticity Conditions"

At present there are two theories available to predict the incipience of plastic yielding in ductile metals. Both theories neglect the effect of the mean stress σ_m and require the knowledge of a single material constant, the "yield stress" in uniaxial state of stress, assumed to be identical for tension and compression, in order to predict the behavior under any given combination of principal stresses.

(*a*) The *maximum-shearing-stress condition*, proposed by Tresca and Saint-Venant as a yield condition, states that plastic yielding begins when $\tau_{max} = (\sigma_I - \sigma_{III})/2$ reaches a critical value. Both in uniaxial tension ($\sigma_I = \sigma_0$, $\sigma_{II} = \sigma_{III} = 0$) and in uniaxial compression ($\sigma_I = \sigma_{II} = 0$, $\sigma_{III} = -\sigma_0$), the maximum shearing stress is $\sigma_0/2$; hence, the yield condition can be stated as

$$\tau_{max} = \frac{\sigma_I - \sigma_{III}}{2} = \frac{\sigma_0}{2}$$

or

$$\sigma_I - \sigma_{III} = \sigma_0 \tag{4.1}$$

(*b*) The *energy-of-distortion condition*, introduced by von Mises and reinterpreted later by Hencky, postulates that yielding sets in when the quantity

$$U' = \frac{1}{12G} [(\sigma_1 - \sigma_2)^2 + (\sigma_2 - \sigma_3)^2 + (\sigma_3 - \sigma_1)^2]$$

reaches a critical value.

For a uniaxial state of stress, for example, $\sigma_1 = \sigma_0$, $\sigma_2 = \sigma_3 = 0$, the energy of distortion becomes

$$U' = \frac{\sigma_0^2}{6G}$$

and the yield condition is stated as

$$\frac{1}{12G} [(\sigma_1 - \sigma_2)^2 + (\sigma_2 - \sigma_3)^2 + (\sigma_3 - \sigma_1)^2] = \frac{\sigma_0^2}{6G}$$

or

$$(\sigma_1 - \sigma_2)^2 + (\sigma_2 - \sigma_3)^2 + (\sigma_3 - \sigma_1)^2 = 2\sigma_0^2 \tag{4.2}$$

Recalling Eq. (3.11), this can be written in the form

$$\tau_{oct} = \frac{\sqrt{2}}{3} \sigma_0 = 0.471\sigma_0 \tag{4.3}$$

which justifies the term of "octahedral-shearing-stress condition" introduced by Nádai and often used for the von Mises–Hencky theory.

The relative merits of the two yield conditions (4.1) and (4.2) will be discussed in Chap. 6 from the standpoint of consistency with experimental data. Both conditions imply the same yield stress σ_0 in uniaxial tension and in uniaxial compression, and both are independent of the mean stress σ_m. The maximum-shearing-stress condition, to be stated in a general fashion, requires that the relative magnitudes of the principal stresses be known in advance and the ordering rule $\sigma_I \geq \sigma_{II} \geq \sigma_{III}$ be applied; hence the use of roman numerals as subscripts in Eq. (4.1). Conversely, the distortion-energy condition can be formulated without advance knowledge of the relative magnitudes of the principal stresses, and, accordingly, arbitrarily assigned arabic numerals are used as subscripts in Eq. (4.2).

The geometrical method of representation to be presented in the next article will afford a direct quantitative comparison between the two yield conditions.

4.3. The Haigh-Westergaard Stress Space

A state of stress, defined by the principal stresses σ_1, σ_2, σ_3, is represented in the "stress space" by a point having the cartesian coordinates σ_1, σ_2, σ_3.

The line Λ that passes through the origin and makes the same angle, $\cos^{-1} 1/\sqrt{3} = 54°44'$, with the three reference axes is defined by the two equations

$$\sigma_1 = \sigma_2 = \sigma_3 \tag{4.4}$$

Hence, for all points on this line the deviatorial part of the stress tensor vanishes, and they represent spherical states of stress.

Lines parallel to Λ but not passing through the origin have the equations

$$\sigma_1 - C_1 = \sigma_2 - C_2 = \sigma_3 - C_3 \tag{4.5}$$

where C_1, C_2, C_3 are three arbitrary constants. All points along such a line represent stress tensors having the same deviatorial component:

$$\mathbf{S'} = \begin{pmatrix} \dfrac{2C_1 - C_2 - C_3}{3} & 0 & 0 \\ 0 & \dfrac{2C_2 - C_3 - C_1}{3} & 0 \\ 0 & 0 & \dfrac{2C_3 - C_1 - C_2}{3} \end{pmatrix} \tag{4.6}$$

The plane Π passing through the origin and perpendicular to the above defined line Λ has the equation

$$\sigma_1 + \sigma_2 + \sigma_3 = 0 \tag{4.7}$$

and all points on this plane represent deviatorial states of stress for which $\mathbf{S''} = 0$.

Planes parallel to Π but not containing the origin have the equation

$$\sigma_1 + \sigma_2 + \sigma_3 = C \tag{4.8}$$

where C is an arbitrary constant. All points on such a plane correspond to states of stress with the same mean normal stress:

$$\sigma_m = \frac{C}{3} \tag{4.9}$$

The properties of the stress space stated above give rise to the following procedure for the resolution of a state of stress represented by a point P in the stress space into its spherical and deviatorial components (see Fig. 4.2). Place a line Λ' parallel to line Λ through the given point P; the point of intersection P' of Λ' with the plane Π represents S', the deviatorial part of the stress tensor S represented by point P. Then,

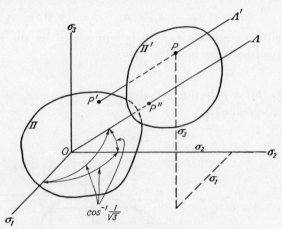

Fig. 4.2. The Haigh-Westergaard stress space.

place a plane Π' parallel to plane Π through the given point P; the point of intersection P'' of Π' with the line Λ represents S'', the spherical component of the stress tensor S.

4.4. Yield Surfaces

A yield condition, analytically expressed in the form

$$F(\sigma_1, \sigma_2, \sigma_3, \sigma_0) = 0$$

is the equation of a so-called "yield surface" in the stress space. As both yield conditions (4.1) and (4.2) are independent of the mean normal stress σ_m, it can be concluded that in both cases the yield surface must be generated by lines parallel to Λ. Such a prismatic or cylindrical surface is fully defined by its intersection with a plane. Select, for example, the (σ_1, σ_2) coordinate plane, having the equation, $\sigma_3 = 0$; obviously the intersection of the yield surface with such a plane represents the yield condition for states of plane stress.

(a) The *maximum-shearing-stress* condition

$$\sigma_\mathrm{I} - \sigma_\mathrm{III} = \sigma_0$$

assumes six different expressions in various regions of the (σ_1, σ_2) plane, depending upon the relative magnitudes and upon the signs of σ_1 and σ_2

(see Fig. 4.3). In the first quadrant, between the σ_1 axis and the bisector of the two axes, the ordering rule requires to put

$$\sigma_{\text{I}} = \sigma_1, \qquad \sigma_{\text{II}} = \sigma_2, \qquad \sigma_{\text{III}} = 0$$

hence, the condition equation becomes $\sigma_1 = \sigma_0$ and yields the line AB. In the same quadrant, between the bisector and the σ_2 axis, one has

$$\sigma_{\text{I}} = \sigma_2, \qquad \sigma_{\text{II}} = \sigma_1, \qquad \sigma_{\text{III}} = 0$$

and the condition equation $\sigma_2 = \sigma_0$ is represented by the line BC. In the second quadrant, one has, throughout,

$$\sigma_{\text{I}} = \sigma_2, \qquad \sigma_{\text{II}} = 0, \qquad \sigma_{\text{III}} = \sigma_1$$

hence, the condition equation is written as $\sigma_2 - \sigma_1 = \sigma_0$, and line CD is obtained correspondingly.

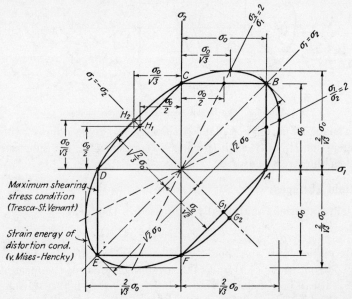

FIG. 4.3. Graphical representation of the yield conditions for plane stress ($\sigma_3 = 0$).

By proceeding similarly for the third and fourth quadrants, it can be found that the yield surface intersects the (σ_1, σ_2) plane along the hexagon $ABCDEF$; and from the interchangeability of the σ_1, σ_2, σ_3 axes it can be concluded that the yield surface is a regular hexagonal prism with the line Λ as its center line (see Fig. 4.4).

(b) The equation expressing the *strain-energy-of-distortion* condition becomes, by putting $\sigma_3 = 0$,

$$\sigma_1^2 - \sigma_1\sigma_2 + \sigma_2^2 = \sigma_0^2 \tag{4.10}$$

This is the equation of an ellipse, with the major and minor axes bisecting the σ_1 and σ_2 axes and passing through the vertices of the hexagon above shown to represent the maximum-shearing-stress condition.

Figure 4.3 affords a comparison between the two yield conditions. They predict the same yield strength for "balanced biaxial states of stress," in which

$$\sigma_1 = \sigma_2 = \pm\sigma_0$$

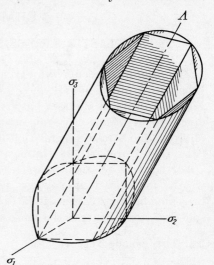

represented by points B and E and for uniaxial stress states, represented by points A, C, D, F. The points of greatest deviation between the two yield conditions are indicated in Fig. 4.3. In particular, for pure shear, $\sigma_1 = -\sigma_2$, represented by points G_1, G_2, H_1, H_2, the maximum-shearing-stress condition predicts yielding at the values

$$\sigma_1 = -\sigma_2 = \pm \frac{\sigma_0}{2}$$

FIG. 4.4. The yield surfaces.

while according to the distortion-energy condition, the yield strength is reached when

$$\sigma_1 = -\sigma_2 = \pm \frac{\sigma_0}{\sqrt{3}}$$

REFERENCES

HAIGH, B. P., The Strain Energy Function and the Elastic Limit, *Engineering*, Vol. 109, p. 158, 1920.

HENCKY, H., Zur Theorie plastischer Deformationen und der hierdurch im Material hervorgerufenen Nachspannungen, *Z. angew. Math. Mechanik*, Vol. 4, pp. 323–334, April, 1924.

MOHR, O., "Abhandlungen aus dem Gebiete der technischen Mechanik," 2d ed., pp. 192–235, Wilhelm Ernst & Sohn, Berlin, 1914.

NÁDAI, A., "Theory of Flow and Fracture of Solids," Vol. I, pp. 175–228, McGraw-Hill Book Company, Inc., New York, 1950.

VON MISES, R., "Mechanik der festen Körper im plastisch deformablen Zustand," pp. 582–592, Göttinger Nachrichten, 1913.

WESTERGAARD, H. M., On the Resistance of Ductile Materials to Combined Stresses, *J. Franklin Inst.*, p. 627, May, 1920.

CHAPTER 5

PLASTIC STRESS-STRAIN RELATIONS

This chapter presents the various theories employed to describe the behavior of ductile metals when the limit of yielding has been exceeded. First, the behavior of strain-hardening metals in the plastic range will be described by means of certain invariantive characteristics of the states of stress and strain, the relationships between which are the so-called "universal" stress-strain relations.

Furthermore, relations between the stress and strain tensors themselves will be formulated; in analogy with the elastic stress-strain relations presented in Chap. 3, this will be done separately for the deviator and the spherical components of the tensors.

5.1. The Tensile Test

The simplest type of loading is represented by the uniaxial stress condition, e.g., the tensile test for which $\sigma_1 > 0$, $\sigma_2 = \sigma_3 = 0$. The well-

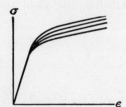

FIG. 5.1. Stress-strain curves at various strain rates.

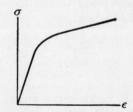

FIG. 5.2. Typical stress-strain curve for strain-hardening material.

known stress-strain diagram in which the axial principal stress σ_1 is plotted against the axial strain ϵ_1 affords a useful representation of the plastic as well as of the elastic behavior.

Figure 5.1 shows a family of typical stress-strain curves for specimens of a strain-hardening metal tested at various strain rates. At room temperature the strain-rate effect is considered negligible for all practical purposes, and the family of curves is replaced by a single curve, as shown in Fig. 5.2, the ordinates of which in the plastic range are termed as "flow stresses."

Among the various attempts at representing analytically the tensile stress-strain curve of a strain-hardening metal, the following two deserve

44

note. One method approximates the continuous curve by two straight lines, thus replacing the smooth transition curve by a sharp breaking point, the ordinate of which is taken as the yield strength or initial flow stress σ_0. (see Fig. 5.3). The first straight-line branch of the diagram corresponds to the elastic range and makes an angle of $\tan^{-1} E$ with the ϵ axis, where E is Young's modulus. The second straight-line branch, which represents in an idealized fashion the strain-hardening range, makes an angle of $\tan^{-1} B$ with the ϵ axis and has the equation

$$\sigma = \sigma_0 + B\left(\epsilon - \frac{\sigma_0}{E}\right) = A + B\epsilon \tag{5.1}$$

where

$$A = \sigma_0\left(1 - \frac{B}{E}\right) \tag{5.2}$$

A similar approximation is sometimes used when a short portion of the stress-strain curve in the strain-hardening range is replaced by its tangent, the slope of which is called the "tangent modulus."

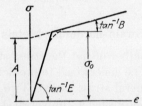

FIG. 5.3. Stress-strain curve approximated by two straight lines.

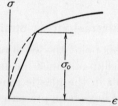

FIG. 5.4. Stress-strain curve approximated by power expression in plastic range.

Another approach uses a power expression of the type

$$\sigma = k\epsilon^m \tag{5.3}$$

where k and m (the "strain-hardening exponent") are two characteristic constants of the metal, to be determined to best fit the experimentally obtained curve. If ϵ represents the *total* strain, the curve should pass through the point representing the yield stress and the corresponding elastic strain; in such case, Eq. (5.2) should be used only in the strain-hardening range (see Fig. 5.4). The power expression is often used to represent only the plastic part of the strain, particularly when the material does not have a definite yield point.

At high temperatures the strain-rate effect cannot be neglected any more; on the other hand, the stress-strain curve has the tendency to flatten out rapidly (see Fig. 5.5), and strain-hardening becomes negligible.

The study of the behavior of metals in the strain-rate sensitive range is rather complex and is beyond the scope of this book.

For many practical applications, the metal is assumed to have negligible strain-hardening, *i.e.*, its stress-strain diagram beyond the yield point is approximated by a horizontal straight line, with the constant ordinate σ_0 (see Fig. 5.6). A further idealization can be obtained by neglecting the elastic strains, as shown in Fig. 5.7. Plastic behavior with constant flow stress is termed "ideally plastic" behavior.

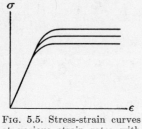 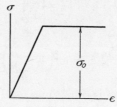 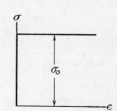

FIG. 5.5. Stress-strain curves at various strain rates with negligible strain-hardening.

FIG. 5.6. Typical stress-strain curve for ideally plastic behavior.

FIG. 5.7. Typical stress-strain curve for ideally plastic behavior and negligible elastic strains.

5.2. Universal Stress-Strain Relations for Strain-hardening Metals

At this point the question arises as to whether or not the stress-strain relationship obtained for uniaxial stress can be generalized to predict the behavior in the plastic range under any general stress state. Two suggestions have been presented in the literature for such a "universal stress-strain relation," and they afford, in a sense, extensions of the two yield conditions, the maximum-shearing-stress condition and the distortion-energy condition, discussed in Art. 4.2.

(*a*) Ludwik was the first to consider this problem in 1909. In line with the then-prevailing concept of the maximum shearing stress as a criterion of yielding, he assumed that such a stress is a unique function of the *plastic* portion of the maximum logarithmic shearing strain defined as $\bar{\gamma}_{max} = \bar{\epsilon}_I - \bar{\epsilon}_{III}$. He pointed out that the maximum shearing stress should be a *true* stress, *i.e.*, calculated with reference to the instantaneous cross-sectional dimensions of the metal specimen.

(*b*) Ros and Eichinger in 1929 proposed to extend the von Mises–Hencky distortion-energy criterion of yielding; they considered the effective stress, defined in Art. 1.7 as

$$\sigma_{eff} = \frac{\sqrt{2}}{2} \sqrt{(\sigma_1 - \sigma_2)^2 + (\sigma_2 - \sigma_3)^2 + (\sigma_3 - \sigma_1)^2} \qquad (5.4)$$

as a function of the following composite invariant of the plastic portion of the logarithmic strain:

$$\frac{1}{\sqrt{6}} \sqrt{(\bar{\epsilon}_1 - \bar{\epsilon}_2)^2 + (\bar{\epsilon}_2 - \bar{\epsilon}_3)^2 + (\bar{\epsilon}_3 - \bar{\epsilon}_1)^2} \qquad (5.5)$$

Nádai, in 1937, introduced the now generally accepted notations of "octahedral shearing stress" and "octahedral shearing strain," discussed in Arts. 1.7 and 2.6, and proposed to represent the strain-hardening behavior of metals by the functional relation

$$\tau_{oct} = F(\bar{\gamma}_{oct}) \qquad (5.6)$$

Here τ_{oct} is determined by Eq. (1.33) from the *true* principal stresses, and $\bar{\gamma}_{oct}$ is defined by the integral

$$\bar{\gamma}_{oct} = \int d\bar{\gamma}_{oct} = \tfrac{2}{3} \int \sqrt{(d\bar{\epsilon}_1 - d\bar{\epsilon}_2)^2 + (d\bar{\epsilon}_2 - d\bar{\epsilon}_3)^2 + (d\bar{\epsilon}_3 - d\bar{\epsilon}_1)^2} \qquad (5.7)$$

where $\bar{\epsilon}_1$, $\bar{\epsilon}_2$, and $\bar{\epsilon}_3$ are the logarithmic principal strains.

Equation (5.7) can be integrated, under conditions of "proportional straining" to be discussed later in Art. 5.6, to yield

$$\bar{\gamma}_{oct} = \tfrac{2}{3} \sqrt{(\bar{\epsilon}_1 - \bar{\epsilon}_2)^2 + (\bar{\epsilon}_2 - \bar{\epsilon}_3)^2 + (\bar{\epsilon}_3 - \bar{\epsilon}_1)^2} \qquad (5.8)$$

and it can be seen that this expression differs from Ros and Eichinger's composite invariant [Eq. (5.5)] only by the constant factor $\sqrt{8/3}$.

It is to be noted, however, that neither one of the two concepts furnishes a fully satisfactory representation of the experimental data on metals, to be discussed later. Points representing actual stress-strain data fall in between the two "generalized stress-strain curves" here discussed.

5.3. Saint-Venant's Theory of Plastic Flow

A universal stress-strain relation for a strain-hardening material, or its specialized form for an ideally plastic material, $\sigma_0 = $ constant, is formulated to interrelate an invariant function of the stress tensor with an invariant function of the strain tensor. Such a relationship, however, is insufficient for solving problems of stress distribution in the plastic state; relationships between the two tensors themselves that can be expanded into relationships between the corresponding tensor components are needed for such a purpose.

The elastic stress-strain relations discussed in Art. 3.1 are examples of linear relations existing separately between the instantaneous values of the deviator tensors and separately between the instantaneous values of the spherical tensors.

There are other tensor relations conceivable and having important applications in the mechanics of continua.

(*a*) The generalized Newton's law for viscous flow establishes the following relationship between the deviator stress tensor and the deviator of the strain-rate tensor:

$$\mathbf{S}' = 2\mu\dot{\mathbf{E}}' \tag{5.9}$$

where $\dot{\mathbf{E}}' = d\mathbf{E}'/dt$ is the rate, or derivative with respect to time, of the deviator strain tensor, or also the deviator of the strain-rate tensor; μ is the coefficient of viscosity.

(*b*) Kelvin's visco-elastic stress-strain relation proposes to describe the behavior of anelastic solids, assumes the deviator stress tensor to be a linear function of the deviator strain tensor and of the deviator strain-rate tensor:

$$\mathbf{S}' = 2G\mathbf{E}' + 2\mu\dot{\mathbf{E}}' \tag{5.10}$$

(*c*) Maxwell's stress-strain relation for elasto-viscous fluids proposes a linear relation between the deviator stress tensor, the deviator stress-rate tensor, and the strain-rate tensor:

$$\mathbf{S}' + \frac{\mu}{G}\dot{\mathbf{S}}' = 2\mu\dot{\mathbf{E}}' \tag{5.11}$$

Saint-Venant's theory, published in 1870 and now considered as the most suitable to describe plastic-flow phenomena, can be condensed into the two tensor equations:

$$\mathbf{S}' = 2\lambda\dot{\mathbf{E}}' \tag{5.12}$$
$$\mathbf{E}'' = 0 \tag{5.13}$$

The first equation expresses proportionality between the deviator stress tensor and the deviator strain-rate tensor. It will be shown that the scalar factor λ is a function of the yield strength σ_0 and of the rate of straining, and hence a function of the space coordinates of the point and of time. Thus, the similarity between Eq. (5.12), which governs the nonviscous plastic flow, and Eq. (5.9), which governs viscous flow and in which μ is a true constant for a given substance at a given temperature, is apparent only.

By rearranging Eq. (5.12) as follows:

$$\mathbf{S}' = \left(\frac{2\lambda}{dt}\right) d\mathbf{E}' \tag{5.14}$$

the *incremental* character of the Saint-Venant theory is better emphasized. The significance of the factor λ can be shown by recalling that according to Eqs. (1.33) and (2.32) the octahedral shearing stress and octahedral shearing strain are composite invariants of the stress and strain tensors and that consequently the same relationship [Eq. (5.12)] existing between the deviator stress tensor and the deviator strain-rate tensor must hold also between τ_{oct} and $\dot{\gamma}_{oct}/2$ that is,

$$\tau_{oct} = \lambda \dot{\gamma}_{oct} \tag{5.15}$$

from which

$$\lambda = \frac{\tau_{oct}}{\dot{\gamma}_{oct}} \tag{5.16}$$

Furthermore, the distortion-energy condition of yielding can be introduced, as expressed by Eq. (4.3),

$$\tau_{oct} = \frac{\sqrt{2}}{3} \sigma_0$$

to obtain

$$\lambda = \frac{\sqrt{2}}{3} \frac{\sigma_0}{\dot{\gamma}_{oct}} \tag{5.17}$$

The second equation of Saint-Venant's theory, Eq. (5.13), is actually a scalar equation. It is usually referred to as the "volume-constancy equation," and expresses that the mean normal strain ϵ_m, and consequently also the volume strain, $\Delta = 3\epsilon_m$, is zero, or, from Eq. (2.23),

$$\epsilon_1 + \epsilon_2 + \epsilon_3 = 0 \tag{5.18}$$

From Eq. (5.13) it follows also that

$$\dot{\mathbf{E}}'' = 0$$

or

$$d\epsilon_1 + d\epsilon_2 + d\epsilon_3 = 0 \tag{5.19}$$

and consequently

$$\dot{\mathbf{E}} = \dot{\mathbf{E}}' + \dot{\mathbf{E}}'' = \dot{\mathbf{E}}' \tag{5.20}$$

Equation (5.14) can now be written as follows:

$$\mathbf{S}' = \left(\frac{2\lambda}{dt}\right) d\mathbf{E} \tag{5.21}$$

This equation expresses proportionality between the deviator stress tensor and the strain-increment tensor. If the components of one of the two tensors are taken with reference to its principal axes, Eq. (5.21) requires that axes be principal axes for the other tensor also. In other words, Saint-Venant's theory implies coaxiality of the deviator stress tensor and the strain-increment tensor, and Eq. (5.21) can be written as a relationship between the matrices of the two tensors referred to the principal axes

$$
\begin{pmatrix}
\dfrac{2\sigma_1 - \sigma_2 - \sigma_3}{3} & 0 & 0 \\[2ex]
0 & \dfrac{2\sigma_2 - \sigma_3 - \sigma_1}{3} & 0 \\[2ex]
0 & 0 & \dfrac{2\sigma_3 - \sigma_1 - \sigma_3}{3}
\end{pmatrix}
= \frac{2\lambda}{dt}
\begin{pmatrix}
d\epsilon_1 & 0 & 0 \\
0 & d\epsilon_2 & 0 \\
0 & 0 & d\epsilon_3
\end{pmatrix}
\tag{5.22}
$$

which can be expanded into the following three equations:

$$
2\sigma_1 - \sigma_2 - \sigma_3 = \frac{6\lambda}{dt} d\epsilon_1
$$

$$
2\sigma_2 - \sigma_3 - \sigma_1 = \frac{6\lambda}{dt} d\epsilon_2 \tag{5.23}
$$

$$
2\sigma_3 - \sigma_1 - \sigma_2 = \frac{6\lambda}{dt} d\epsilon_3
$$

Eliminating $6\lambda/dt$ from the first and second equation and from the first and third equation, one obtains

$$
\frac{2\sigma_1 - \sigma_2 - \sigma_3}{2\sigma_2 - \sigma_3 - \sigma_1} = \frac{d\epsilon_1}{d\epsilon_2}
$$

$$
\frac{2\sigma_1 - \sigma_2 - \sigma_3}{2\sigma_3 - \sigma_1 - \sigma_2} = \frac{d\epsilon_1}{d\epsilon_3}
\tag{5.24}
$$

which together with the volume-constancy relation [Eq. (5.19)]

$$
d\epsilon_1 + d\epsilon_2 + d\epsilon_3 = 0
$$

form a system of differential equations. This system must be integrated along a given stress path or given strain path to obtain in any specific case finite stress-strain relations. If the resultant deformations are small, in the sense indicated in Art. 2.7, conventional strains can be used in integrating this system of equations without serious error.

If the resultant deformations are large, however, the $d\epsilon$ strain increments are to be considered as expressed in terms of the instantaneous dimensions and replaced by $d\bar{\epsilon}$ terms, *i.e.*, by increments of the logarithmic strain.

It should be pointed out that Saint-Venant's theory establishes relationship between stresses and strain increments in the plastic range only, during loading ($d\tau_{oct} > 0$) or in neutral load condition ($d\tau_{oct} = 0$). In the range below the yield limit and during unloading ($d\tau_{oct} < 0$), the elastic stress-strain relations presented in Art. 3.1 apply. Whatever elastic strains may persist in the plastic range, they are neglected in this theory.

5.4. Reuss's Theory of Elasto-plastic Deformations

In conditions of constrained plastic flow, *e.g.*, in the presence of elastic regions adjacent to the plastic region, the deformations may be so small that the basic assumption of Saint-Venant's theory that elastic strains are negligible may lead to erroneous conclusions. Reuss's theory is intended to cover such cases by including in the expression of the total deviator strain tensor the elastic part of it, so that

$$E' = E'_e + E'_p \tag{5.25}$$

where the elastic deviator strain tensor E'_e obeys Hooke's law [see Eq. (3.1)]:

$$E'_e = \frac{1}{2G} S' \tag{5.26}$$

and the plastic deviator strain tensor E'_p is assumed to be related to the stress deviator according to the Saint-Venant theory:

$$dE'_p = \left(\frac{dt}{2\lambda}\right) S' \tag{5.27}$$

The volume changes are assumed to be purely elastic, *i.e.*,

$$S'' = 3KE'' \tag{5.28}$$

By differentiating both sides of Eq. (5.26), one obtains

$$dE'_e = \frac{1}{2G} dS' \tag{5.29}$$

and this in conjunction with Eqs. (5.25) and (5.27) gives the differential equation expressing Reuss's theory

$$S' + \left(\frac{\lambda}{G\,dt}\right) dS' = \left(\frac{2\lambda}{dt}\right) dE' \tag{5.30}$$

Coaxiality of the stress tensor and the strain tensor is not implicit in this equation, and unless coaxiality is imposed by the conditions of the problem, it cannot be expanded into differential equations between principal values of the two tensors; indeed, tensor equations have meaning only if all tensor components are referred to the same reference axes.

The differential equations, represented in condensed form by Eq. (5.30), are very intricate, even in case of assured coaxiality; their solution has been explored so far only in a few special cases by Reuss, and by Hill, Lee, and Tupper. It is to be recognized, however, that Reuss's theory is a realistic approach which takes into account the persistency of elastic strains during plastic flow, a fact that cannot be neglected in a rigorous treatment of the transition areas between elastic and plastic regions.

5.5. Hencky's Theory of Small Plastic Deformations

For small plastic strains Saint-Venant's differential equation (5.12) has been replaced by Hencky (1924) by an approximate relation between the deviator stress tensor and the deviator strain tensor:

$$\mathbf{S}' = 2G_p\mathbf{E}' \tag{5.31}$$

where G_p is variable from one point to another and can be considered, by analogy to the elastic relations, as a "plastic shear modulus."

Assuming here, as in Saint-Venant's theory, volume constancy, that is, $\mathbf{E}'' = 0$, Eq. (5.31) becomes

$$\mathbf{S}' = 2G_p\mathbf{E} \tag{5.32}$$

The proportionality between the two tensors implies coaxiality; hence this equation can be expanded in terms of principal stresses and strains as follows:

$$
\begin{aligned}
\epsilon_1 &= \frac{2\sigma_1 - \sigma_2 - \sigma_3}{6G_p} = \frac{1}{3G_p}\left(\sigma_1 - \frac{\sigma_2 + \sigma_3}{2}\right) = \frac{1}{E_p}\left(\sigma_1 - \frac{\sigma_2 + \sigma_3}{2}\right) \\
\epsilon_2 &= \frac{2\sigma_2 - \sigma_3 - \sigma_1}{6G_p} = \frac{1}{3G_p}\left(\sigma_2 - \frac{\sigma_3 + \sigma_1}{2}\right) = \frac{1}{E_p}\left(\sigma_2 - \frac{\sigma_3 + \sigma_1}{2}\right) \\
\epsilon_3 &= \frac{2\sigma_3 - \sigma_1 - \sigma_2}{6G_p} = \frac{1}{3G_p}\left(\sigma_3 - \frac{\sigma_1 + \sigma_2}{2}\right) = \frac{1}{E_p}\left(\sigma_3 - \frac{\sigma_1 + \sigma_2}{2}\right)
\end{aligned} \tag{5.33}
$$

E_p can be interpreted as a variable "plastic modulus" having the same role in these equations as Young's modulus has in the elastic equations. The factor $\frac{1}{2}$ takes the place of Poisson's ratio in consistence with the assumed volume constancy $(K \to \infty)$.

It is to be emphasized that the ϵ values in Eqs. (5.33) are small finite strains, and it is not permissible to calculate large total deformations by integrating Eqs. (5.33). The Hencky theory furnishes results identical with those of Saint-Venant's theory under two conditions: (a) that the principal axes of stress and strain for a particle do not rotate with respect to the particle during the process of straining; and (b) that the straining is "proportional," i.e., the following relations are fulfilled:

$$\frac{d\epsilon_1}{\epsilon_1} = \frac{d\epsilon_2}{\epsilon_2} = \frac{d\epsilon_3}{\epsilon_3}$$

5.6. Work of Plastic Deformation

The following developments are intended to obtain the expression for the work spent in plastic deformation of an ideally plastic material obeying von Mises' yield condition and Saint-Venant's theory of plastic flow. Consider an infinitesimal straining defined by infinitesimal increments $d\epsilon_1$, $d\epsilon_2$, $d\epsilon_3$ of the principal strains under the instantaneous stress state defined by σ_1, σ_2, σ_3; the work per unit volume dW, dissipated during such an infinitesimal straining, is

$$dW = \sigma_1\, d\epsilon_1 + \sigma_2\, d\epsilon_2 + \sigma_3\, d\epsilon_3 \qquad (5.34)$$

or, by recalling the volume-constancy relation [Eq. (5.19)] and expressing $d\epsilon_3$ in terms of $d\epsilon_1$ and $d\epsilon_2$, that is, $d\epsilon_3 = -d\epsilon_1 - d\epsilon_2$,

$$dW = (\sigma_1 - \sigma_3)\, d\epsilon_1 + (\sigma_2 - \sigma_3)\, d\epsilon_2 \qquad (5.35)$$

From Eq. (5.24) it follows that

$$d\epsilon_2 = d\epsilon_1 \frac{2\sigma_2 - \sigma_3 - \sigma_1}{2\sigma_1 - \sigma_2 - \sigma_3}$$

and, introducing this expression into Eq. (5.35), one obtains, after obvious manipulations,

$$dW = d\epsilon_1 \frac{(\sigma_1 - \sigma_2)^2 + (\sigma_2 - \sigma_3)^2 + (\sigma_3 - \sigma_1)^2}{2\sigma_1 - \sigma_2 - \sigma_3} \qquad (5.36)$$

With reference to Eq. (4.2) expressing von Mises' yield condition and to Eqs. (5.23) expressing Saint-Venant's theory, one has

$$dW = \frac{\sigma_0{}^2}{3\lambda}\, dt \qquad (5.37)$$

To integrate this equation, the variable λ is to be known as a function of the path of straining. By recalling the von Mises' yield condition formulated in terms of the octahedral shearing stress and the expression for λ given by Eq. (5.17), the following expressions result:

$$dW = \frac{\sqrt{2}}{2}\, \sigma_0\, \dot{\gamma}_{oct}\, dt = \frac{\sqrt{2}}{2}\, \sigma_0\, d\gamma_{oct} \qquad (5.38)$$

or also, by introducing the "effective strain" defined in Art. 2.6 as $\epsilon_{eff} = (\sqrt{2}/2)\gamma_{oct}$,

$$dW = \sigma_0\, d\epsilon_{eff} \qquad (5.39)$$

When the deformations are large, logarithmic strain increments are to be introduced in the above formulas before integrating them. The increment of the logarithmic octahedral shearing strain is defined by the expression

$$d\bar{\gamma}_{oct} = \tfrac{2}{3}\, \sqrt{(d\bar{\epsilon}_1 - d\bar{\epsilon}_2)^2 + (d\bar{\epsilon}_2 - d\bar{\epsilon}_3)^2 + (d\bar{\epsilon}_3 - d\bar{\epsilon}_1)^2} \qquad (5.40)$$

which, with reference to the volume-constancy relation,

$$d\bar{\epsilon}_1 + d\bar{\epsilon}_2 + d\bar{\epsilon}_3 = 0,$$

reduces to

$$d\bar{\gamma}_{oct} = \sqrt{\tfrac{8}{3}} \sqrt{d\bar{\epsilon}_1{}^2 + d\bar{\epsilon}_1\, d\bar{\epsilon}_2 + d\bar{\epsilon}_2{}^2} \qquad (5.41)$$

Nádai has shown that in case of "proportional straining," with

$$\frac{d\bar{\epsilon}_1}{\bar{\epsilon}_1} = \frac{d\bar{\epsilon}_2}{\bar{\epsilon}_2} = \frac{d\bar{\epsilon}_3}{\bar{\epsilon}_3},$$

this expression can be integrated to yield

$$\bar{\gamma}_{oct} = \sqrt{\tfrac{8}{3}} \sqrt{\bar{\epsilon}_1{}^2 + \bar{\epsilon}_1\bar{\epsilon}_2 + \bar{\epsilon}_2{}^2} \qquad (5.42)$$

which defines the logarithmic octahedral shearing strain. From the discussion presented in Art. 2.7 it is obvious that $\bar{\gamma}_{oct}$ does not represent necessarily the logarithmic shearing strain of planes parallel to the octahedral planes.

In the special case of large "proportional straining," the total work W is obtained by integrating the right side of Eq. (5.38):

$$W = \int dW = \frac{2}{\sqrt{3}}\, \sigma_0 \sqrt{\bar{\epsilon}_1{}^2 + \vec{\epsilon}_1\bar{\epsilon}_2 + \bar{\epsilon}_2{}^2} \qquad (5.43)$$

REFERENCES

HENCKY, H., Zur Theorie plastischer Deformationen und der hierdurch im Material hervorgerufenen Nachspannungen, *Z. angew. Math. Mechanik*, Vol. 4, pp. 323–334, April, 1924.

HILL, R., General Features of Plastic-Elastic Problems as Exemplified by Some Particular Solutions, *J. Applied Mechanics*, Vol. 16, p. 295, September, 1949.

HILL, R., E. H. LEE, and S. J. TUPPER, The Theory of Combined Plastic and Elastic Deformation with Particular Reference to a Thick Tube under Internal Pressure, *Proc. Roy. Soc. (London)*, Series *A*, Vol. 191, p. 278, 1947.

LÉVY, M., Mémoire sur les équations générales des mouvements intérieurs des corps solides ductiles . . . , *Compt. rend. acad. sci. Paris*, Vol. 70, p. 1323, 1870.

LUDWIK, P., "Elemente der technologischen Mechanik," Springer-Verlag, Berlin, 1909.

NÁDAI, A., Plastic Behavior of Metals in the Strain-hardening Range. Part I, *J. Appl. Phys.*, Vol. 8, p. 205, March, 1937.

REUSS, A., Berücksichtigung der elastischen Formänderung in der Plastizitätstheorie, *Z. angew. Math. Mechanik*, Vol. 10, pp. 266–274, June, 1930.

ROS, M., and A. EICHINGER, Versuche zur Klärung der Frage der Bruchgefahr, *Eidgenöss. Materialprüf. u. Versuchsanstalt Ind.*, *Bauw. u. Gewerbe, Zürich*, Diskussionsbericht No. 34, February, 1929.

SAINT-VENANT, B., Mémoire sur l'établissement des equations différentielles des mouvements intérieurs opérés dans les corps solides ductiles . . . , *Compt. rend. acad. sci. Paris*, Vol. 70, p. 473, 1870.

CHAPTER 6

EXPERIMENTAL DATA

6.1. Plasticity Conditions

The two currently used conditions of plasticity, the maximum-shearing-stress condition and the distortion-energy condition, have the feature in common that they predict the beginning of yielding in terms of certain functions of the state of stress. Both functions are invariant with respect to various possible orientations of the principal stress axes; hence, their adoption implies the (statistical) isotropy of the polycrystalline metal. It is also common to both conditions that the same value of the stress function employed can be obtained from an infinite number of combinations of the principal stresses, or, in other words, various stress states can be considered as being equivalent to each other as far as the beginning of yielding is concerned. In particular, the addition of a hydrostatic state of stress of any magnitude is without influence on the plasticity conditions.

It should be pointed out that the plasticity conditions are purely phenomenological attempts to describe the metal behavior, without any real physical significance. There is no reason to assume that a material consisting of a large number of small crystals will deform plastically either along certain planes of maximum shearing stress or because a certain distortion-energy level has been reached. However, it is a well-established fact that each single crystallite deforms by slippage along certain crystallographic planes in certain crystallographic directions when the shearing-stress component along those directions reaches a critical value. Sachs (1928) proposed to evaluate the yield strength of a polycrystalline aggregate, subjected to simple stress states, by averaging the shearing-stress components along the critical slip directions for the various orientations of the principal directions with respect to the crystallographic axes· This averaging principle, applied to aggregates of face-centered cubic crystals and to two stress states, pure tension and pure torsion, yielded the ratio $1:1.15$ for the maximum shearing stress at the beginning of plastic flow. This is very closely the same ratio as that furnished by the distortion-energy condition $(2/\sqrt{3} = 1.155)$. Moreover, Dehlinger (1943) has shown that this conclusion can be generalized and that the distortion-energy condition of plasticity can be obtained, for any state of stress, by the process of averaging the yield strength of the cubic crystals which constitute the polycrystalline aggregate. This relationship is a most significant link between the phenomenological and physical approach to the problem of plastic flow.

6.2. Experiments on Thin-walled Tubes under Combined Axial Load and Internal Pressure

Most metals and alloys do not have a well-defined yield strength corresponding to zero plastic strain; furthermore, metal specimens are usually anisotropic to a certain extent. Therefore, among the many tests made to verify the validity of the two conditions of plasticity, those conducted on the same specimen and in such a way to eliminate the strain as a variable appear to be the most convincing. This applies particularly to the tests carried out by Lode (1928) on thin-walled tubes of steel, copper, and nickel. In these tests, the specimens were strained progressively under a variety of stress states obtained by various combinations of longitudinal tension and internal hydrostatic pressure.

A highly sensitive method of discerning between the two conditions of plasticity is that of examining the influence of the intermediate principal stress σ_{II}, upon the yielding. According to the maximum-shearing-stress condition, such influence is nonexistent, *i.e.*, Eq. (4.1),

$$\sigma_I - \sigma_{III} = \sigma_0$$

is valid regardless of the value of σ_{II}, or

$$\frac{\sigma_I - \sigma_{III}}{\sigma_0} = 1 \tag{6.1}$$

On the other hand, according to the distortion-energy condition, the ratio on the left side of the above equation is a function of σ_{II}. Lode introduced the parameter

$$\mu = \frac{\sigma_{II} - (\sigma_I + \sigma_{III})/2}{(\sigma_1 - \sigma_{III})/2} = \frac{2\sigma_{II} - \sigma_{III} - \sigma_I}{\sigma_I - \sigma_{III}} \tag{6.2}$$

to characterize the influence of the intermediate principal stress. From this equation one obtains

$$\sigma_{II} = \frac{\sigma_I + \sigma_{III}}{2} + \mu \frac{\sigma_I - \sigma_{III}}{2} \tag{6.3}$$

and substituting this expression into the distortion-energy condition [Eq. (4.2)]

$$(\sigma_I - \sigma_{II})^2 + (\sigma_{II} - \sigma_{III})^2 + (\sigma_{III} - \sigma_I)^2 = 2\sigma_0{}^2$$

one has, after simplifying,

$$\frac{\sigma_I - \sigma_{III}}{\sigma_0} = \frac{2}{\sqrt{3 + \mu^2}} \tag{6.4}$$

This relationship replaces Eq. (6.1) if the distortion-energy condition is valid. Figure 6.1 shows the experimental values $(\sigma_I - \sigma_{III})/\sigma_0$ plotted versus the parameter μ, and it indicates that they conform closely with Eq. (6.4).

A number of additional results of tests on tubular steel specimens by Ros and Eichinger (1929) confirm Lode's results and indicate a rather close consistency with the distortion-energy condition. It should be pointed out, however, that the observed deviations from the latter

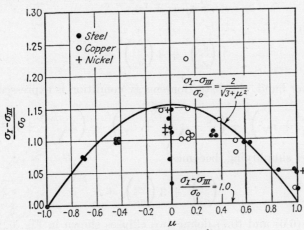

FIG. 6.1. Lode's test results.

condition are generally larger than the limits of accuracy; in most cases they are toward the maximum-shearing-stress condition, *i.e.*, the observed differences in $\sigma_I - \sigma_{III}$ are smaller than those predicted by the distortion-energy theory.

6.3. Experiments on Thin-walled Tubes under Combined Axial Tension and Torsion

A series of stress states can be obtained by combining axial tension with torsion. Tests on solid cylinders are not reliable because of the uncertainty of the stress distribution due to torsion after small amounts of plastic flow have taken place. Taylor and Quinney (1931) used thin-walled tubular specimens in which a uniform state of plane stress is assumed across the wall thickness. With respect to a reference system having the x axis oriented parallel to the tube axis and the y axis in tangential direction, the stress components in the xy plane are: $\sigma_x = $ normal stress due to axial tension load; $\sigma_y = 0$; $\tau_{xy} = $ torsional shearing stress.   Then the principal stresses become [see Eq. (1.43)]

$$\sigma_\mathrm{I} = \frac{\sigma_x}{2} + \sqrt{\frac{\sigma_x{}^2}{4} + \tau_{xy}{}^2}$$

$$\sigma_\mathrm{II} = 0 \tag{6.5}$$

$$\sigma_\mathrm{III} = \frac{\sigma_x}{2} - \sqrt{\frac{\sigma_x{}^2}{4} + \tau_{xy}{}^2}$$

With these expressions the maximum-shearing-stress condition becomes

$$2\sqrt{\frac{\sigma_x{}^2}{4} + \tau_{xy}{}^2} = \sigma_0$$

from which

$$\left(\frac{\sigma_x}{\sigma_0}\right)^2 + 4\left(\frac{\tau_{xy}}{\sigma_0}\right)^2 = 1 \tag{6.6}$$

On the other hand, the distortion-energy condition is expressed by

$$\left(\frac{\sigma_x}{2} + \sqrt{\frac{\sigma_x{}^2}{4} + \tau_{xy}{}^2}\right)^2 + \left(\frac{\sigma_x}{2} - \sqrt{\frac{\sigma_x{}^2}{4} + \tau_{xy}{}^2}\right)^2 + \left(2\sqrt{\frac{\sigma_x{}^2}{4} + \tau_{xy}{}^2}\right)^2 = 2\sigma_0{}^2$$

which, after simplifying, becomes

$$\left(\frac{\sigma_x}{\sigma_0}\right)^2 + 3\left(\frac{\tau_{xy}}{\sigma_0}\right)^2 = 1 \tag{6.7}$$

Equations (6.6) and (6.7) define two ellipses shown in Fig. 6.2 together with points which represent experimental results and again agree well with the distortion-energy condition of plasticity.

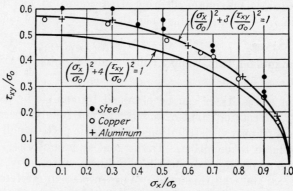

Fig. 6.2. Test results of Taylor and Quinney.

6.4. Experimental Verification of Saint-Venant's Theory of Plastic Flow

In addition to the plasticity conditions, both Lode's and Taylor and Quinney's experiments yielded additional information concerning Saint-Venant's theory of plastic flow (see Art. 5.3). The latter implies two postulates: (a) that the deviator stress tensor and the deviator strain-increment tensor are coaxial; and (b) that the corresponding terms of the two tensors are proportional.

In Lode's experiments the principal directions of stress and strain were fixed by the geometry of the specimens and by the loading; hence, they could furnish evidence neither for nor against the coaxiality of the two tensors. Taylor and Quinney calculated the angle of obliquity of the principal directions of stress and strain for various stages of straining and found the coaxiality postulate well confirmed.

In experimental investigations of postulate b infinitesimal increments of strain $(d\epsilon)$ are replaced by finite increments $(\Delta\epsilon)$. Denoting the increments of principal strain in the I, II, III directions with $\Delta\epsilon_I$, $\Delta\epsilon_{II}$, $\Delta\epsilon_{III}$, respectively, one obtains the following approximate version of Eqs. (5.24):

$$\frac{2\sigma_I - \sigma_{II} - \sigma_{III}}{2\sigma_{II} - \sigma_{III} - \sigma_I} = \frac{\Delta\epsilon_I}{\Delta\epsilon_{II}}$$
$$\frac{2\sigma_I - \sigma_{II} - \sigma_{III}}{2\sigma_{III} - \sigma_I - \sigma_{II}} = \frac{\Delta\epsilon_I}{\Delta\epsilon_{III}} \tag{6.8}$$

These equations, in conjunction with the volume-constancy relation

$$\Delta\epsilon_I + \Delta\epsilon_{II} + \Delta\epsilon_{III} = 0 \tag{6.9}$$

yield, after simple transformations,

$$\frac{2\sigma_{II} - \sigma_{III} - \sigma_I}{\sigma_I - \sigma_{III}} = \frac{2\Delta\epsilon_{II} - \Delta\epsilon_{III} - \Delta\epsilon_I}{\Delta\epsilon_I - \Delta\epsilon_{III}} \tag{6.10}$$

Finally, by introducing the notation

$$\nu = \frac{\Delta\epsilon_{II} - (\Delta\epsilon_I + \Delta\epsilon_{III})/2}{(\Delta\epsilon_I - \Delta\epsilon_{III})/2} = \frac{2\Delta\epsilon_{II} - \Delta\epsilon_{III} - \Delta\epsilon_I}{\Delta\epsilon_I - \Delta\epsilon_{III}} \tag{6.11}$$

Eqs. (6.8) can be condensed into the relationship

$$\mu = \nu \tag{6.12}$$

which affords a graphical representation of the experimental results by plotting the ν values calculated from measured strains versus the μ values corresponding to the applied stresses. Saint-Venant's theory, expressed approximately by Eq. (6.12), requires that points representing test data should fall on the straight line which makes 45° angles with the $+\mu$ and

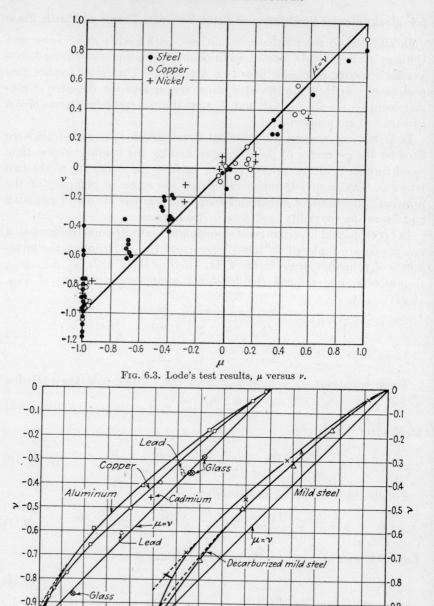

FIG. 6.3. Lode's test results, μ versus ν.

FIG. 6.4. Results of tests by Taylor and Quinney, μ versus ν. Dotted lines indicate actual trend of test points.

$+\nu$ axes.   Both Lode's experiments (Fig. 6.3) and Taylor and Quinney's experiments (Fig. 6.4) show deviations from Saint-Venant's theory.

6.5. Critical Remarks on Plasticity Experiments

The experimental work of recent years devoted to the verification of plasticity relations should be critically examined from the viewpoint of the properties of the materials used, which, in many respects, do not conform with the two basic assumptions of the theories in question.   In the first place, the material is assumed to possess certain characteristics which permit determining without ambiguity the limit of stress at which plastic flow begins, as well as the change in this yield strength, or flow stress, with progressive straining under conditions where the ratios of the principal stresses remain constant, independently of the orientation of the principal stress axes.   In the second place, all stress states which satisfy a plasticity condition are assumed to be equivalent among themselves, *i.e.*, certain variations in the stress state are assumed to be without influence.

(*a*) *Deviations from Isotropy.*   A metal is considered to approach the isotropic condition if it consists of a sufficiently large number of crystals and if these crystals are oriented according to a purely statistical or random distribution.   Anisotropy can be due either to a preferred orientation, or "texture," of the crystal structure ("crystallographic anisotropy") or to directional arrangement of certain phases, inclusions, porosities, cracks, etc. ("mechanical anisotropy"), or to cold-working ("anelastic anisotropy").   Anisotropy manifests itself in only slight variations of the yield strength, but most obviously in differences in plastic strains in various directions.   The most sensitive test for anisotropy lies in the behavior in uniaxial tension (or compression).   If changes in the density of the metal are neglected, the plastic strains in all directions normal to the direction of the applied uniaxial stress must be equal to half the principal strain in the latter direction taken with negative sign, *e.g.*, for uniaxial tension

$$\epsilon_{II} = \epsilon_{III} = -\frac{\epsilon_I}{2}$$

It follows that in the most common specimen shape used in plasticity experiments, the thin-walled tube, if the material is isotropic, plastic straining by an axial load should produce the same strain in circumferential direction (change in diameter) as in radial direction (change in wall thickness).   Lode's stress parameter μ becomes for uniaxial tension $(\sigma_I > 0; \quad \sigma_{II} = \sigma_{III} = 0)$

$$\mu = -1.0$$

and the strain parameter ν for isotropic behavior

$$\Delta\epsilon_{II} = \Delta\epsilon_{III} = -\frac{\Delta\epsilon_I}{2}$$

becomes
$$\nu = -1.0$$

Lode's tests indicate a lack of isotropy inasmuch as specimens of three different materials in uniaxial tension show average values of ν considerably larger than -1.0 (algebraically).   Taylor and Quinney's μ versus ν

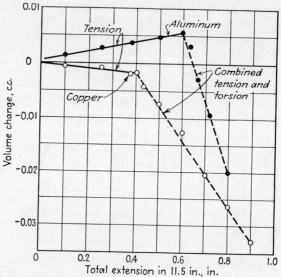

FIG. 6.5. Volume changes in tests by Taylor and Quinney.

diagrams do not contain any experimental points for $\mu = -1.0$; however, the trend of their curves clearly indicates an anisotropic behavior when extrapolated to the $\mu = -1.0$ line.   Taylor and Quinney introduced a method of checking on the isotropy of tubular specimens by measuring their internal volume.   Isotropy requires that this volume remain constant if the changes in density are negligible.   They discarded specimens which showed large changes in internal volume, but those considered acceptable still showed definite changes in internal volume under uniaxial tension loading (see Fig. 6.5).

(b) *Equivalence of Stress States.*   Both conditions of plasticity predict yielding to occur under a variety of stress states having the same deviator stress tensor, or, in other words, they imply that the value of the mean stress

$$\sigma_m = \frac{\sigma_I + \sigma_{II} + \sigma_{III}}{3}$$

is without influence on plastic yielding. Indeed, the addition (or subtraction) of a hydrostatic state of stress affects solely the magnitude of the mean stress σ_m but leaves the deviator stress tensor unchanged.

Ros and Eichinger found the yield strength (yield point) of annealed cast-steel specimens in compression to be constant (28.4 ± 0.5 kg/mm²) over the following range of the mean stress (see Fig. 6.6):

$$0 < \sigma_m < 0.7\sigma_{\text{III}}$$

Bridgman (1945) determined stress-strain curves for various steel specimens subjected to simultaneous axial tension and hydrostatic

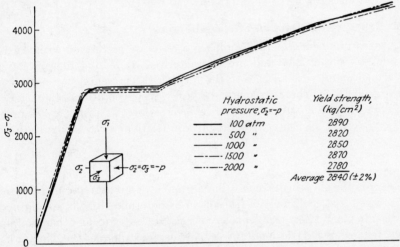

FIG. 6.6. Results of tests by Ros and Eichinger. Stress-strain diagrams of annealed cast-steel specimens subjected to axial compression combined with various hydrostatic pressures.

pressure up to mean stress values slightly larger than the applied tensile stress. The flow stress for the beginning of yielding and for small strains was found to be practically independent of the mean stress; in the range of large strains, however, the flow-stress curves became different for different values of hydrostatic pressure, assuming steeper slopes for increasing values of the latter. Thus, experimental findings confirm the assumption, implicit in the plasticity theories, that the mean stress has no influence on the beginning of yielding; however, this conclusion applies only to dense metals but not to materials, such as cast metals, minerals, etc., in which the effects of the mean stress may be rather pronounced.

It is also implicitly assumed in the plasticity conditions that reversing the signs of all three principal stresses is without influence on the beginning of yielding. The experimental evidence on this point is not decisive. For the simplest reversal in stress state, namely, for uniaxial tension and compression, most of the known experimental data furnish slightly higher yield strength values in compression than in tension. The average difference in such tests is in the neighborhood of 5 per cent. It also appears that this difference is smaller for pure metals than for alloys.

If a uniaxial tension state of stress is taken with reversed sign and combined with a hydrostatic stress of equal intensity, one obtains a state of "balanced" biaxial tension stress which, according to both plasticity conditions, is equivalent to the uniaxial tension stress state in producing plastic yielding. This conclusion needs a more complete experimental confirmation inasmuch as most investigators report higher values for balanced biaxial tension than for uniaxial tension.

6.6. Experimental Data on Frictional Forces

A great number of metal-forming processes are performed with the aid of metal tools or dies and are characterized by sliding motion of the deformed metal with respect to the tools in the presence of compressive stresses between the two metal bodies. Such conditions give rise to shearing stresses along the contact surfaces, which, as a rule, are assumed to be governed by Coulomb's law of "dry friction" or "sliding friction":

$$\frac{\tau}{\sigma} = f \tag{6.13}$$

where τ is the shearing stress, σ the normal stress on the die-metal interface, and f the coefficient of friction to be determined from test data.

Certain plastic-flow problems have been treated by using other assumptions regarding the frictional forces. Thus, for example, the friction has been assumed to depend on the speed of relative motion of the two bodies according to the laws of viscous friction. Such an assumption has not been confirmed experimentally; in fact, it was found that at high speeds of relative motion the friction decreases (instead of increasing, as the viscous-friction assumption would require), a fact that can be explained by an improvement of the lubrication at higher speeds.

From the wealth of experimental data heretofore accumulated in connection with various forming processes it can be concluded that the assumption of a constant frictional coefficient over the contact areas between metal and tools furnishes the best approximation for any particular series of tests. In addition, for many forming processes the friction coefficients between the same or similar metals and under otherwise comparable conditions were found to be of the same order of magnitude. On the other hand, important differences were found for conditions which differ in respect to the surface conditions of metals and tools and to lubrication. Thus, the lowest friction coefficients, of the order of 0.05, were found to occur under such conditions where the tool surfaces were well polished, the sliding motions were relatively small, and the lubrication was ideal. This applies, for example, to the cold-rolling of mild (low-carbon) steel strip with flood lubrication using a soluble oil. Only slightly higher values, between 0.05 and 0.15, have been reported for other conditions of cold-working and favorable friction, such as wire drawing, tube drawing, and deep drawing of steel, copper, and brass with cemented carbide dies or hardened steel dies and efficient lubricants. For the rolling of mild steel strip under commercial conditions friction coefficients between 0.07 and 0.09 are usually assumed. On rolling this metal with polished rolls but without lubrication, the friction coefficient is probably also close to 0.10; and approximately the same value applies to the cold-rolling of other metals, including various steel types. Slightly higher values, of the order of 0.15, may be encountered if the roll surface is ground rather than polished.

The friction coefficient may be much higher under conditions where either the tool surface or the metal surface is very rough. Thus, with increasing temperature of rolling, the surface of steel strip oxidizes increasingly, and this also causes the friction coefficient to increase until it reaches an apparently constant value of about 0.4 during rolling at temperatures between 700 and 1650°F. At still higher temperatures the friction coefficient decreases again to become as low as 0.2 at temperatures above 2000°F. This may be explained by the fact that oxide layers may act either as friction-increasing or as lubricating media, depending upon their nature and temperature, and possibly also upon other processing conditions.

The amount of shearing stress that can be transferred by friction is limited by the shearing strength of the metal. High friction coefficients may lead to a condition in which the frictional forces per unit area are larger than the shearing strength. In such cases the metal sticks to the die or tool surface and no sliding motion can take place, so that Coulomb's law ceases to be applicable.

In evaluating production and experimental data, it must be taken into consideration that the work consumed both in plastic deformation and in friction is transformed into heat. So far, little attention has been given to this phenomenon. The analysis of forming processes has been restricted to date to conditions in which the heating of the metal surfaces and of the metal body appears to have little influence on the stress and strain characteristics of the process.

REFERENCES

BARON, H. G., and F. C. THOMPSON, Friction in Wire Drawing, *J. Inst. Metals*, Voi. 78, pp. 415–462, 1950/51.

BRIDGMAN, P. W., Effects of High Hydrostatic Pressure on the Plastic Properties of Metals, *Revs. Modern Phys.*, Vol. 17, p. 3, January, 1945.

COX, H. L., and D. G. SOPWITH, The Effect of Orientation on Stresses in Single Crystals and of Random Orientation on Strength of Polycrystalline Aggregates, *Proc. Phys. Soc. (London)*, Vol. 49, p. 134, 1937.

DEHLINGER, U., Die Fliessbedingung bei mehrachsigem Spannungszustand vielkristalliner Metalle, *Z. Metallkunde*, Vol. 35, No. 9, pp. 182–184, September, 1943.

ESPEY, G., and G. SACHS, Experimentation on Tube Drawing with a Moving Mandrel, *J. Applied Mechanics*, Vol. 14, pp. 81–87, 1947.

EVANS, E. A., H. SILMAN, and H. W. SWIFT, "Lubrication in Drawing Operations," paper presented to the Sheet and Strip Metal Users' Technical Association, England.

KLINGLER, L. J., and G. SACHS, Plastic Flow Characteristics of Aluminum-alloy Plate, *J. Aeronaut. Sci.*, Vol. 15, pp. 599–604, 1948.

LODE, W., Versuche ueber den Einfluss der mittleren Hauptspannung auf das Fliessen der Metalle Eisen, Kupfer und Nickel, *Z. Physik*, Vol. 36, p. 913, 1926.

LUDWIK, P., and R. SCHEU, Vergleichende Zug-, Druck-, Dreh- und Walzversuche, *Stahl u. Eisen*, Vol. 45, p. 373, 1925.

MARIN, J., and R. L. STANLEY, Failure of Aluminum Subjected to Combined Stresses, *J. Am. Welding Soc. Res. Suppl.*, Vol. 19, p. 74, 1940.

OSGOOD, W. R., Combined-stress Tests on 24S-T Aluminum-alloy Tubes, *J. Applied Mechanics*, Vol. 14, p. 147, 1947.

ROS, M., and A. EICHINGER, Versuche zur Klaerung der Frage der Bruchgefahr, III. Metalle, *Eidgenöss. Materialprüf. u. Versuchsanstalt Ind. Bauw. u. Gewerbe, Zürich*, Diskussionsbericht No. 34, 1929.

SACHS, G., Zur Ableitung einer Fliessbedingung, *Z. Ver. deut. Ing.*, Vol. 72, p. 734, 1928.

SACHS, G., and W. M. BALDWIN, Stress Analysis of Tube Sinking, *Trans. ASME*, Vol. 68, pp. 655–662, 1946.

SACHS, G., and K. R. VAN HORN, "Practical Metallurgy," American Society for Metals, Cleveland, 1940.

TAYLOR, G. I., and H. QUINNEY, The Plastic Distortion of Metals, *Trans. Roy. Soc. (London)*, Series *A*, Vol. 230, pp. 323–362, 1931.

UNDERWOOD, L. R., "The Rolling of Metals, Theory and Experiment," John Wiley & Sons, Inc., New York, 1950.

Part II

PROBLEMS IN PLASTIC FLOW
OF IDEALLY PLASTIC MATERIALS

The problems to be discussed in the following chapters have certain common simple features, such as the assumedly simple and symmetrical body shapes, boundary conditions, and loading conditions. The problems are typical for structural applications of the theory of plasticity in which elastic and plastic areas exist adjacently and consequently the plastic deformations are contained and limited to small values. The material will be assumed throughout to be incompressible both in the elastic and plastic range; furthermore, it will be assumed to possess ideal plasticity and to obey Saint-Venant's theory of flow above the limit of yielding. Under such conditions, solutions in closed form are obtainable by employing comparatively simple mathematical tools, and this circumstance makes these examples particularly adapted as an introduction to more complex applications of the theory of plasticity.

CHAPTER 7

THICK-WALLED SPHERICAL SHELL
UNDER INTERNAL PRESSURE

7.1. Incompressible Three-dimensional Radial Flow

Consider a thick-walled spherical shell, having the internal radius a, external radius b, subjected to a uniform pressure p on its inner surface. From the central symmetry of the shell and of the applied forces it can be concluded that the field of displacement vectors also possesses central symmetry. Accordingly, all points on a concentric spherical surface with radius r have the same radially directed displacement vector u_r. During an infinitesimal deformation a radial line element 1, emanating from the point under consideration, remains parallel to itself, and it is deformed into another radial line element, with length $l(1 + \epsilon_r)$ where

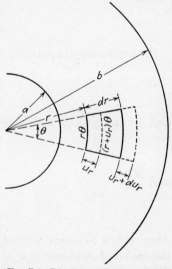

$$\epsilon_r = \frac{du_r}{dr} \qquad (7.1)$$

is the linear strain in the radial direction. Hence, it can be concluded that the radial direction is a principal direction, and for reason of symmetry so are all tangential directions, i.e., all directions perpendicular to the radial direction. The length of a

FIG. 7.1. Displacements of a volume element in three-dimensional radial flow.

tangential element corresponding to a central angle θ is $r\theta$; the entire element will displace parallel to itself by u_r, and its length becomes $(r + u_r)\theta$ and consequently the tangential strain becomes (see Fig. 7.1)

$$\epsilon_\theta = \frac{(r + u_r)\theta - r\theta}{r\theta} = \frac{u_r}{r} \qquad (7.2)$$

69

The strain tensor matrix can be written as follows:

$$
E = \begin{pmatrix} \epsilon_r & 0 & 0 \\ 0 & \epsilon_\theta & 0 \\ 0 & 0 & \epsilon_\theta \end{pmatrix} = \begin{pmatrix} \dfrac{du_r}{dr} & 0 & 0 \\ 0 & \dfrac{u_r}{r} & 0 \\ 0 & 0 & \dfrac{u_r}{r} \end{pmatrix} \tag{7.3}
$$

The incompressibility assumption means that

$$
E'' = 0, \qquad \epsilon_m = \frac{\epsilon_r + 2\epsilon_\theta}{3} = 0
$$

or

$$
\epsilon_r + 2\epsilon_\theta = 0 \tag{7.4}
$$

Substituting expressions for ϵ_r and ϵ_θ from Eqs. (7.1) and (7.2), one obtains

$$
\frac{du_r}{dr} + 2\frac{u_r}{r} = 0 \tag{7.5}
$$

By separating the variables, one has

$$
\frac{du_r}{u_r} = -\frac{2\,dr}{r}
$$

and, by integrating both sides of the equation,

$$
\ln u_r = \ln \frac{C}{r^2}
$$

and

$$
u_r = \frac{C}{r^2} \tag{7.6}
$$

where C is a constant of integration. This equation furnishes essentially the ratios of displacements of various points of the shell. Expressing all displacements in terms of that of a conveniently selected point, e.g., a point on the inner surface, $u_a = (u_r)_{r=a}$, the constant C is actually being replaced by another one:

$$
u_a = \frac{C}{a^2}
$$

With such substitution the expression for u_r becomes

$$
u_r = \frac{u_a a^2}{r^2} \tag{7.7}
$$

and the principal strains become

$$\epsilon_r = \frac{du_r}{dr} = -\frac{2a^2 u_a}{r^3} \tag{7.8}$$

$$\epsilon_\theta = \frac{u_r}{r} = \frac{a^2 u_a}{r^3} \tag{7.9}$$

7.2. Differential Equation of Equilibrium

It can be seen that, because of symmetry, the same state of stress exists at all points of a concentric spherical surface; furthermore, at any point the radial direction is a principal direction, with the principal stress σ_r, and all tangential directions are also principal directions, with a constant principal stress σ_θ. In other words, a so-called "cylindrical" state of stress, defined in Art. 1.3, exists throughout the shell.

In order to investigate the state of stress as a function of the radial distance r, consider the equilibrium of a volume element bounded by two concentric spherical surfaces, with radii r and $r + dr$, respectively, and by four meridian planes such that they intersect the concentric spherical surfaces along spherical squares (see Fig. 7.2). Owing to symmetry, the only significant equilibrium equation is the one expressing that the

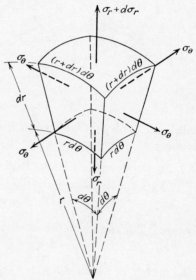

FIG. 7.2. Dimensions of volume element and stresses on volume element.

sum of the radial components of all forces acting on the element is zero (see Fig. 7.3). The tangential forces acting on two opposite meridian planes yield a radial resultant to be included in the sum of forces; thus the equilibrium equation is written as

$$\left(\sigma_r + \frac{d\sigma_r}{dr}\, dr \right)(r + dr)^2 (d\theta)^2 - \sigma_r r^2 (d\theta)^2 - 2\sigma_\theta r\, dr\,(d\theta)^2 = 0$$

Neglecting differentials of higher order, one obtains the following differential equation governing the stress distribution in a spherical shell:

$$\frac{d\sigma_r}{dr} + 2\frac{\sigma_r - \sigma_\theta}{r} = 0 \tag{7.10}$$

This equation has general validity under the assumed conditions of symmetry, regardless of the mechanical properties of the material. But it contains the two unknown functions σ_r and σ_θ of the independent variable r; hence, it cannot be integrated without making use of an additional

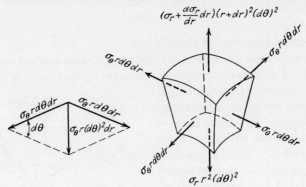

FIG. 7.3. Forces on volume element.

relation. This will be derived from assumptions concerning the specialized stress-strain properties of the material.

7.3. Incompressible Elastic Shell

The elastic stress-strain relation, expressed by Eq. (3.1),

$$\mathbf{S}' = 2G\mathbf{E}'$$

becomes, for the incompressibility condition, $\mathbf{E}'' = 0$,

$$\mathbf{S}' = 2G\mathbf{E} \qquad (7.11)$$

The matrix of the deviator stress tensor is

$$\mathbf{S}' = \begin{pmatrix} \frac{2}{3}(\sigma_r - \sigma_\theta) & 0 & 0 \\ 0 & \frac{1}{3}(\sigma_\theta - \sigma_r) & 0 \\ 0 & 0 & \frac{1}{3}(\sigma_\theta - \sigma_r) \end{pmatrix} \qquad (7.12)$$

and that of the strain tensor

$$\mathbf{E} = \begin{pmatrix} \epsilon_r & 0 & 0 \\ 0 & \epsilon_\theta & 0 \\ 0 & 0 & \epsilon_\theta \end{pmatrix}$$

or, because from Eq. (7.4) $\epsilon_\theta = -\dfrac{\epsilon_r}{2}$,

$$\mathbf{E} = \begin{pmatrix} \epsilon_r & 0 & 0 \\ 0 & -\dfrac{\epsilon_r}{2} & 0 \\ 0 & 0 & -\dfrac{\epsilon_r}{2} \end{pmatrix} \qquad (7.13)$$

Expanding Eq. (7.11) furnishes a single relation

$$\tfrac{2}{3}(\sigma_r - \sigma_\theta) = 2G\epsilon_r$$

from which, by recalling Eq. (7.8), one has

$$\sigma_r - \sigma_\theta = -\frac{6Ga^2}{r^3} u_a \tag{7.14}$$

Substituting in the equilibrium equation (7.10), it becomes

$$\frac{d\sigma_r}{dr} - \frac{12Ga^2}{r^4} u_a = 0$$

and the integration of this yields

$$\sigma_r = C - \frac{4Ga^2}{r^3} u_a \tag{7.15}$$

C is a constant of integration, which together with u_a is to be determined from the boundary conditions expressing that the radial stress σ_r assumes the value $-p$ at the inner surface and vanishes at the outer surface, or

$$(\sigma_r)_{r=a} = -p = C - \frac{4G}{a} u_a$$
$$(\sigma_r)_{r=b} = 0 = C - \frac{4Ga^2}{b^3} u_a \tag{7.16}$$

From solving these two equations simultaneously one has

$$C = p\,\frac{a^3/b^3}{1 - a^3/b^3}, \qquad u_a = \frac{p}{4G}\frac{a}{1 - a^3/b^3} \tag{7.17}$$

With these values Eq. (7.15) becomes

$$\sigma_r = p\,\frac{a^3/b^3 - a^3/r^3}{1 - a^3/b^3} \tag{7.18}$$

and, with reference to Eq. (7.14), one finds also

$$\sigma_\theta = p\,\frac{a^3/b^3 + a^3/2r^3}{1 - a^3/b^3} \tag{7.19}$$

7.4. Condition of Incipient Yielding

Inspection of Eqs. (7.18) and (7.19) shows that σ_r is always negative or zero and σ_θ is always positive; hence, the notations σ_I, σ_II, σ_III are to be assigned as follows:

$$\sigma_\mathrm{I} = \sigma_\mathrm{II} = \sigma_\theta, \qquad \sigma_\mathrm{III} = \sigma_r$$

and the Tresca–Saint-Venant condition [Eq. (4.1)] becomes

$$\sigma_I - \sigma_{III} = \sigma_\theta - \sigma_r = \sigma_0 \tag{7.20}$$

It can be easily verified that the von Mises–Hencky condition [Eq. (4.2)], with $\sigma_1 = \sigma_2 = \sigma_\theta$ and $\sigma_3 = \sigma_r$, yields the same equation (7.20) as the Tresca–Saint-Venant condition. This holds generally for a "cylindrical" state of stress, defined by $\sigma_1 = \sigma_2$ or $\sigma_2 = \sigma_3$ or $\sigma_3 = \sigma_1$, and represented in the "stress space" by two common generators of the Tresca–Saint-Venant prism and the von Mises–Hencky cylinder.

Substituting expressions (7.18) and (7.19) into Eq. (7.20) yields

$$\sigma_\theta - \sigma_r = p\,\frac{\frac{3}{2}(a^3/r^3)}{1 - a^3/b^3}$$

an expression that assumes its largest value at the inner surface, $r = a$, where, it can be concluded, the yielding will start when the pressure reaches a value p_i, defined by the equation

$$\sigma_0 = p_i\,\frac{\frac{3}{2}}{1 - a^3/b^3}$$

from which

$$p_i = \frac{2\sigma_0}{3}\left(1 - \frac{a^3}{b^3}\right) \tag{7.21}$$

7.5. Stresses in the Elasto-plastic Shell

As the internal pressure assumes values larger than p_i, a plastic zone develops, adjacently to the inner surface, extended to a depth depending upon the applied pressure. Consider an instantaneous condition, when the "plastic front," a spherical surface with radius ρ, separates the inner plastic shell from the outer elastic portion. The differential equation of equilibrium, Eq. (7.10), becomes for the plastic shell, in conjunction with the yield condition, $\sigma_\theta - \sigma_r = \sigma_0$,

$$\frac{d\sigma_r}{dr} - \frac{2\sigma_0}{r} = 0 \tag{7.22}$$

With constant σ_0, according to the assumption of ideally plastic behavior, integration of this equation furnishes

$$\sigma_r = C + \sigma_0 \ln r^2 \tag{7.23}$$

and

$$\sigma_\theta = \sigma_r + \sigma_0 = C + \sigma_0(1 + \ln r^2) \tag{7.24}$$

where C is a constant of integration. The condition available for determining C is the continuity of the radial stress σ_r across the plastic front.

From Eq. (7.23) for the plastic region:

$$(\sigma_r)_{r=\rho} = C + \sigma_0 \ln \rho^2 \tag{7.25}$$

This expression must be equal to the pressure p_i, taken with negative sign, that produces incipient yielding in the outer shell, and whose value is obtained from Eq. (7.21) by replacing a by ρ as

$$p_i = \frac{2\sigma_0}{3}\left(1 - \frac{\rho^3}{b^3}\right) \tag{7.26}$$

Then, the condition

$$(\sigma_r)_{r=\rho} = -p_i$$

yields

$$C = -\frac{2\sigma_0}{3}\left(1 - \frac{\rho^3}{b^3}\right) - \sigma_0 \ln \rho^2 = -\frac{2\sigma_0}{3}\left(3 \ln \rho + 1 - \frac{\rho^3}{b^3}\right)$$

and by substituting into Eqs. (7.23) and (7.24), the stresses in the plastic zone ($a \leq r \leq \rho$) are obtained as follows:

$$\sigma_r = \frac{2\sigma_0}{3}\left(3 \ln \frac{r}{\rho} - 1 + \frac{\rho^3}{b^3}\right) \tag{7.27}$$

$$\sigma_\theta = \frac{2\sigma_0}{3}\left(3 \ln \frac{r}{\rho} + \frac{1}{2} + \frac{\rho^3}{b^3}\right) \tag{7.28}$$

The stresses in the elastic zone ($\rho \leq r \leq b$) are obtained from Eqs. (7.18) and (7.19), after putting $p = p_i$ and $a = \rho$, as

$$\sigma_r = \frac{2\sigma_0}{3}\left(\frac{\rho^3}{b^3} - \frac{\rho^3}{r^3}\right) \tag{7.29}$$

$$\sigma_\theta = \frac{2\sigma_0}{3}\left(\frac{\rho^3}{b^3} + \frac{\rho^3}{2r^3}\right) \tag{7.30}$$

The solution represented by Eqs. (7.27) through (7.30) is complete only if the radius of the plastic front ρ is known for a given value of the internal pressure p. To determine ρ, one can make use of the condition that at the inner surface of the plastic zone, $r = a$, the radial stress σ_r, expressed from Eq. (7.27), must be equal to the internal pressure p, taken with negative sign, or

$$p = \frac{2\sigma_0}{3}\left(3 \ln \frac{\rho}{a} + 1 - \frac{\rho^3}{b^3}\right) \tag{7.31}$$

This is a transcendental equation for ρ, and no explicit formulas can be given to express ρ in terms of p; but a trial-and-error procedure furnishes ρ for a given p, with all the practically required accuracy.

The state of full plasticity is reached when $\rho = b$, and the internal pressure has the value, according to Eq. (7.31),

$$p_f = \sigma_0 \ln \frac{b^2}{a^2} \qquad (7.32)$$

and the stresses have the expressions

$$\sigma_r = \sigma_0 \ln \frac{r^2}{b^2} \qquad (7.33)$$

$$\sigma_\theta = \sigma_0 \left(1 + \ln \frac{r^2}{b^2}\right) \qquad (7.34)$$

In concluding it can be pointed out that the stresses in the elasto-plastic and in the plastic shell were obtained without making use of a

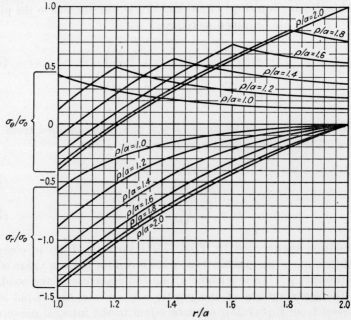

Fig. 7.4. Stress distributions in elasto-plastic shell ($b/a = 2$).

plastic stress-strain relation, so that the problem here solved can be termed as "statically determinate," although the use of the elastic stress-strain relation was essential in deriving the expressions for the elasto-plastic state.

Figure 7.4 shows the distribution of the σ_r and σ_θ stresses for the various positions of the plastic front for a shell with $b/a = 2$.

7.6. Deformations of the Elasto-plastic Shell

As long as the internal pressure p is smaller than p_f and hence $\rho < b$, there is an outer elastic shell, the deformations of which are uniquely determined and govern the deformations of the inner plastic shell also, by virtue of Eq. (7.6).

Apply the second of Eqs. (7.17) to the elastic shell by putting $p = p_i$ and $a = \rho$ and obtain

$$u_\rho = \frac{p_i}{4G} \frac{\rho}{1 - \rho^3/b^3}$$

and, by substituting for p_i the expression given in Eq. (7.26),

$$u_\rho = \frac{\sigma_0 \rho}{6G}$$

On the other hand, from Eq. (7.7), with $r = \rho$,

$$u_\rho = \frac{u_a a^2}{\rho^2}$$

so that eventually the displacement of the inner surface becomes

$$u_a = \frac{u_\rho \rho^2}{a^2} = \frac{\sigma_0 \rho^3}{6G a^2} \tag{7.35}$$

At the instant of incipient yielding, $\rho = a$,

$$u_a = \frac{\sigma_0 a}{6G} \tag{7.36}$$

and at the instant of full plasticity, $\rho = b$,

$$u_a = \frac{\sigma_0 b^3}{6G a^2} \tag{7.37}$$

From the above analysis it follows that, after the plastic front has reached the outer surface of the shell, unconstrained plastic flow begins to take place under the constant internal pressure, $p_f = \sigma_0 \ln (b^2/a^2)$. However, this conclusion is of limited validity, because it is based on the assumption that the changes in dimensions of the shell are negligible with respect to the original dimensions themselves. Actually, in the above expression for p_f the values of a and b *after deformation*, that is, $a + u_a$ and $b + u_b$, should be used instead of a and b themselves. This would imply a decrease in the value of p_f with increasing u_a and indicates that a loss of the stable character of the equilibrium has taken place at the inset of unconstrained plastic flow. Such instability phenomena play an important role in plastic metal forming and in metal testing and will be analyzed in more detail in Chap. 14.

Figure 7.5 shows the ratio p/σ_0 plotted against u_a/a for an example in which $b/a = 2$ and $\sigma_0/G = 10^{-3}$ were assumed.

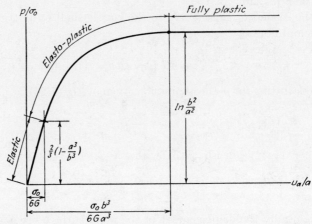

F<small>IG</small>. 7.5. Diagram of internal pressure versus displacement of inner surface for thick-walled spherical shell.

Once the displacement of the inner surface u_a is known, the strains at any point are obtained from Eqs. (7.8) and (7.9). By taking derivatives with respect to u_a one finds

$$\frac{d\epsilon_r}{du_a} = -\frac{2a^2}{r^3}$$

$$\frac{d\epsilon_\theta}{du_a} = \frac{a^2}{r^3}$$

hence, it is found that

$$\frac{d\epsilon_r}{\epsilon_r} = \frac{d\epsilon_\theta}{\epsilon_\theta} = \frac{du_a}{u_a} \tag{7.38}$$

and it can be concluded that the straining is "proportional" in the sense defined in Art. 5.5. As it was mentioned previously, the stresses and strains in the spherical shell could be obtained without making use of Saint-Venant's plastic stress-strain relation, which nevertheless has full validity for this problem. It is interesting to derive the expression for the factor λ which appears in Saint-Venant's theory [Eq. (5.12)]; this can be done by using its definition given by Eq. (5.17)

$$\lambda = \frac{\sqrt{2}}{3} \frac{\sigma_0}{\dot{\gamma}_{oct}}$$

From its definition [Eq. (2.32)], the octahedral shearing strain is, in the present case,

$$\gamma_{oct} = \sqrt{8}\,\epsilon_\theta = \sqrt{8}\,\frac{a^2 u_a}{r^3} \tag{7.39}$$

and the rate of octahedral shearing strain

$$\dot{\gamma}_{oct} = \sqrt{8}\,\frac{a^2 \dot{u}_a}{r^3} \tag{7.40}$$

where $\dot{u}_a = du_a/dt$ is the rate of displacement of the inner surface. Substituting into the expression for λ, it becomes

$$\lambda = \frac{\sigma_0 r^3}{6a^2 \dot{u}_a} \tag{7.41}$$

CHAPTER 8

THICK-WALLED TUBE UNDER INTERNAL PRESSURE

The problem of the thick-walled tube subjected to internal pressure presents several variations according to the restraints imposed upon the tube in longitudinal direction. This chapter will cover the following cases: (a) the "plane-strain" condition, characterized by vanishing axial strains; (b) the "generalized plane-strain" condition, with constant nonvanishing axial strains; (c) the "plane-stress" condition with vanishing stresses on transverse planes.

8.1. Two-dimensional Radial Flow

Consider a thick-walled tube, with internal radius a and external radius b, loaded with a uniform pressure p on its inner surface and subjected to the condition that any annular portion of it, bounded by two transverse planes before deformation, remains bounded by the same planes after deformation. From this imposed condition of so-called "plane strain" and from the axial symmetry of the tube, it follows that all points on a concentric cylindrical surface will have the same displacement vector lying in the transverse plane and directed radially. With reference to the cylindrical coordinates r, θ, z, assumed to make the z axis coincide with the tube axis, the components of the displacement vector $\mathbf{u}$ are then $u_r = f(r)$, $u_\theta = 0$, $u_z = 0$. Hence, at any point the radial, tangential, and longitudinal directions are principal directions of strain, and similarly to the derivation given in Art. 7.1 one obtains the following expressions for the principal strains:

$$\epsilon_r = \frac{du_r}{dr} \tag{8.1}$$

$$\epsilon_\theta = \frac{u_r}{r} \tag{8.2}$$

$$\epsilon_z = \frac{du_z}{dz} = 0 \tag{8.3}$$

The incompressibility condition, assumed henceforth to be valid both in the elastic and the plastic range, is expressed by

$$E'' = 0 \qquad \epsilon_r + \epsilon_\theta + \epsilon_z = 0 \qquad \epsilon_r + \epsilon_\theta = 0 \tag{8.4}$$

Substituting expressions for ϵ_r and ϵ_θ from Eqs. (8.1) and (8.2), one has the differential equation for the unknown function u_r

$$\frac{du_r}{dr} + \frac{u_r}{r} = 0 \tag{8.5}$$

which can be integrated by separating the variables and yields the solution

$$u_r = \frac{C}{r} \tag{8.6}$$

where C is a constant of integration. It is convenient to introduce the radial displacement of the inner surface $u_a = (u_r)_{r=a}$, which is related to C by the equation

$$u_a = \frac{C}{a}$$

so that Eq. (8.6) becomes

$$u_r = \frac{u_a a}{r} \tag{8.7}$$

The expressions for the principal strains are then

$$\epsilon_r = \frac{du_r}{dr} = -\frac{u_a a}{r^2} \tag{8.8}$$

$$\epsilon_\theta = \frac{u_r}{r} = \frac{u_a a}{r^2} \tag{8.9}$$

$$\epsilon_z = 0 \tag{8.10}$$

8.2. Differential Equation of Equilibrium

From the axial symmetry of the tube and that of the applied forces it can be concluded that all points of a concentric cylindrical surface are

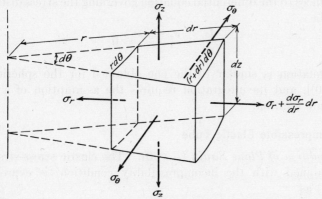

FIG. 8.1. Dimensions of volume element and stresses on volume element.

in the same state of stress and that radial, tangential, and longitudinal directions are principal directions of stress, the respective principal stresses being σ_r, σ_θ, σ_z.

Consider the equilibrium of a volume element bounded by two concentric cylindrical surfaces, with radii r and $r + dr$, respectively, by two radial planes making a dihedral angle $d\theta$, and by two transverse planes at distance dz (see Fig. 8.1). The only significant equilibrium

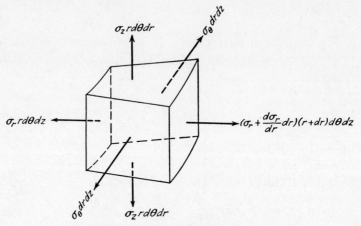

Fig. 8.2. Forces on volume element.

equation that can be written expresses that the sum of the radial components of all forces acting on the element vanishes (see Fig. 8.2), *i.e.*,

$$\left(\sigma_r + \frac{d\sigma_r}{dr}\, dr\right)(r + dr)\, d\theta\, dz - \sigma_r r\, d\theta\, dz - \sigma_\theta\, dr\, d\theta\, dz = 0$$

which reduces to the differential equation governing the stress distribution in the tube

$$\frac{d\sigma_r}{dr} + \frac{\sigma_r - \sigma_\theta}{r} = 0 \tag{8.11}$$

This equation is similar to the one obtained for the spherical shell [Eq. (7.10)], and its integration requires the assumption of a specific stress-strain relation.

8.3. Incompressible Elastic Tube

(a) *Condition of Plane Strain* ($\epsilon_z = 0$). The elastic stress-strain relation, combined with the incompressibility condition, is expressed by Eq. (7.11) as

$$\mathbf{S'} = 2G\mathbf{E}$$

or in matrix form by

$$\begin{pmatrix} \dfrac{2\sigma_r - \sigma_\theta - \sigma_z}{3} & 0 & 0 \\[2mm] 0 & \dfrac{2\sigma_\theta - \sigma_z - \sigma_r}{3} & 0 \\[2mm] 0 & 0 & \dfrac{2\sigma_z - \sigma_r - \sigma_\theta}{3} \end{pmatrix} = 2G \begin{pmatrix} \epsilon_r & 0 & 0 \\ 0 & -\epsilon_r & 0 \\ 0 & 0 & 0 \end{pmatrix}$$

(8.12)

which yields the following three equations:

$$2\sigma_r - \sigma_\theta - \sigma_z = 6G\epsilon_r \qquad (8.13)$$
$$2\sigma_\theta - \sigma_z - \sigma_r = -6G\epsilon_r \qquad (8.14)$$
$$2\sigma_z - \sigma_r - \sigma_\theta = 0 \qquad (8.15)$$

From the last equation it follows that

$$\sigma_z = \frac{\sigma_r + \sigma_\theta}{2} \qquad (8.16)$$

and substituting this expression into Eqs. (8.13) and (8.14), they yield the same relation:

$$\sigma_r - \sigma_\theta = 4G\epsilon_r \qquad (8.17)$$

which, with reference to Eq. (8.8), becomes

$$\sigma_r - \sigma_\theta = -\frac{4Gau_a}{r^2} \qquad (8.18)$$

Entering with such expression into the equilibrium equation (8.11), it becomes

$$\frac{d\sigma_r}{dr} - \frac{4Gau_a}{r^3} = 0$$

the solution of which is obtained, by separating the variables and integrating, as follows.

$$\sigma_r = C - \frac{2Gau_a}{r^2} \qquad (8.19)$$

C and u_a are determined from the boundary conditions at the inner and outer surfaces:

$$(\sigma_r)_{r=a} = -p = C - \frac{2Gu_a}{a}$$

$$(\sigma_r)_{r=b} = 0 = C - \frac{2Gau_a}{b^2}$$

(8.20)

as follows:

$$C = p \frac{a^2/b^2}{1 - a^2/b^2}$$

$$u_a = \frac{p}{2G} \frac{a}{1 - a^2/b^2}$$

$$(8.21)$$

With these values, Eq. (8.19) becomes

$$\sigma_r = p \frac{a^2/b^2 - a^2/r^2}{1 - a^2/b^2} \tag{8.22}$$

and from Eqs. (8.18) and (8.16)

$$\sigma_\theta = p \frac{a^2/b^2 + a^2/r^2}{1 - a^2/b^2} \tag{8.23}$$

$$\sigma_z = p \frac{a^2/b^2}{1 - a^2/b^2} \tag{8.24}$$

The σ_z stresses are constant throughout a transverse section of the tube; they yield the resultant

$$\sigma_z(b^2 - a^2)\pi = p \frac{a^2/b^2}{1 - a^2/b^2} (b^2 - a^2)\pi = pa^2\pi \tag{8.25}$$

which is equal to the resultant of the pressure acting on the end sections of a closed cylindrical vessel, with a diameter $2a$, subjected to the inner pressure p. This result can be interpreted to indicate that the plane-strain condition here investigated exists in a long closed tube, made of an incompressible elastic material, at a sufficient distance from the ends. In the immediate adjacencies of the ends, owing to the connection with the end plates, the distribution of the σ_z stresses differs from the above-indicated uniformity; but their resultant will still be $pa^2\pi$, and hence, by virtue of the well-known Saint-Venant principle, the effect of the nonuniformity tapers off with increasing distance from the ends.

(b) *Condition of Plane Stress.* By superimposing a uniaxial state of stress, consisting of $\sigma_z = -p \dfrac{a^2/b^2}{1 - a^2/b^2}$, upon the condition of plane strain above investigated, a state of stress results in which all σ_z stresses vanish and consequently their resultant vanishes also. This state of stress corresponds at the same time to the "condition of zero longitudinal load" in a long open tube and to the "condition of plane stress" in a short tube or annular disk. The σ_r and σ_θ stresses are not affected by this superimposed state of stress, and for them Eqs. (8.22) and (8.23) still hold. It should be made clear that the principle of superposition of effects used in reaching the above conclusions is valid only in the range of elastic behavior and ceases to be applicable in the plastic state.

8.4. Incipience of Plasticity

The conditions under which plastic flow begins in an originally elastic tube require separate considerations for the two cases of (*a*) plane strain, (*b*) plane stress; the latter, for the incompressible elastic tube, includes the zero longitudinal load condition.

(*a*) *Plane Strain.* The von Mises–Hencky condition of yielding is expressed by the following equation:

$$(\sigma_r - \sigma_\theta)^2 + (\sigma_\theta - \sigma_z)^2 + (\sigma_z - \sigma_r)^2 = 2\sigma_0^2 \qquad (8.26)$$

which, by substituting σ_r, σ_θ, σ_z from Eqs. (8.22), (8.23), and (8.24), becomes

$$p \frac{2a^2/r^2}{1 - a^2/b^2} = \frac{2}{\sqrt{3}} \sigma_0 \qquad (8.27)$$

Yielding begins at the inner face of the tube, $r = a$, where the expression on the left side reaches its maximum, at a value of the internal pressure

$$p_i = \frac{1 - a^2/b^2}{\sqrt{3}} \sigma_0 \qquad (8.28)$$

(*b*) *Plane Stress.* Substituting $\sigma_z = 0$ in Eq. (8.26) that expresses the von Mises–Hencky yield condition, it becomes

$$\sigma_r^2 - \sigma_r \sigma_\theta + \sigma_\theta^2 = \sigma_0^2 \qquad (8.29)$$

and, with reference to Eqs. (8.22) and (8.23),

$$p \frac{\sqrt{3 \dfrac{a^4}{r^4} + \dfrac{a^4}{b^4}}}{1 - a^2/b^2} = \sigma_0 \qquad (8.30)$$

The internal pressure that gives rise to incipient yielding at the inner surface of the tube results, by putting $r = a$, as

$$p_i = \frac{1 - a^2/b^2}{\sqrt{3 + a^4/b^4}} \sigma_0 \qquad (8.31)$$

8.5. Stresses in the Elasto-plastic Tube in Plane Strain

To investigate the progress of the plastic front from the inner face toward the outer face of the tube when the internal pressure $p > p_i$, consider the state of stress for an instantaneous value of ρ, the radius of the plastic front. Conditions throughout the inner plastic region are governed by the von Mises–Hencky yield condition, expressed by Eq. (8.26), and by Saint-Venant's theory of plastic flow, expressed by Eqs. (5.24).

The first of Eqs. (5.24) becomes, by putting $\sigma_1 = \sigma_z, \sigma_2 = \sigma_r, \sigma_3 = \sigma_\theta$

$$\frac{2\sigma_z - \sigma_r - \sigma_\theta}{2\sigma_r - \sigma_\theta - \sigma_z} = \frac{d\epsilon_z}{d\epsilon_r} \tag{8.32}$$

Recalling that $\epsilon_z = 0$, and consequently $d\epsilon_z = 0$, this yields

$$2\sigma_z - \sigma_r - \sigma_\theta = 0$$

and finally one obtains

$$\sigma_z = \frac{\sigma_r + \sigma_\theta}{2} \tag{8.33}$$

i.e., the same equation previously obtained for the incompressible elastic tube. It can be recognized that it holds generally, in the state of plane strain, for any incompressible material obeying a linear stress-strain relation (Hooke's law) or a linear stress-strain-rate relation (Saint-Venant's law). Substituting σ_z from Eq. (8.33), the von Mises–Hencky yield condition [Eq. (8.26)] becomes

$$\sigma_\theta - \sigma_r = \frac{2}{\sqrt{3}} \sigma_0 \tag{8.34}$$

and the differential equation of equilibrium becomes

$$\frac{d\sigma_r}{dr} - \frac{2}{\sqrt{3}} \frac{\sigma_0}{r} = 0 \tag{8.35}$$

The solution of this equation is

$$\sigma_r = \frac{2\sigma_0}{\sqrt{3}} \ln r + C \tag{8.36}$$

The integration constant C is determined from the condition that the radial stress σ_r is continuous across the plastic front, a concentric cylindrical surface with radius ρ. From Eq. (8.36), governing the stresses in the plastic region,

$$(\sigma_r)_{r=\rho} = \frac{2\sigma_0}{\sqrt{3}} \ln \rho + C$$

and this value must equal, with negative sign, the pressure at the inner surface of the elastic portion of the tube, which is in a state of incipient yielding, as expressed by Eq. (8.28), or

$$\frac{2\sigma_0}{\sqrt{3}} \ln \rho + C = -\frac{1 - \rho^2/b^2}{\sqrt{3}} \sigma_0$$

From this equation one obtains

$$C = -\frac{\sigma_0}{\sqrt{3}} \left(2 \ln \rho + 1 - \frac{\rho^2}{b^2} \right)$$

and entering with this value into Eq. (8.36), one has

$$\sigma_r = \frac{\sigma_0}{\sqrt{3}}\left(2\ln\frac{r}{\rho} - 1 + \frac{\rho^2}{b^2}\right) \qquad (8.37)$$

and furthermore, from Eq. (8.34),

$$\sigma_\theta = \frac{\sigma_0}{\sqrt{3}}\left(2\ln\frac{r}{\rho} + 1 + \frac{\rho^2}{b^2}\right) \qquad (8.38)$$

$$\sigma_z = \frac{\sigma_0}{\sqrt{3}}\left(2\ln\frac{r}{\rho} + \frac{\rho^2}{b^2}\right) \qquad (8.39)$$

The above three equations furnish the stresses in the plastic zone ($a \leq r \leq \rho$); for the outer elastic shell ($\rho \leq r \leq b$), the expressions for the stresses are obtained from Eqs. (8.22) to (8.24) by putting $p = p_i$ [See Eq. (8.31)] and $a = \rho$ as follows:

$$\sigma_r = \frac{\sigma_0}{\sqrt{3}}\left(\frac{\rho^2}{b^2} - \frac{\rho^2}{r^2}\right) \qquad (8.40)$$

$$\sigma_\theta = \frac{\sigma_0}{\sqrt{3}}\left(\frac{\rho^2}{b^2} + \frac{\rho^2}{r^2}\right) \qquad (8.41)$$

$$\sigma_z = \frac{\sigma_0}{\sqrt{3}}\frac{\rho^2}{b^2} \qquad (8.42)$$

To find the relationship between the applied pressure p and the radius of the plastic front ρ, it should be recalled that the radial stress at $r = a$, furnished by Eq. (8.37), should be equal to $-p$ or

$$p = \frac{\sigma_0}{\sqrt{3}}\left(2\ln\frac{\rho}{a} + 1 - \frac{\rho^2}{b^2}\right) \qquad (8.43)$$

For any given value of p, the radius ρ can be found by a trial-and-error procedure.

Full plasticity is reached when the plastic front has progressed to the outer face of the tube, or $\rho = b$, and the internal pressure assumes the value

$$p_f = \frac{2\sigma_0}{\sqrt{3}}\ln\frac{b}{a} \qquad (8.44)$$

The stresses have the following expressions in the fully plastic state:

$$\sigma_r = \frac{2\sigma_0}{\sqrt{3}}\ln\frac{r}{b} \qquad (8.45)$$

$$\sigma_\theta = \frac{2\sigma_0}{\sqrt{3}}\left(1 + \ln\frac{r}{b}\right) \qquad (8.46)$$

$$\sigma_z = \frac{2\sigma_0}{\sqrt{3}}\left(\frac{1}{2} + \ln\frac{r}{b}\right) \qquad (8.47)$$

Figure 8.3 shows the distribution of the σ_r, σ_θ, σ_z stresses for various positions ρ/a of the plastic front for a tube with $b/a = 2$. The resultant of the σ_z stresses acting on a transverse section of the tube, $\int_a^b \sigma_z 2\pi r \, dr$, is the longitudinal force to be applied to the tube in order to

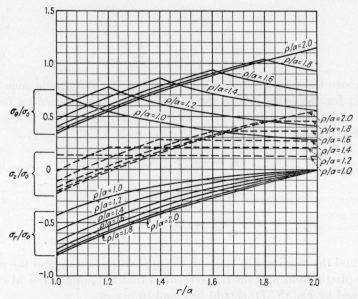

Fig. 8.3. Stress distributions in elasto-plastic tube in plane strain ($b/a = 2$).

maintain a state of "plane strain." This integral can be determined as the sum of the integrals for the plastic and elastic zones:

$$\int_a^b \sigma_z 2\pi r \, dr = \int_a^\rho \sigma_z 2\pi r \, dr + \int_\rho^b \sigma_z 2\pi r \, dr$$

By substituting the expressions for σ_z from Eq. (8.39) (for $a \leq r \leq \rho$) and from Eq. (8.42) (for $\rho \leq r \leq b$), the integral furnishes the value $pa^2\pi$ for the elasto-plastic tube, identically with the result obtained in Art. 8.3 for the incompressible elastic tube. Hence, it can be concluded that a "plane-strain" condition can be expected to exist in a closed tube in the elasto-plastic and fully plastic state, as well as in the elastic state, when incompressibility is assumed. It is reasonable to admit that an extension of Saint-Venant's principle for elastic bodies applies to elasto-plastic and fully plastic conditions and that only a limited portion of the tube, immediately adjacent to the closed ends, is in a stress state that is essentially different from that obtained in this article.

8.6. Deformations of the Elasto-plastic Tube in Condition of Plane Strain

Until the plastic front has not reached the outer face of the tube, that is, $\rho < b$ and $p < p_f$, there remains an elastic region, the deformations of which determine uniquely the deformations of all points of the tube, according to Eq. (8.6). Substituting $p = p_i$ and $a = \rho$ into the second equation (8.21), the displacement of the points of the plastic front is obtained as

$$u_\rho = \frac{p_i}{2G} \frac{\rho}{1 - \rho^2/b^2} \qquad (8.48)$$

and by using the expression for p_i from Eq. (8.28), this becomes

$$u_\rho = \frac{\sigma_0 \rho}{2\sqrt{3}\,G} \qquad (8.49)$$

To obtain the displacement of the inner face u_a that can be used as a characteristic parameter of the process of deformation, substitute $r = \rho$ into Eq. (8.7) and solve to obtain

$$u_a = \frac{u_\rho \rho}{a} = \frac{\sigma_0 \rho^2}{2\sqrt{3}\,Ga} \qquad (8.50)$$

At the beginning of plastic yielding, $\rho = a$, this becomes

$$u_a = \frac{\sigma_0 a}{2\sqrt{3}\,G} \qquad (8.51)$$

and, at reaching full plasticity, $\rho = b$,

$$u_a = \frac{\sigma_0 b^2}{2\sqrt{3}\,Ga} \qquad (8.52)$$

After the plastic front has reached the outer surface, free plastic flow occurs, under a constant internal pressure, $p_f = (2\sigma_0/\sqrt{3}) \ln (b/a)$, according to the above analysis based upon small deformations. When the deformations become large, conditions similar to those

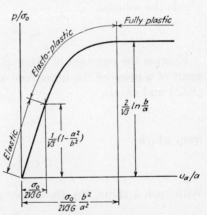

FIG. 8.4. Diagram of internal pressure versus displacement of inner surface for thick-walled tube in plane strain.

previously found for the spherical shell are encountered; the ratio b/a, and with it the pressure needed to maintain the tube in a plastic equilibrium, tend to decrease, giving rise to a condition of instability.

Figure 8.4 shows values of p/σ_0 plotted against value of u_a/a for $b/a = 2$ and $\sigma_0/G = 10^{-3}$.

8.7. Fully Plastic Tube in Generalized Plane-strain Condition

The condition of "generalized plane strain" is hereby defined as a state of deformation in which certain planes (in the present problem the planes normal to the tube axis) maintain their planar shape and their orientation but undergo a change in their mutual distances. In the problem of the thick-walled tube, such a condition is characterized by a constant, but not necessarily zero, longitudinal strain ϵ_z.

Equations (8.1) and (8.2)

$$\epsilon_r = \frac{du_r}{dr}, \qquad \epsilon_\theta = \frac{u_r}{r}$$

apply to the present problem also, u_r being the radial component of the displacement vector of a point at the radial distance r. Substituting these expressions into the volume-constancy equation

$$\epsilon_r + \epsilon_\theta + \epsilon_z = 0 \tag{8.53}$$

one obtains the following differential equation:

$$\frac{du_r}{dr} + \frac{u_r}{r} + \epsilon_z = 0 \tag{8.54}$$

Since the longitudinal strain ϵ_z is constant in the present case, this equation yields the solution

$$u_r = -\frac{\epsilon_z r}{2} + \frac{C_1}{r} \tag{8.55}$$

Express the constant of integration C_1 in terms of the radial displacement of a point of the inner face u_a; for this purpose put $r = a$ into Eq. (8.55) and obtain

$$u_a = -\frac{\epsilon_z a}{2} + \frac{C_1}{a}$$

from which

$$C_1 = \frac{\epsilon_z a^2}{2} + u_a a \tag{8.56}$$

With such a value, Eq. (8.55) becomes

$$u_r = \frac{\epsilon_z}{2}\left(\frac{a^2}{r} - r\right) + u_a \frac{a}{r} \tag{8.57}$$

and finally the radial and tangential strains are obtained as

$$\epsilon_r = \frac{du_r}{dr} = -\frac{\epsilon_z}{2}\left(\frac{a^2}{r^2} + 1\right) - u_a \frac{a}{r^2} \tag{8.58}$$

$$\epsilon_\theta = \frac{u_r}{r} = \frac{\epsilon_z}{2}\left(\frac{a^2}{r^2} - 1\right) + u_a \frac{a}{r^2} \tag{8.59}$$

Saint-Venant's plastic stress-strain relations [Eqs. (5.24)] are written, by using the notations of the present problem, as follows:

$$\frac{2\sigma_r - \sigma_\theta - \sigma_z}{2\sigma_z - \sigma_r - \sigma_\theta} = \frac{d\epsilon_r}{d\epsilon_z} \tag{8.60}$$

$$\frac{2\sigma_\theta - \sigma_z - \sigma_r}{2\sigma_z - \sigma_r - \sigma_\theta} = \frac{d\epsilon_\theta}{d\epsilon_z} \tag{8.61}$$

Differentiation of Eqs. (8.58) and (8.59) with respect to ϵ_z furnishes the expressions

$$\frac{d\epsilon_r}{d\epsilon_z} = -\frac{1}{2}\left(\frac{a^2}{r^2} + 1\right) - \frac{du_a}{d\epsilon_z}\frac{a}{r^2}$$

$$\frac{d\epsilon_\theta}{d\epsilon_z} = \frac{1}{2}\left(\frac{a^2}{r^2} - 1\right) + \frac{du_a}{d\epsilon_z}\frac{a}{r^2}$$

and with these, Eqs. (8.60) and (8.61) become

$$\frac{2\sigma_r - \sigma_\theta - \sigma_z}{2\sigma_z - \sigma_r - \sigma_\theta} = -\frac{1}{2}\left(\frac{a^2}{r^2} + 1\right) - \frac{du_a}{d\epsilon_z}\frac{a}{r^2} \tag{8.62}$$

$$\frac{2\sigma_\theta - \sigma_z - \sigma_r}{2\sigma_z - \sigma_r - \sigma_\theta} = \frac{1}{2}\left(\frac{a^2}{r^2} - 1\right) + \frac{du_a}{d\epsilon_z}\frac{a}{r^2} \tag{8.63}$$

Subtracting Eq. (8.62) from Eq. (8.63), one has

$$\frac{3(\sigma_\theta - \sigma_r)}{2\sigma_z - \sigma_r - \sigma_\theta} = \frac{a^2}{r^2} + 2\frac{a}{r^2}\frac{du_a}{d\epsilon_z}$$

from which

$$\sigma_z = \frac{\sigma_r + \sigma_\theta}{2} + \frac{\sigma_\theta - \sigma_r}{\dfrac{2}{3}\left(\dfrac{a^2}{r^2} + 2\dfrac{a}{r^2}\dfrac{du_a}{d\epsilon_z}\right)} \tag{8.64}$$

or also, by introducing the notation

$$c = \frac{\sqrt{3}}{a^2 + 2a(du_a/d\epsilon_z)} = \frac{\sqrt{3}}{a}\frac{d\epsilon_z/du_a}{2 + a(d\epsilon_z/du_a)} \tag{8.65}$$

$$\sigma_z = \frac{\sigma_r + \sigma_\theta}{2} + \frac{\sigma_\theta - \sigma_r}{2}\sqrt{3}\,cr^2 \tag{8.66}$$

The von Mises–Hencky plasticity condition

$$(\sigma_\theta - \sigma_r)^2 + (\sigma_r - \sigma_z)^2 + (\sigma_z - \sigma_\theta)^2 = 2\sigma_0^2$$

becomes, by substituting for σ_z the expression from Eq. (8.66) and simplifying,

$$\sigma_\theta - \sigma_r = \frac{(2/\sqrt{3})\sigma_0}{\sqrt{1 + c^2 r^4}} \tag{8.67}$$

Substituting this expression into the differential equation of equilibrium, Eq. (8.11), it becomes

$$\frac{d\sigma_r}{dr} - \frac{(2/\sqrt{3})\sigma_0}{r\sqrt{1 + c^2 r^4}} = 0 \tag{8.68}$$

The solution of this equation is

$$\sigma_r = C_2 - \frac{\sigma_0}{\sqrt{3}} \coth^{-1}\sqrt{1 + c^2 r^4} \tag{8.69}$$

The constant of integration C_2 is determined from the condition that at the outer surface, $r = b$, the radial stress vanishes, $\sigma_r = 0$, from which

$$C_2 = \frac{\sigma_0}{\sqrt{3}} \coth^{-1}\sqrt{1 + c^2 b^4}$$

and the equation for σ_r becomes

$$\sigma_r = \frac{\sigma_0}{\sqrt{3}}[\coth^{-1}\sqrt{1 + c^2 b^4} - \coth^{-1}\sqrt{1 + c^2 r^4}] \tag{8.70}$$

Also, from Eq. (8.67) one has

$$\begin{aligned}
\sigma_\theta &= \sigma_r + \frac{(2/\sqrt{3})\sigma_0}{\sqrt{1 + c^2 r^4}} \\
&= \frac{\sigma_0}{\sqrt{3}}\left[\coth^{-1}\sqrt{1 + c^2 b^4} - \coth^{-1}\sqrt{1 + c^2 r^4} + \frac{2}{\sqrt{1 + c^2 r^4}}\right] \tag{8.71}
\end{aligned}$$

and from Eq. (8.66)

$$\sigma_z = \frac{\sigma_0}{\sqrt{3}}\left[\coth^{-1}\sqrt{1 + c^2 b^4} - \coth^{-1}\sqrt{1 + c^2 r^4} + \frac{1 + \sqrt{3}\,cr^2}{\sqrt{1 + c^2 r^4}}\right] \tag{8.72}$$

It can be seen that the state of plastic equilibrium described by Eqs. (8.70) to (8.72) depends eventually, for given tube dimensions, upon the derivative $d\epsilon_z/du_a$. The complexity of the above-developed equations suggests a procedure consisting in assuming values of $d\epsilon_z/du_a$, calculating the corresponding c values from Eq. (8.65) and determining the external forces necessary to maintain plastic equilibrium. These forces are (a) the longitudinal force

$$\int_a^b \sigma_z 2\pi r\, dr$$

distributed on transverse sections according to Eq. (8.72); and (b) the internal pressure, obtained from Eq. (8.70) by putting $r = a$ and taking the resulting σ_r with negative sign, *i.e.*,

$$p = -(\sigma_r)_{r=a} = \frac{\sigma_0}{\sqrt{3}}(\coth^{-1}\sqrt{1 + c^2b^4} - \coth^{-1}\sqrt{1 + c^2a^4}) \quad (8.73)$$

The c value for which the resultant of the σ_z stresses vanishes,

$$\int_a^b \sigma_z 2\pi r \, dr = 0$$

furnishes the solution for a long open tube.

8.8. Fully Plastic Tube in Plane-stress Condition

If the open tube is very short, the longitudinal stress vanishes for all points, $\sigma_z = 0$, and the von Mises–Hencky condition of plasticity becomes

$$\sigma_r{}^2 - \sigma_r\sigma_\theta + \sigma_\theta{}^2 = \sigma_0{}^2 \quad (8.74)$$

The problem of plastic equilibrium in a short tube (or in other words, in a flat ring) has been solved first by Nádai. The discussion of the problem given in this article follows the solution given by Sachs and Lubahn.

Solving Eq. (8.74) for σ_θ, one has

$$\sigma_\theta = \tfrac{1}{2}(\sigma_r + \sqrt{4\sigma_0{}^2 - 3\sigma_r{}^2}) \quad (8.75)$$

and substituting this expression in the differential equation of equilibrium, Eq. (8.11), the latter becomes

$$\frac{d\sigma_r}{dr} - \frac{\sqrt{4\sigma_0{}^2 - 3\sigma_r{}^2} - \sigma_r}{2r} = 0 \quad (8.76)$$

The solution of this equation is

$$\ln r = \frac{\sqrt{3}}{2}\sin^{-1}\left(\frac{\sqrt{3}}{2}\frac{\sigma_r}{\sigma_0}\right) - \frac{1}{2}\ln\left[\sqrt{1 - \frac{3}{4}\frac{\sigma_r{}^2}{\sigma_0{}^2}} - \frac{\sigma_r}{2\sigma_0}\right] + C \quad (8.77)$$

The constant of integration C is obtained from the condition at the outer surface, $r = b$, where $\sigma_r = 0$, as $C = \ln b$, and with this value the solution of the differential equation becomes

$$\ln\frac{r}{b} = \frac{\sqrt{3}}{2}\sin^{-1}\left(\frac{\sqrt{3}}{2}\frac{\sigma_r}{\sigma_0}\right) - \frac{1}{2}\ln\left(\sqrt{1 - \frac{3}{4}\frac{\sigma_r{}^2}{\sigma_0{}^2}} - \frac{\sigma_r}{2\sigma_0}\right) \quad (8.78)$$

or

$$\frac{r}{b} = \frac{e^{\frac{\sqrt{3}}{2}\sin^{-1}\left(\frac{\sqrt{3}}{2}\frac{\sigma_r}{\sigma_0}\right)}}{\sqrt{\sqrt{1 - \frac{3}{4}\frac{\sigma_r{}^2}{\sigma_0{}^2}} - \frac{\sigma_r}{2\sigma_0}}} \quad (8.79)$$

This equation indicates that the σ_r/σ_0 ratio is a function of r/b but is independent of the inner radius a. The same statement holds for the σ_θ/σ_0 ratio, by virtue of Eq. (8.75). Figure 8.5 shows the plot of σ_r/σ_0 and σ_θ/σ_0 versus r/b.

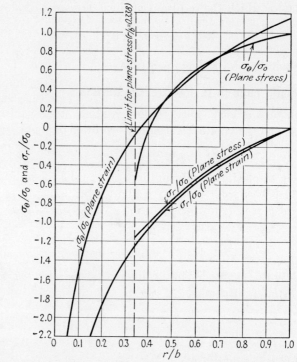

Fɪɢ. 8.5. Stress distribution in fully plastic tube in plane stress and plane strain.

The relationship between the internal pressure p which is consistent with the state of plastic equilibrium and the a/b ratio of a given tube is obtained by substituting in Eq. (8.79) $r = a$ and $\sigma_r = -p$.

$$\frac{a}{b} = \frac{e^{-\frac{\sqrt{3}}{2}\sin^{-1}\left(\frac{\sqrt{3}}{2}\frac{p}{\sigma_0}\right)}}{\sqrt{\sqrt{1 - \frac{3}{4}\frac{p^2}{\sigma_0^2}} + \frac{p}{2\sigma_0}}} \tag{8.80}$$

From Eq. (8.75) it can be seen that the absolute value of the ratio σ_r/σ_0 cannot become larger than $2/\sqrt{3} = 1.155$. Substituting this value for $-p/\sigma_0$ into Eq. (8.80) furnishes $a/b = 0.338$, the smallest ratio for which full plasticity is possible in the plane-stress state.

For comparison, σ_r/σ_0 and σ_θ/σ_0 for the plane-strain condition, based on Eqs. (8.45) and (8.46), are also plotted in Fig. 8.5.

REFERENCES

HILL, R., E. H. LEE, and S. J. TUPPER, The Theory of Combined Plastic and Elastic Deformation with Particular Reference to a Thick Tube under Internal Pressure, *Proc. Roy. Soc. (London)*, Series *A*, Vol. 191, pp. 278–303, 1947.

NÁDAI, A., "Theory of the Plastic Distortion of Thick-walled Cylinders," Reissner Anniversary Volume, pp. 430–448, Edwards Bros., Inc., Ann Arbor, Mich., 1949.

NÁDAI, A., "Theory of Flow and Fracture of Solids," Vol. I, pp. 436–481, McGraw-Hill Book Company, Inc., New York, 1950.

SACHS, G., and J. D. LUBAHN, Strength of Cylindrical Dies, *J. Applied Mechanics*, Vol. 10, pp. A-147–A-155, 1943.

TIMOSHENKO, S., "Theory of Elasticity," pp. 55–58, McGraw-Hill Book Company, Inc., New York, 1934.

CHAPTER 9

ROTATING CYLINDERS AND DISKS

The problems to be discussed in this chapter present many similarities to those of the preceding one, because of the axial symmetry of the bodies and of the forces acting on them in both cases; hence, frequent reference will be made to notations and basic relations used and results obtained in Chap. 8.

According to the longitudinal dimensions of the rotating body, distinction is being made between "long cylinders" with vanishing longitudinal load and very short cylinders or "disks" with vanishing stresses on planes normal to the cylinder axis.

9.1. Elastic Rotating Cylinder

The equilibrium equation for problems of rotating cylindrical bodies is obtained by a procedure similar to that followed in deriving Eq. (8.11), except that the sum of the forces acting on the volume element in the radial direction will contain the following term that represents the centrifugal force:

$$D\omega^2 r^2 \, dr \, d\theta \, dz$$

where D is the density of the material and ω the angular velocity of rotation. Thus, the differential equation of equilibrium becomes

$$\frac{d\sigma_r}{dr} + \frac{\sigma_r - \sigma_\theta}{r} + D\omega^2 r = 0 \tag{9.1}$$

The volume-constancy condition, $\epsilon_r + \epsilon_\theta + \epsilon_z = 0$, becomes, with reference to the relations $\epsilon_r = du_r/dr$ and $\epsilon_\theta = u_r/r$,

$$\frac{du_r}{dr} + \frac{u_r}{r} + \epsilon_z = 0 \tag{9.2}$$

In a long cylinder, at sufficient distance from the ends, a "generalized plane-strain" condition can be expected to exist with a constant, but not necessarily zero, longitudinal strain ϵ_z. Under such condition, the solution of Eq. (9.2) is

$$u_r = -\frac{\epsilon_z r}{2} + \frac{C_1}{r} \tag{9.3}$$

The constant of integration C_1 must be zero in the present case, in order to avoid the physically impossible result of infinitely large displacement at the center, so that the expression for u_r becomes

$$u_r = -\frac{\epsilon_z r}{2} \tag{9.4}$$

and the ϵ_r and ϵ_θ strains become

$$\epsilon_r = \epsilon_\theta = -\frac{\epsilon_z}{2} \tag{9.5}$$

Hence, the assumption of a "generalized plane strain" yields a uniform state of strain for all points of the cylinder, regardless of the mechanical properties of the material.

The stress-strain relations for an incompressible elastic body become with reference to Eq. (9.5)

$$2\sigma_r - \sigma_\theta - \sigma_z = -3G\epsilon_z \tag{9.6}$$
$$2\sigma_\theta - \sigma_z - \sigma_r = -3G\epsilon_z \tag{9.7}$$
$$2\sigma_z - \sigma_r - \sigma_\theta = 6G\epsilon_z \tag{9.8}$$

From Eqs. (9.6) and (9.7) one concludes that $\sigma_r = \sigma_\theta$, and the differential equation of equilibrium, Eq. (9.1), becomes

$$\frac{d\sigma_r}{dr} + D\omega^2 r = 0 \tag{9.9}$$

The solution of this equation is

$$\sigma_r = C_2 - \frac{D\omega^2 r^2}{2} \tag{9.10}$$

and the constant of integration C_2 is obtained from the condition that at the surface of the cylinder, where $r = b$, $\sigma_r = 0$, as follows:

$$C_2 = \frac{D\omega^2 b^2}{2} \tag{9.11}$$

With this value the σ_r and σ_θ stresses become

$$\sigma_r = \sigma_\theta = \frac{D\omega^2(b^2 - r^2)}{2} \tag{9.12}$$

and from Eq. (9.8),

$$\sigma_z = \frac{\sigma_r + \sigma_\theta}{2} + 3G\epsilon_z = \frac{D\omega^2}{2}(b^2 - r^2) + 3G\epsilon_z \tag{9.13}$$

The condition of vanishing longitudinal load furnishes the equation

$$\int_0^b \sigma_z 2\pi r \, dr = 0$$

which, with the above value for σ_z, becomes

$$\int^b \left[\frac{D\omega^2}{2}(b^2 - r^2) + 3G\epsilon_z \right] 2\pi r\, dr = \frac{\pi D\omega^2 b^4}{4} + 3G\epsilon_z\pi b^2 = 0$$

from which

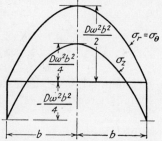

$$\epsilon_z = -\frac{D\omega^2 b^2}{12G} \qquad (9.14)$$

Substituting this expression into Eq. (9.13), one has

$$\sigma_z = \frac{D\omega^2}{2}\left(\frac{b^2}{2} - r^2\right) \qquad (9.15)$$

FIG. 9.1. Stress distribution in elastic incompressible rotating cylinder.

Figure 9.1 shows the stress distribution across the cylinder in the elastic state.

9.2. Rotating Cylinder in the Plastic State

The stress state at all points of the incompressible elastic rotating cylinder is, because of $\sigma_r = \sigma_\theta$, of the type previously defined as a "cylindrical" stress state, in which both the maximum-shearing-stress condition and the distortion-energy condition furnish the same relation to be satisfied at the instant of yielding:

$$\sigma_r - \sigma_z = \sigma_0 \qquad (9.16)$$

Substituting in this equation the expressions of σ_r and σ_z from Eqs. (9.12) and (9.15), respectively, it becomes

$$\frac{D\omega^2 b^2}{4} = \sigma_0 \qquad (9.17)$$

and it can be seen that yielding begins simultaneously at all points of the cylinder, at the following value of the angular velocity of rotation:

$$\omega_i = \frac{2}{b}\sqrt{\frac{\sigma_0}{D}} \qquad (9.18)$$

The stresses in the fully plastic state are obtained from Eqs. (9.12) and (9.15) that govern the elastic state, by substituting for ω the above expression for ω_i,

$$\sigma_r = \sigma_\theta = 2\sigma_0\left(1 - \frac{r^2}{b^2}\right) \qquad (9.19)$$

$$\sigma_z = 2\sigma_0\left(\frac{1}{2} - \frac{r^2}{b^2}\right) \qquad (9.20)$$

9.3. Elastic Rotating Circular Disk

When the transverse planes that bound the very short cylinder are free of external forces, a state of plane stress, in this case with $\sigma_z = 0$, can be assumed to exist throughout the body. The stress-strain relations for an incompressible elastic body become in this case

$$2\sigma_r - \sigma_\theta = 6G\epsilon_r \tag{9.21}$$
$$2\sigma_\theta - \sigma_r = 6G\epsilon_\theta \tag{9.22}$$
$$\sigma_r + \sigma_\theta = 6G(\epsilon_r + \epsilon_\theta) \tag{9.23}$$

Actually, these are only two independent equations, the third being always derivable from any two of these equations. Solving for σ_r and σ_θ, one has

$$\sigma_r = 2G(2\epsilon_r + \epsilon_\theta) \tag{9.24}$$
$$\sigma_\theta = 2G(\epsilon_r + 2\epsilon_\theta) \tag{9.25}$$

and with these values the equilibrium equation (9.1) becomes

$$2G \frac{d}{dr}(2\epsilon_r + \epsilon_\theta) + 2G \frac{\epsilon_r - \epsilon_\theta}{r} + D\omega^2 r = 0 \tag{9.26}$$

Recalling that, according to Eqs. (7.1) and (7.2),

$$\epsilon_r = \frac{du_r}{dr} \quad \text{and} \quad \epsilon_\theta = \frac{u_r}{r}$$

the following differential equation is obtained for u_r:

$$\frac{d^2 u_r}{dr^2} + \frac{1}{r}\frac{du_r}{dr} - \frac{u_r}{r^2} + \frac{D\omega^2 r}{4G} = 0 \tag{9.27}$$

the solution of which is

$$u_r = C_1 r + \frac{C_2}{r} - \frac{D\omega^2}{32G} r^3 \tag{9.28}$$

To avoid infinitely large u_r values along the z axis, C_2 must be zero, or

$$u_r = C_1 r - \frac{D\omega^2}{32G} r^3 \tag{9.29}$$

Then, the strains become

$$\epsilon_r = \frac{du_r}{dr} = C_1 - \frac{3}{32}\frac{D\omega^2}{G} r^2 \tag{9.30}$$

$$\epsilon_\theta = \frac{u_r}{r} = C_1 - \frac{D\omega^2}{32G} r^2 \tag{9.31}$$

and substituting into Eqs. (9.24) and (9.25), one has

$$\sigma_r = 6GC_1 - \tfrac{7}{16}D\omega^2 r^2 \tag{9.32}$$
$$\sigma_\theta = 6GC_1 - \tfrac{5}{16}D\omega^2 r^2 \tag{9.33}$$

The integration constant C_1 is determined from the condition that at the cylindrical surface $r = b$, $\sigma_r = 0$, so that

$$C_1 = \frac{7}{96} \frac{D\omega^2 b^2}{G}$$

and with this value the stresses become

$$\sigma_r = \frac{D\omega^2}{16} (7b^2 - 7r^2) \qquad (9.34)$$

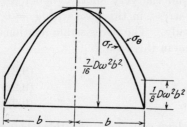

FIG. 9.2. Stress distribution in elastic incompressible rotating disk.

$$\sigma_\theta = \frac{D\omega^2}{16} (7b^2 - 5r^2) \qquad (9.35)$$

Figure 9.2 shows the distribution of the σ_r and σ_θ stresses in the circular disk.

9.4. Rotating Circular Disk in the Plastic State

The distortion-energy condition of plasticity, expressed in the present case of "plane stress" by Eq. (8.74) as

$$\sigma_r{}^2 - \sigma_r\sigma_\theta + \sigma_\theta{}^2 = \sigma_0{}^2$$

involves considerable analytical difficulties when applied to the problem of rotating disks. A comparatively simple solution can be obtained by adopting, as suggested by Nádai, the maximum-shearing-stress condition of plasticity:

$$\sigma_{\mathrm{I}} - \sigma_{\mathrm{III}} = \sigma_0 \qquad (9.36)$$

The use of this condition requires caution because it is predicated upon the advance knowledge of the relative magnitudes of the principal stresses in order to assign proper values to σ_{I} and σ_{III}. For the present problem, inspection of the elastic stress distribution shows that $\sigma_\theta \geq \sigma_r \geq 0$ throughout the disk; hence, $\sigma_{\mathrm{I}} = \sigma_\theta$ and $\sigma_{\mathrm{III}} = \sigma_z = 0$ should be substituted in Eq. (9.36), which becomes

$$\sigma_\theta = \sigma_0 \qquad (9.37)$$

With reference to Fig. 4.3, which represents the yield conditions in the plane-stress state, it can be seen that by using this equation the elliptic arc CB is replaced by the straight line CB.

Yielding starts where σ_θ reaches its largest value, *i.e.*, at the center of the disk, where $r = 0$ and

$$\sigma_\theta = \frac{7D\omega^2 b^2}{16}$$

The yield condition [Eq. (9.37)] is satisfied when the angular velocity assumes the value

$$\omega_i = \frac{4}{b} \sqrt{\frac{\sigma_0}{7D}} \tag{9.38}$$

The fully plastic condition can be investigated under the tentative assumption that the inequalities $\sigma_\theta \geq \sigma_r \geq 0$ hold for that condition also, and it will be shown that this assumption is confirmed by the obtained results. The differential equation of equilibrium becomes, with $\sigma_\theta = \sigma_0$ and $\omega = \omega_f$, the angular velocity that produces full plasticity:

$$\frac{d\sigma_r}{dr} + \frac{\sigma_r - \sigma_0}{r} + D\omega_f^2 r = 0 \tag{9.39}$$

and its solution is

$$\sigma_r = \sigma_0 + \frac{C}{r} - \frac{D\omega_f^2 r^2}{3} \tag{9.40}$$

Again, C must vanish to avoid infinitely large stresses at $r = 0$; hence,

$$\sigma_r = \sigma_0 - \frac{D\omega_f^2 r^2}{3} \tag{9.41}$$

The expression for ω_f is found from the condition at the rim of the disk, where $r = b$, $\sigma_r = 0$, or

$$\sigma_0 - \frac{D\omega_f^2 b^2}{3} = 0$$

from which

$$\omega_f = \frac{1}{b} \sqrt{\frac{3\sigma_0}{D}} \tag{9.42}$$

and finally the expression for the σ_r stress becomes

$$\sigma_r = \sigma_0 \left(1 - \frac{r^2}{b^2}\right) \tag{9.43}$$

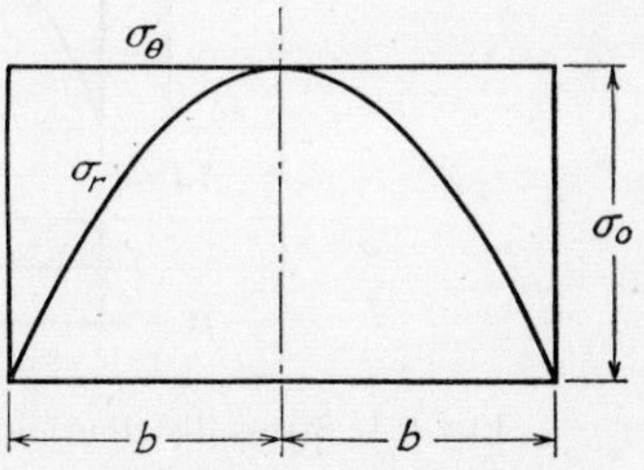

Fig. 9.3. Stress distribution in fully plastic rotating disk.

Figure 9.3 shows the stress distribution in the fully plastic state, and it is seen that the tentatively assumed relation $\sigma_\theta \geq \sigma_r \geq 0$ is fulfilled throughout the disk.

9.5. Elastic Rotating Annular Disk

Investigating the stress state in a rotating annular disk, with inner radius a, outer radius b, use can be made of the relations developed in Art. 9.3 for a *solid* circular disk, including Eq. (9.28), which furnishes the solution of the equilibrium equation in terms of the radial displacement u_r. However, in the case of the *annular* disk, both integration constants

C_1 and C_2 must be maintained, so that the complete expressions for the strains ϵ_r and ϵ_θ become

$$\epsilon_r = \frac{du_r}{dr} = C_1 - \frac{c_2}{r^2} - \frac{3}{32} \frac{D\omega^2}{G} r^2 \tag{9.44}$$

$$\epsilon_\theta = \frac{u_r}{r} = C_1 + \frac{c_2}{r^2} - \frac{1}{32} \frac{D\omega^2}{G} r^2 \tag{9.45}$$

and the expressions for the stresses become, from Eqs. (9.24) and (9.25),

$$\sigma_r = 6GC_1 - \frac{2GC_2}{r^2} - \frac{7}{16} D\omega^2 r^2 \tag{9.46}$$

$$\sigma_\theta = 6GC_1 + \frac{2GC_2}{r^2} - \frac{5}{16} D\omega^2 r^2 \tag{9.47}$$

The integration constants C_1 and C_2 are determined from the conditions that both at the inner rim, $r = a$, and at the outer rim, $r = b$, the σ_r

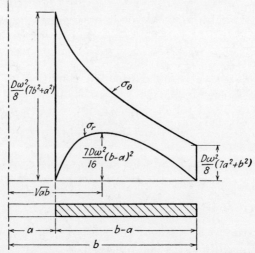

Fig. 9.4. Stress distribution in incompressible elastic rotating annular disk.

stress vanishes, or

$$6GC_1 - \frac{2GC_2}{a^2} - \frac{7}{16} D\omega^2 a^2 = 0 \tag{9.48}$$

$$6GC_1 - \frac{2GC_2}{b^2} - \frac{7}{16} D\omega^2 b^2 = 0 \tag{9.49}$$

Solving these two equations simultaneously, one obtains

$$C_1 = \frac{7D\omega^2}{96G} (a^2 + b^2) \tag{9.50}$$

$$C_2 = \frac{7D\omega^2}{32G} a^2 b^2 \tag{9.51}$$

and with these values the expressions for the stresses become

$$\sigma_r = \frac{7D\omega^2}{16}\left[a^2 - r^2 + b^2\left(1 - \frac{a^2}{r^2}\right)\right] \tag{9.52}$$

$$\sigma_\theta = \frac{D\omega^2}{16}\left[7\left(a^2 + b^2 + \frac{a^2b^2}{r^2}\right) - 5r^2\right] \tag{9.53}$$

In Fig. 9.4 the stress distribution calculated here is represented graphically.

9.6. Annular Disk in the Plastic State

Here, as in the analysis of the *solid* plastic disk in Art. 9.4, the maximum-shearing-stress yield condition will be used, expressed by Eq. (9.37),

$$\sigma_\theta = \sigma_0$$

Yielding starts at the inner rim of the disk, where σ_θ reaches its maximum value of

$$\frac{D\omega^2}{8}(7b^2 + a^2)$$

and when the angular velocity reaches the value

$$\omega_i = \sqrt{\frac{8\sigma_0}{D(7b^2 + a^2)}} \tag{9.54}$$

In the full plastic state, Eq. (9.40) applies:

$$\sigma_r = \sigma_0 + \frac{C}{r} - \frac{D\omega_f^2 r^2}{3}$$

in the present case as in the case of the solid disk; however, C and ω_f are to be determined from the following equations expressing that $\sigma_r = 0$ at the inner and the outer rim of the disk:

$$\sigma_0 + \frac{C}{a} - \frac{D\omega_f^2 a^2}{3} = 0 \tag{9.55}$$

$$\sigma_0 + \frac{C}{b} - \frac{D\omega_f^2 b^2}{3} = 0 \tag{9.56}$$

from which

$$C = \sigma_0 a \frac{a^2/b^2 - 1}{1 - a^3/b^3} \tag{9.57}$$

$$\omega_f = \sqrt{\frac{3\sigma_0}{D}\frac{b - a}{b^3 - a^3}} \tag{9.58}$$

and the expression for σ_r becomes

$$\sigma_r = \sigma_0 \left(1 - \frac{a}{r} \frac{1 - a^2/b^2}{1 - a^3/b^3} - \frac{r^2}{b^2} \frac{1 - a/b}{1 - a^3/b^3} \right) \tag{9.59}$$

Figure 9.5 shows the stress distribution in the plastic annular disk.

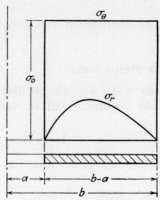

FIG. 9.5. Stress distribution in fully plastic rotating annular disk.

REFERENCES

LASZLO, F., Geschleuderte Umdrehungskoerper im Gebiet bleibender Deformation, *Z. angew. Math. Mechanik*, Vol. 9, p. 281, 1929.

NÁDAI, A., and L. H. DONNELL, Stress Distribution in Rotating Disks of Ductile Material after the Yield Point Has Been Reached, *Trans. ASME*, Vol. 51, pp. 173–181, 1929.

NÁDAI, A., "Theory of Flow and Fracture of Solids," Vol. I, pp. 482–489, McGraw-Hill Book Company, Inc., New York, 1950.

CHAPTER 10

TORSION AND BENDING

This chapter is devoted to the simplest problems that arise in connection with plastic flow in slender structural members: the torsion of a shaft of circular cross section and the bending of a beam of narrow rectangular cross section.

10.1. Torsion of Cylindrical Bars of Solid Circular Cross Section

Consider a long cylindrical bar of circular cross section subjected to two equal and opposite torques T applied at the ends. The state of strain and stress at sufficient distance from the ends can be expected to be independent of the applied forces that yield the torques and to be uniform along lines parallel to the bar axis.

From the above assumptions and the condition of axial symmetry, it can be concluded that the displacement vector $\mathbf{u}$ at any point is in the plane of the cross section, perpendicular to the radius passing through the point, and that it represents a rigid rotation of the cross-sectional plane about the axis. Furthermore, the relative rotation of two cross sections must be proportional to their mutual distance.

With reference to a system of cylindrical coordinates, r, θ, z, with z along the bar axis, the components of $\mathbf{u}$ are then

$$u_r = 0 \tag{10.1}$$
$$u_\theta = \vartheta z r \tag{10.2}$$
$$u_z = 0 \tag{10.3}$$

where ϑ is the constant angle of twist per unit length.

By applying Eqs. (2.10) that define the components of strain, it is found that they all vanish except for $\gamma_{\theta z}$, that is,

$$\epsilon_r = \epsilon_\theta = \epsilon_z = \gamma_{r\theta} = \gamma_{zr} = 0 \tag{10.4}$$

and

$$\gamma_{\theta z} = \frac{\partial u_\theta}{\partial z} + \frac{1}{r} \frac{\partial u_z}{\partial \theta} = \vartheta r \tag{10.5}$$

so that the matrix of the strain tensor becomes

$$\mathbf{E} = \begin{pmatrix} 0 & 0 & 0 \\ 0 & 0 & \dfrac{\gamma_{\theta z}}{2} \\ 0 & \dfrac{\gamma_{\theta z}}{2} & 0 \end{pmatrix} = \begin{pmatrix} 0 & 0 & 0 \\ 0 & 0 & \dfrac{\vartheta r}{2} \\ 0 & \dfrac{\vartheta r}{2} & 0 \end{pmatrix} \tag{10.6}$$

Because of $\mathbf{E}'' = 0$, one can state that $\mathbf{E} = \mathbf{E}'$ so that the strain tensor is a deviator tensor, independently of the assumptions concerning the incompressibility of the material.

Considering first the behavior in the elastic range, governed by the stress-strain relation, $\mathbf{S}' = 2G\mathbf{E}'$, one finds that all stress components

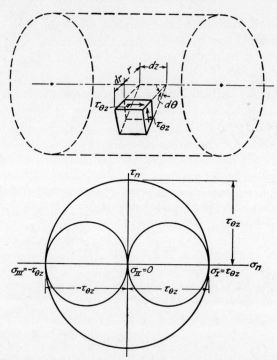

Fig. 10.1. Stresses on volume element and Mohr's diagram.

except $\tau_{\theta z}$ must vanish, and the matrix of the deviator stress tensor $\mathbf{S}'$ (and at the same time that of the stress tensor $\mathbf{S}$ itself) is written as

$$\mathbf{S} = \mathbf{S}' = \begin{pmatrix} 0 & 0 & 0 \\ 0 & 0 & \tau_{\theta z} \\ 0 & \tau_{\theta z} & 0 \end{pmatrix} = \begin{pmatrix} 0 & 0 & 0 \\ 0 & 0 & G\vartheta r \\ 0 & G\vartheta r & 0 \end{pmatrix} \tag{10.7}$$

From Eqs. (10.6) and (10.7) it can be seen that the same state of strain and stress exists at all points of a concentric cylindrical surface. From the vanishing of the shearing stress components on a tangential plane element, $\tau_{r\theta} = \tau_{zr} = 0$, it can be concluded that the radial direction is a principal direction with zero principal stress. Hence a "plane-stress" condition exists, with the directions of the nonvanishing principal stresses σ_1 and σ_2 lying in the tangential plane.

With reference to Art. 1.9, in which the "plane-stress" condition is discussed in detail, one finds that the principal directions are oriented so as to make $\pm 45°$ angles with the z direction, and the principal stresses are

$$\sigma_1 = \tau_{\theta z}, \qquad \sigma_2 = -\tau_{\theta z} \tag{10.8}$$

Figure 10.1 shows the stresses acting on a volume element bounded by two transverse planes, two concentric cylindrical surfaces, and two planes containing the bar axis; and also the Mohr diagram of the state of stress.

The angle of twist ϑ is found from the condition that the moment of all stresses acting on a cross section is equal to the applied torque:

$$T = \int_0^a \tau_{\theta z} 2r^2\pi \, dr = \int_0^a G\vartheta 2r^3\pi \, dr = \frac{\pi G\vartheta a^4}{2} \tag{10.9}$$

where a is the radius of the circular cross section.

Solving for ϑ, one has

$$\vartheta = \frac{2T}{\pi G a^4} \tag{10.10}$$

and the expression for $\tau_{\theta z}$ becomes

$$\tau_{\theta z} = \frac{2Tr}{\pi a^4} \tag{10.11}$$

It was shown in Art. 4.4 that, in the present case of "plane stress" with $\sigma_1 = -\sigma_2$, the distortion-energy condition of plasticity is expressed by

$$\sigma_1 = -\sigma_2 = \frac{\sigma_0}{\sqrt{3}}$$

or in the present problem

$$\tau_{\theta z} = \frac{\sigma_0}{\sqrt{3}} \tag{10.12}$$

Yielding begins at the surface where $\tau_{\theta z}$ has its maximum value:

$$\max \tau_{\theta z} = \frac{2T}{\pi a^3} \tag{10.13}$$

when the torque reaches the value

$$T_i = \frac{\pi \sigma_0 a^3}{2\sqrt{3}} \tag{10.14}$$

For values of $T > T_i$, a plastic zone will develop between the outer surface and a certain concentric cylindrical surface, the "plastic front," the radius of which, ρ, depends on the magnitude of the applied torque.

In the plastic zone, the same state of deformation, defined at the beginning of this article, will exist. Applying Saint-Venant's stress-strain relation to an infinitesimal increment of the strain components, the matrix of the stress tensor and of its deviator is found to be

$$\mathbf{S} = \mathbf{S}' = \begin{pmatrix} 0 & 0 & 0 \\ 0 & 0 & \tau_{\theta z} \\ 0 & \tau_{\theta z} & 0 \end{pmatrix} \tag{10.15}$$

In other words, the state of stress in the plastic zone is similar to that in the elastic zone, except that $\tau_{\theta z}$ has the constant value

$$\tau_{\theta z} = \frac{\sigma_0}{\sqrt{3}} \tag{10.16}$$

During the progressive development of the plastic zone, the deformation of the inner elastic core, defined by the angle of twist ϑ, determines uniquely that of the entire cylinder.

At the plastic front, $r = \rho$, the elastic shearing stress

$$\tau_{\theta z} = G\vartheta\rho$$

equals the value of $\sigma_0/\sqrt{3}$ previously obtained for the plastic zone, that is,

$$G\vartheta\rho = \frac{\sigma_0}{\sqrt{3}}$$

from which

$$\rho = \frac{\sigma_0}{\sqrt{3}G\vartheta} \tag{10.17}$$

The torque corresponding to a given value of ϑ is then

$$T = \int_0^a \tau_{\theta z} 2\pi r^2 \, dr = \int_0^\rho (G\vartheta r) 2\pi r^2 \, dr + \int_\rho^a \frac{\sigma_0}{\sqrt{3}} 2\pi r^2 \, dr$$

$$= \frac{2\pi}{\sqrt{27}} \sigma_0 a^3 - \frac{\pi}{54} \frac{\sigma_0{}^4}{(G\vartheta)^3} \tag{10.18}$$

This equation indicates that an elastic core persists at the center of the bar and that the torque T_f corresponding to full plasticity

$$T_f = \frac{2\pi}{\sqrt{27}} \sigma_0 a^3$$

can be reached only for a theoretically infinitely large angle of twist. It is to be recalled, however, that the relations here developed are based on the assumption of small strains.   Figure 10.2 shows a diagram of the torque T versus the angle of twist ϑ.

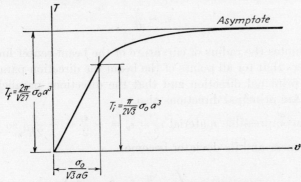

FIG. 10.2. Diagram of torque versus angle of twist.

10.2. Bending of Prismatic Bars of Narrow Rectangular Cross Section

Consider a long prismatic bar (or "beam") having a rectangular cross section of width b and depth h subjected to two equal and opposite

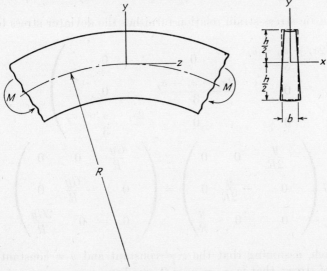

FIG. 10.3. Dimensions in bending of prismatic bar of narrow rectangular cross section.

end moments, as shown in Fig. 10.3, where the cartesian reference axes are shown also.   Excluding two short portions near the ends, it can be expected that lines parallel to the edges change into concentric circular arcs.   Assuming that the width of the beam is very small in comparison with its depth, it can be concluded that elongated prismatic elements, of width b and depth dy, are deformed as if they would be isolated from the rest of the beam and undergo an axial strain

$$\epsilon_z = \frac{y}{R} \qquad (10.19)$$

where R denotes the radius of curvature of the beam center line.   From this it follows that for all points of the beam the direction parallel to the z axis is a principal direction and that the directions parallel to the x and y axes are principal directions also.

For an incompressible material $\epsilon_x = \epsilon_y = -\dfrac{\epsilon_z}{2} = -\dfrac{y}{2R}$, so that both the strain tensor and its deviator become

$$\mathbf{E} = \mathbf{E'} = \begin{pmatrix} -\dfrac{y}{2R} & 0 & 0 \\[2ex] 0 & -\dfrac{y}{2R} & 0 \\[2ex] 0 & 0 & \dfrac{y}{R} \end{pmatrix} \qquad (10.20)$$

The elastic stress-strain relation furnishes the deviator stress tensor

$$\mathbf{S'} = \begin{pmatrix} \dfrac{2\sigma_x - \sigma_y - \sigma_z}{3} & 0 & 0 \\[2ex] 0 & \dfrac{2\sigma_y - \sigma_z - \sigma_x}{3} & 0 \\[2ex] 0 & 0 & \dfrac{2\sigma_z - \sigma_x - \sigma_y}{3} \end{pmatrix}$$

$$= 2G \begin{pmatrix} -\dfrac{y}{2R} & 0 & 0 \\[2ex] 0 & -\dfrac{y}{2R} & 0 \\[2ex] 0 & 0 & \dfrac{y}{R} \end{pmatrix} = \begin{pmatrix} -\dfrac{Gy}{R} & 0 & 0 \\[2ex] 0 & -\dfrac{Gy}{R} & 0 \\[2ex] 0 & 0 & \dfrac{2Gy}{R} \end{pmatrix} \qquad (10.21)$$

from which, assuming that the $x =$ constant and $y =$ constant planes are free of stress, that is, $\sigma_x = \sigma_y = 0$, one has

$$\sigma_z = \frac{3Gy}{R} \qquad (10.22)$$

The radius of curvature R of the beam axis is calculated from the equilibrium equation which expresses that the sum of the moments about the x axis of all σ_z stresses acting on a cross section is equal to the applied moment M.

$$M = \int_{-h/2}^{+h/2} \sigma_z by \, dy = \int_{-h/2}^{+h/2} \frac{3Gb}{R} y^2 \, dy = \frac{Gbh^3}{4R} \qquad (10.23)$$

From the definition of the bulk modulus K (see Art. 3.1) it follows that the value of $\frac{1}{2}$ for Poisson's ratio ν is consistent with the assumption of incompressibility. With such a value, the shear modulus becomes $G = E/3$, and substituting this expression into Eq. (10.23), one has

$$M = \frac{Ebh^3}{12R} \qquad \text{or} \qquad \frac{1}{R} = \frac{12M}{Ebh^3} \qquad (10.24)$$

the well-known relationship of the elastic-beam theory. Substituting $1/R$ into Eq. (10.22), it becomes

$$\sigma_z = \frac{12My}{bh^3} = \frac{Ey}{R} \qquad (10.25)$$

For the uniaxial stress condition here existing, the yield condition is simply $\sigma_z = \pm\sigma_0$; and yielding begins at the extreme "fibers," where $y = \pm h/2$, when the bending moment reaches the value

$$M_i = \sigma_0 \frac{bh^2}{6} \qquad (10.26)$$

and the curvature of the beam center line becomes

$$\frac{1}{R} = \frac{2\sigma_0}{Eh} \qquad (10.27)$$

The elasto-plastic behavior, corresponding to $M > M_i$, is characterized by a central portion of the beam, $-\eta \leq y \leq \eta$, being in the elastic state with σ_z stresses given by the equation

$$\sigma_z = \sigma_0 \frac{y}{\eta} \qquad (10.28)$$

and two outer plastic portions with $\sigma_z = \pm\sigma_0$.

The bending moment corresponding to an assumed value of η is

$$M = \int_{-h/2}^{+h/2} \sigma_z by \, dy = b\sigma_0 \left(\frac{h^2}{4} - \frac{\eta^2}{3} \right) = \frac{b\sigma_0 h^2}{4} - \frac{1}{3} \frac{b\sigma_0^3}{E^2} R^2 \qquad (10.29)$$

In this case, similarly to the torsion of a circular cylindrical bar, an elastic core persists, and the bending moment M_f for full plasticity,

$$M_f = \sigma_0 \frac{bh^2}{4} \qquad (10.30)$$

requires, theoretically, an infinitely large curvature. However, the theory here developed, based on small strains, will cease to be valid before the changes in cross-sectional dimensions of the beam become comparable with the original dimensions.

Figure 10.4 shows the diagram of the bending moment M as a function of the curvature $1/R$.

Nádai has shown how the above-developed theory can be extended to beams having other than a narrow rectangular cross section by assuming

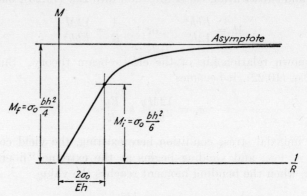

Fig. 10.4. Diagram of bending moment versus curvature.

a stress distribution analogous to that defined by Eq. (10.28). It should be pointed out, however, that, as the width of the beam increases, the basic assumptions of the above theory, especially those concerning the uniaxial state of stress and the free lateral deformation of the particles, become increasingly inadmissible. For an analysis of the bending of plates (*i.e.*, beams having a very wide rectangular cross section) see Chap. 23 of this book.

REFERENCES

Nádai, A., "Theory of Flow and Fracture of Solids," Vol. I, pp. 347–370, McGraw-Hill Book Company, Inc., New York, 1950.

Timoshenko, S., "Theory of Elasticity," pp. 220–221, McGraw-Hill Book Company, Inc., New York, 1934.

CHAPTER 11

TWO-DIMENSIONAL PLASTIC-FLOW PROBLEMS

It is the purpose of this chapter to give a review of the fundamentals of the general theory of two-dimensional plastic flow together with a few examples of application. These problems do not necessarily possess the simple symmetry properties of the problems discussed in the preceding chapters, yet they afford several methods of approach which are not available for the more general three-dimensional cases.

11.1. Incompressible Two-dimensional Flow

Assume a state of deformation of an incompressible material in which there is a direction, say the z direction of a cartesian system of reference, such that displacements of all points occur in planes parallel to the xy plane and are identical for all points with the same x, y coordinates, so that the cartesian components of the displacement vector $\mathbf{u}$ are $u_x(x,y)$; $u_y(x,y)$; $u_z = 0$.

The components of strain are then, according to their definitions by Eqs. (2.10),

$$
\begin{aligned}
\epsilon_x &= \frac{\partial u_x}{\partial x} & \gamma_{xy} &= \frac{\partial u_x}{\partial y} + \frac{\partial u_y}{\partial x} \\
\epsilon_y &= \frac{\partial u_y}{\partial y} & \gamma_{yz} &= \frac{\partial u_y}{\partial z} + \frac{\partial u_z}{\partial y} = 0 \\
\epsilon_z &= \frac{\partial u_z}{\partial z} = 0 & \gamma_{zx} &= \frac{\partial u_z}{\partial x} + \frac{\partial u_x}{\partial z} = 0
\end{aligned}
\tag{11.1}
$$

Hence, a condition of "plane strain" can be said to exist; and the z direction is that of the vanishing principal strain, while the other two principal directions lie in the xy plane. The corresponding principal strains are $\epsilon_1 > \epsilon_2$.

From the volume-constancy relation $\epsilon_x + \epsilon_y + \epsilon_z = 0$, one obtains

$$
\epsilon_x = -\epsilon_y
\tag{11.2}
$$

and the matrix of the strain tensor is written as

$$
\mathbf{E} = \mathbf{E}' =
\begin{pmatrix}
\epsilon_x & \dfrac{\gamma_{xy}}{2} & 0 \\
\dfrac{\gamma_{xy}}{2} & -\epsilon_x & 0 \\
0 & 0 & 0
\end{pmatrix}
\tag{11.3}
$$

Equation (2.17), from which the principal strains are to be calculated, becomes

$$\epsilon_i{}^3 - \left(\epsilon_x{}^2 + \frac{\gamma_{xy}{}^2}{4}\right)\epsilon_i = 0 \tag{11.4}$$

from which

$$\epsilon_i = (\epsilon_1,\ \epsilon_2) = \pm \sqrt{\epsilon_x{}^2 + \frac{\gamma_{xy}{}^2}{4}} \tag{11.5}$$

Figure 11.1 shows the Mohr diagram of the state of strain. The greatest principal circle with the diameter $2\epsilon_1$ represents the strains cor-

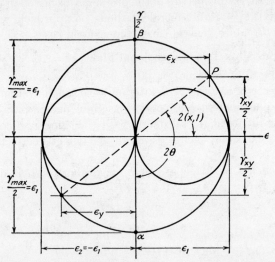

Fig. 11.1. Mohr's diagram of the state of strain in plane strain.

responding to the various orientations of the line elements contained in the xy plane. A point P on the greatest principal circle, with the coordinates ϵ_x, $\gamma_{xy}/2$, represents the strain of a line element that makes an angle $(x,1)$ with the principal direction of strain "1," and from the figure it can be seen that

$$\tan 2(x,1) = \frac{\gamma_{xy}}{2\epsilon_x} \tag{11.6}$$

On the same circle, point α represents the strain for a line element that makes a counterclockwise 45° angle with the principal direction "1," and a counterclockwise angle θ with the x direction so that

$$\tan 2\theta = - \frac{2\epsilon_x}{\gamma_{xy}} \tag{11.7}$$

For the line element α, the components of strain are

$$\epsilon_\alpha = 0, \qquad \gamma_\alpha = -2\epsilon_1 = -\gamma_{max} \qquad (11.8)$$

and similarly, for the line element β, perpendicular to α,

$$\epsilon_\beta = 0, \qquad \gamma_\beta = 2\epsilon_1 = \gamma_{max} \qquad (11.9)$$

In other words, at each point of an incompressible material in the state of plane strain, there are two directions, the α and β directions, that bisect the directions of principal strain and are characterized by vanishing linear strain and by the maximum angular strain among all possible directions. Curves in the xy plane which are tangential everywhere to the α and β directions form two families of orthogonal curves, the so-called "slip lines."

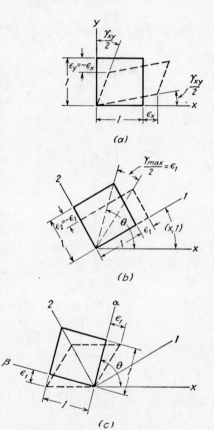

(a)

(b)

(c)

Figure 11.2a shows the deformed shape of a prismatic volume element with its edges oriented parallel to the cartesian axes; Fig. 11.2b shows a volume element with edges parallel to the "1" and "2" principal directions; Fig. 11.2c shows a volume element with edges originally parallel to the α and β directions.

The state of strain, described above for a given point by the tensor **E** [Eq. (11.3)], considered as a function of the coordinates of the point, has to satisfy certain conditions of continuity. It is convenient to express such conditions with reference to the slip lines; for this purpose, calculate the components of the displacement vector **u** with respect to the α and β directions. Given the cartesian components u_x and u_y, elementary rules of geometry furnish the expressions (see Fig. 11.3):

Fig. 11.2. Deformations of volume elements in plane strain: (a) edges of element are parallel to cartesian coordinate axes; (b) edges of element are parallel to the principal directions; (c) edges of element are parallel to the slip lines.

$$u_\alpha = u_x \cos\theta + u_y \sin\theta$$
$$u_\beta = -u_x \sin\theta + u_y \cos\theta \qquad (11.10)$$

Conversely, for given u_α and u_β components, the u_x and u_y components are

$$u_x = u_\alpha \cos \theta - u_\beta \sin \theta$$
$$u_y = u_\alpha \sin \theta + u_\beta \cos \theta \qquad (11.11)$$

In order to express the conditions $\epsilon_\alpha = 0$, $\epsilon_\beta = 0$ [see Eqs. (11.8) and (11.9)] orient the x axis so as to coincide with the α direction, that is, $\theta = 0$; then these conditions are written, by definition of the strain ϵ,

$$\epsilon_\alpha = \left(\frac{\partial u_x}{\partial x}\right)_{\theta=0} = 0$$
$$\epsilon_\beta = \left(\frac{\partial u_y}{\partial y}\right)_{\theta=0} = 0 \qquad (11.12)$$

By taking the partial derivatives of u_x and u_y, as expressed by Eqs. (11.11), these equations become

$$\frac{\partial u_x}{\partial x} = \left(\frac{\partial u_\alpha}{\partial x} - u_\beta \frac{\partial \theta}{\partial x}\right) \cos \theta - \left(\frac{\partial u_\beta}{\partial x} + u_\alpha \frac{\partial \theta}{\partial x}\right) \sin \theta = 0$$
$$\frac{\partial u_y}{\partial y} = \left(\frac{\partial u_\beta}{\partial y} + u_\alpha \frac{\partial \theta}{\partial y}\right) \cos \theta + \left(\frac{\partial u_\alpha}{\partial y} - u_\beta \frac{\partial \theta}{\partial y}\right) \sin \theta = 0 \qquad (11.13)$$

Denote with ds_α a line element along the α slip line and with ds_β a line element along the β slip line; in terms of the radii of curvature R_α and R_β of the slip lines they become

$$ds_\alpha = R_\alpha \, d\theta$$
and
$$ds_\beta = -R_\beta \, d\theta \qquad (11.14)$$

from which

$$\left(\frac{\partial \theta}{\partial x}\right)_{\theta=0} = \frac{\partial \theta}{\partial s_\alpha} = \frac{1}{R_\alpha}$$
$$\left(\frac{\partial \theta}{\partial y}\right)_{\theta=0} = \frac{\partial \theta}{\partial s_\beta} = -\frac{1}{R_\beta} \qquad (11.15)$$

The sign convention for the radii of curvature is such that they are positive for the slip lines shown in Fig. 11.3.

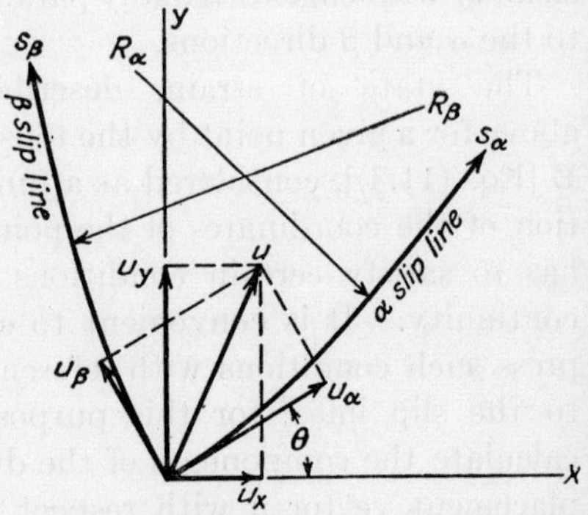

Fig. 11.3. Components of displacement of a point.

With the above values, and because of

$$\left(\frac{\partial u_\alpha}{\partial x}\right)_{\theta=0} = \frac{\partial u_\alpha}{\partial s_\alpha}, \qquad \left(\frac{\partial u_\beta}{\partial y}\right)_{\theta=0} = \frac{\partial u_\beta}{\partial s_\beta}$$

Eqs. (11.13) become, for $\theta = 0$,

$$
\begin{aligned}
\left(\frac{\partial u_x}{\partial x}\right)_{\theta=0} &= \frac{\partial u_\alpha}{\partial s_\alpha} - u_\beta \frac{\partial \theta}{\partial s_\alpha} = \frac{\partial u_\alpha}{\partial s_\alpha} - \frac{u_\beta}{R_\alpha} = 0 \\
\left(\frac{\partial u_y}{\partial y}\right)_{\theta=0} &= \frac{\partial u_\beta}{\partial s_\beta} + u_\alpha \frac{\partial \theta}{\partial s_\beta} = \frac{\partial u_\beta}{\partial s_\beta} - \frac{u_\alpha}{R_\beta} = 0
\end{aligned}
\tag{11.16}
$$

By taking the time derivatives of above equations and using the notations $v_\alpha = \partial u_\alpha / \partial t$, $v_\beta = \partial u_\beta / \partial t$, one has the following equations derived by Geiringer in 1937:

$$
\begin{aligned}
\frac{\partial v_\alpha}{\partial s_\alpha} - \frac{v_\beta}{R_\alpha} &= 0 \\
\frac{\partial v_\beta}{\partial s_\beta} - \frac{v_\alpha}{R_\beta} &= 0
\end{aligned}
\tag{11.17}
$$

It should be pointed out that these are the continuity equations for incompressible two-dimensional flow, of general validity, regardless of the stress-strain relations that govern the mechanical behavior of the material.

11.2. Stresses in Plastic Materials in Condition of "Plane Strain"

Saint-Venant's stress-strain relation for incompressible plastic materials [Eq. (5.12)]

$$
\mathbf{S}' = 2\lambda \dot{\mathbf{E}}
$$

can be written, with reference to arbitrary x, y, z axes and by using Eq. (11.3), as follows:

$$
\begin{pmatrix}
\dfrac{2\sigma_x - \sigma_y - \sigma_z}{3} & \tau_{xy} & \tau_{zx} \\[2ex]
\tau_{xy} & \dfrac{2\sigma_y - \sigma_z - \sigma_x}{3} & \tau_{yz} \\[2ex]
\tau_{zx} & \tau_{yz} & \dfrac{2\sigma_z - \sigma_x - \sigma_y}{3}
\end{pmatrix}
$$

$$
= 2\lambda \begin{pmatrix}
\dot{\epsilon}_x & \dfrac{\dot{\gamma}_{xy}}{2} & 0 \\[2ex]
\dfrac{\dot{\gamma}_{xy}}{2} & -\dot{\epsilon}_x & 0 \\[2ex]
0 & 0 & 0
\end{pmatrix}
\tag{11.18}
$$

From this tensor equation it can be concluded that

$$
\tau_{yz} = \tau_{zx} = 0 \quad \text{and} \quad \frac{2\sigma_z - \sigma_x - \sigma_y}{3} = 0
\tag{11.19}
$$

Hence,

$$\sigma_z = \frac{\sigma_x + \sigma_y}{2} \tag{11.20}$$

so that the matrix of the stress tensor becomes

$$\mathbf{S} = \begin{pmatrix} \sigma_x & \tau_{xy} & 0 \\ \tau_{xy} & \sigma_y & 0 \\ 0 & 0 & \dfrac{\sigma_x + \sigma_y}{2} \end{pmatrix} \tag{11.21}$$

From Eq. (11.19) it follows that the z direction is a principal direction of stress, the other two principal directions being contained in the xy plane; the corresponding principal stresses are calculated by the method outlined in Art. 1.3.   Equations (1.10) reduce in the present case to

$$\begin{aligned}(\sigma_x - \sigma_i)\cos(i,x) + \tau_{xy}\cos(i,y) &= 0 \\ \tau_{xy}\cos(i,x) + (\sigma_y - \sigma_i)\cos(i,y) &= 0\end{aligned} \tag{11.22}$$

and Eq. (1.12), expressing the vanishing of the determinant of the coefficients of these equations, reduces to

$$\begin{aligned}\begin{vmatrix} \sigma_x - \sigma_i & \tau_{xy} \\ \tau_{xy} & \sigma_y - \sigma_i \end{vmatrix} &= (\sigma_x - \sigma_i)(\sigma_y - \sigma_i) - \tau_{xy}^2 \\ &= \sigma_i^2 - (\sigma_x + \sigma_y)\sigma_i + \sigma_x\sigma_y - \tau_{xy}^2 = 0 \end{aligned} \tag{11.23}$$

The solution of this equation is

$$\sigma_i = (\sigma_1, \sigma_2) = \frac{\sigma_x + \sigma_y}{2} \pm \sqrt{\left(\frac{\sigma_x - \sigma_y}{2}\right)^2 + \tau_{xy}^2} \tag{11.24}$$

The third principal stress is

$$\sigma_3 = \sigma_z = \frac{\sigma_1 + \sigma_2}{2} = \frac{\sigma_x + \sigma_y}{2} \tag{11.25}$$

Figure 11.4 shows the Mohr diagram for the state of stress.   The greatest principal circle, with diameter $\sigma_1 - \sigma_2$, represents the stresses on plane elements normal to the xy plane; its radius is

$$\tau_{\max} = \frac{\sigma_1 - \sigma_2}{2} = \sqrt{\left(\frac{\sigma_x - \sigma_y}{2}\right)^2 + \tau_{xy}^2}$$

and its center is at distance $\sigma_m = (\sigma_1 + \sigma_2)/2 = (\sigma_x + \sigma_y)/2$ from the origin.   Point P on the greatest circle has the coordinates σ_x, τ_{xy} and represents the stress on the plane element normal to the x axis; the angle $(x,1)$ is obtained from the equation

$$\tan 2(x,1) = \frac{2\tau_{xy}}{\sigma_x - \sigma_y} \tag{11.26}$$

Point α on the same circle represents the stress on a plane that makes an angle of counterclockwise 45° with the plane of principal stress σ_1 and

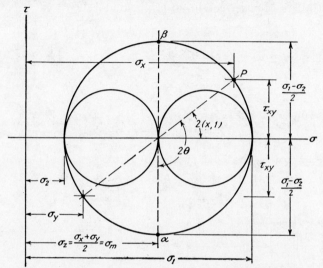

FIG. 11.4. Mohr's diagram of the state of stress in plane strain.

the counterclockwise angle θ with the x axis. The angle θ is calculated from

$$\tan 2\theta = \frac{\sigma_y - \sigma_x}{2\tau_{xy}} \tag{11.27}$$

The components of stress represented by point α are

$$\sigma_\alpha = \sigma_m = \frac{\sigma_1 + \sigma_2}{2}, \qquad \tau_\alpha = -\tau_{\max} = \frac{\sigma_2 - \sigma_1}{2} \tag{11.28}$$

Similarly, point β represents the state of stress on a plane perpendicular to the plane corresponding to point α, and it represents the stress with the components

$$\sigma_\beta = \sigma_m = \frac{\sigma_1 + \sigma_2}{2}, \qquad \tau_\beta = \tau_{\max} = \frac{\sigma_1 - \sigma_2}{2} \tag{11.29}$$

From Saint-Venant's plastic stress-strain relation [Eq. (11.18)] one can conclude that the Mohr diagrams representing the deviator stress tensor and the strain-rate tensor are similar, *i.e.*, in both cases the two smaller principal circles have diameters equal to half of that of the largest circle; also the coaxiality of the stress tensor and of the strain-rate tensor is implicit in Saint-Venant's theory.

It can be concluded also that the α and β directions of the state of stress, which define the planes of maximum shearing stresses, coincide with the α and β slip-line tangents of the state of strain produced during an infinitesimal time interval, at constant strain rates.

The von Mises–Hencky condition of plasticity:

$$(\sigma_1 - \sigma_2)^2 + (\sigma_2 - \sigma_3)^2 + (\sigma_3 - \sigma_1)^2 = 2\sigma_0^2$$

becomes, with $\sigma_3 = \sigma_z = (\sigma_1 + \sigma_2)/2$,

$$\sigma_1 - \sigma_2 = \frac{2}{\sqrt{3}} \sigma_0 \tag{11.30}$$

or, in terms of σ_x, σ_y, τ_{xy},

$$(\sigma_x - \sigma_y)^2 + 4\tau_{xy}^2 = \tfrac{4}{3}\sigma_0^2 \tag{11.31}$$

Conversely, σ_x, σ_y, τ_{xy} can be expressed in terms of σ_m and σ_0, with refer-

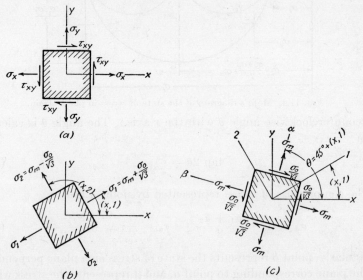

Fig. 11.5. Stresses on volume elements in plane strain: (*a*) edges of element are parallel to cartesian coordinate axes; (*b*) edges of element are parallel to principal directions; (*c*) edges of element are parallel to slip directions.

ence to the Mohr diagram of stress and to Eqs. (11.26) to (11.28), as follows:

$$\sigma_x = \frac{\sigma_1 + \sigma_2}{2} + \frac{\sigma_1 - \sigma_2}{2} \cos 2(x,1) = \sigma_m + \frac{\sigma_0}{\sqrt{3}} \sin 2\theta$$

$$\sigma_y = \frac{\sigma_1 + \sigma_2}{2} - \frac{\sigma_1 - \sigma_2}{2} \cos 2(x,1) = \sigma_m - \frac{\sigma_0}{\sqrt{3}} \sin 2\theta \tag{11.32}$$

$$\tau_{xy} = \frac{\sigma_1 - \sigma_2}{2} \sin 2(x,1) = -\frac{\sigma_0}{\sqrt{3}} \cos 2\theta$$

Figure 11.5a shows the stresses acting on a prismatic volume element with faces oriented parallel to the x, y axes; the matrices of the stress tensor and of the deviator stress tensor, with respect to such axes, are

$$
\mathbf{S} = \begin{pmatrix} \sigma_x & \tau_{xy} & 0 \\ \tau_{xy} & \sigma_y & 0 \\ 0 & 0 & \dfrac{\sigma_x + \sigma_y}{2} \end{pmatrix}, \quad
\mathbf{S'} = \begin{pmatrix} \dfrac{\sigma_x - \sigma_y}{2} & \tau_{xy} & 0 \\ \tau_{xy} & \dfrac{-\sigma_x + \sigma_y}{2} & 0 \\ 0 & 0 & 0 \end{pmatrix} \quad (11.33)
$$

Figure 11.5b shows the stresses on a volume element oriented parallel to the principal planes; the matrices of $\mathbf{S}$ and $\mathbf{S'}$, with reference to these axes, are

$$
\mathbf{S} = \begin{pmatrix} \sigma_m + \dfrac{\sigma_0}{\sqrt{3}} & 0 & 0 \\ 0 & \sigma_m - \dfrac{\sigma_0}{\sqrt{3}} & 0 \\ 0 & 0 & \sigma_m \end{pmatrix}, \quad
\mathbf{S'} = \begin{pmatrix} \dfrac{\sigma_0}{\sqrt{3}} & 0 & 0 \\ 0 & -\dfrac{\sigma_0}{\sqrt{3}} & 0 \\ 0 & 0 & 0 \end{pmatrix}
$$
$$(11.34)$$

Finally, Fig. 11.5c shows the stresses on a volume element with faces perpendicular to the α and β slip-line directions; $\mathbf{S}$ and $\mathbf{S'}$, with respect to such axes, are

$$
\mathbf{S} = \begin{pmatrix} \sigma_m & \dfrac{\sigma_0}{\sqrt{3}} & 0 \\ \dfrac{\sigma_0}{\sqrt{3}} & \sigma_m & 0 \\ 0 & 0 & \sigma_m \end{pmatrix}, \quad
\mathbf{S'} = \begin{pmatrix} 0 & \dfrac{\sigma_0}{\sqrt{3}} & 0 \\ \dfrac{\sigma_0}{\sqrt{3}} & 0 & 0 \\ 0 & 0 & 0 \end{pmatrix} \quad (11.35)
$$

11.3. Equilibrium Equations Referred to Arbitrary Cartesian Coordinates

A rectangular prismatic volume element with edges parallel to the x, y, z and with edge lengths dx, dy, dz is shown in Fig. 11.6 with the forces acting on its six faces. The equilibrium of the x and y components of such forces furnishes the only two significant equilibrium equations:

$$
\left(\sigma_x + \frac{\partial \sigma_x}{\partial x}\, dx \right) dy\, dz - \sigma_x\, dy\, dz + \left(\tau_{xy} + \frac{\partial \tau_{xy}}{\partial y}\, dy \right) dx\, dz - \tau_{xy}\, dx\, dz = 0
$$
$$
\left(\tau_{xy} + \frac{\partial \tau_{xy}}{\partial x}\, dx \right) dy\, dz - \tau_{xy}\, dy\, dz + \left(\sigma_y + \frac{\partial \sigma_y}{\partial y}\, dy \right) dx\, dz - \sigma_y\, dx\, dz = 0
$$

from which, by dividing both sides by $dx\, dy\, dz$ and simplifying, the following well-known differential equations are obtained:

$$\frac{\partial \sigma_x}{\partial x} + \frac{\partial \tau_{xy}}{\partial y} = 0 \tag{11.36}$$

$$\frac{\partial \tau_{xy}}{\partial x} + \frac{\partial \sigma_y}{\partial y} = 0 \tag{11.37}$$

These equations, in conjunction with the plasticity condition for plane strain [Eq. (11.31)],

$$(\sigma_x - \sigma_y)^2 + 4\tau_{xy}^2 = \tfrac{4}{3}\sigma_0^2 \tag{11.38}$$

are, theoretically, sufficient to determine the stress components σ_x, σ_y, τ_{xy} as functions of the coordinates x, y for boundary conditions estab-

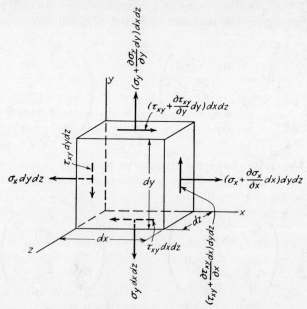

FIG. 11.6. Stress resultants on volume element.

lished in terms of boundary forces. Problems of this type are often called "statically determinate" problems because they admit solutions without further reference to stress-strain relations, although, it should be noted, Eq. (11.31) was derived with the aid of Saint-Venant's plastic stress-strain relation.

There are three procedures by which solutions of this type can be constructed:

(a) Taking the partial derivative of Eq. (11.36) with respect to y and of Eq. (11.37) with respect to x and subtracting the latter from the former, one obtains

$$\frac{\partial^2 (\sigma_x - \sigma_y)}{\partial x\, \partial y} + \frac{\partial^2 \tau_{xy}}{\partial y^2} - \frac{\partial^2 \tau_{xy}}{\partial x^2} = 0 \tag{11.39}$$

Eliminating $\sigma_x - \sigma_y$ from Eqs. (11.38) and (11.39) yields

$$\pm \frac{\partial^2}{\partial x\, \partial y} \sqrt{\frac{4}{3}\sigma_0{}^2 - 4\tau_{xy}{}^2} + \frac{\partial^2 \tau_{xy}}{\partial y^2} - \frac{\partial^2 \tau_{xy}}{\partial x^2} = 0 \tag{11.40}$$

a partial differential equation for the unknown function $\tau_{xy}(x,y)$. When a solution of Eq. (11.40), satisfying the boundary conditions of the problem, is known, σ_x and σ_y are obtained by integrating Eqs. (11.36) and (11.37).

(b) An alternate of the above procedure consists in eliminating τ_{xy} from Eqs. (11.38) and (11.39), by which the following differential equation is obtained for $\sigma_x - \sigma_y$ as an unknown function of x and y:

$$\frac{\partial^2 (\sigma_x - \sigma_y)}{\partial x\, \partial y} = \pm \frac{\partial^2}{\partial x^2} \sqrt{\frac{\sigma_0{}^2}{3} - \left(\frac{\sigma_x - \sigma_y}{2}\right)^2} \mp \frac{\partial^2}{\partial y^2} \sqrt{\frac{\sigma_0{}^2}{3} - \left(\frac{\sigma_x - \sigma_y}{2}\right)^2} \tag{11.41}$$

(c) In analogy to the well-known procedure for two-dimensional elastic problems, a stress function $F(x,y)$ can be introduced so that the cartesian stress components derived from it according to the following equations:

$$\sigma_x = \frac{\partial^2 F}{\partial y^2}, \qquad \sigma_y = \frac{\partial^2 F}{\partial x^2}, \qquad \tau_{xy} = -\frac{\partial^2 F}{\partial x \partial y} \tag{11.42}$$

identically satisfy the equilibrium equations (11.36) and (11.37).

Substituting the above expressions into the plasticity condition [Eq. (11.38)], one has the following partial differential equation of second order and second degree:

$$\left(\frac{\partial^2 F}{\partial y^2} - \frac{\partial^2 F}{\partial x^2}\right)^2 + 4\left(\frac{\partial^2 F}{\partial x\, \partial y}\right)^2 = \frac{4}{3}\sigma_0{}^2 \tag{11.43}$$

to be satisfied by the unknown stress function F.

11.4. Equilibrium Equations Referred to Slip Lines

Substitute into the equilibrium equations (11.36) and (11.37) the expressions for σ_x, σ_y, τ_{xy} in terms of σ_m, σ_0, and θ, as given in Eqs. (11.32), and obtain

$$\frac{\partial \sigma_m}{\partial x} + \frac{2\sigma_0}{\sqrt{3}}\left(\cos 2\theta\, \frac{\partial \theta}{\partial x} + \sin 2\theta\, \frac{\partial \theta}{\partial y}\right) = 0$$

$$\frac{\partial \sigma_m}{\partial y} + \frac{2\sigma_0}{\sqrt{3}}\left(\sin 2\theta\, \frac{\partial \theta}{\partial x} - \cos 2\theta\, \frac{\partial \theta}{\partial y}\right) = 0 \tag{11.44}$$

The arbitrary x, y axes can be oriented so as to coincide with the α and β slip-line tangents, respectively; then, by putting $\theta = 0$, $dx \equiv ds_\alpha$, $dy \equiv ds_\beta$, one has

$$\frac{\partial \sigma_m}{\partial s_\alpha} + \frac{2\sigma_0}{\sqrt{3}} \frac{\partial \theta}{\partial s_\alpha} = 0$$

$$\frac{\partial \sigma_m}{\partial s_\beta} - \frac{2\sigma_0}{\sqrt{3}} \frac{\partial \theta}{\partial s_\beta} = 0$$

(11.45)

These equations were derived by Hencky in 1923 essentially in the above form, except that the factor $2/\sqrt{3}$ was omitted in the second terms, as Hencky's work was based on the maximum-shearing-stress condition of plasticity.

A solution of Eqs. (11.45) must satisfy the boundary conditions of the problem where they are given in terms of stresses (or forces). In addition, where the boundary conditions are given in terms of velocities, Geiringer's equations (11.17) have to be satisfied. Various boundary conditions in terms of stresses and slip lines are illustrated in Fig. 11.7. From the ambiguity of the plastic-flow problem it follows that a given slip-line configuration always admits two distinct solutions; they are both indicated for the examples of Fig. 11.7, and the selection depends upon the general physical significance of the problem.

(a) Where the plastic material flows along a rigid solid body so that the mutual forces between the two bodies are limited to *normal* forces, in other words, where frictionless sliding occurs along the boundary surface, the slip lines intersect the boundary line under 45°. The principal stresses assume the values shown in Fig. 11.7a in the two cases depending upon the orientation of the α and β slip lines.

(b) A stress-free boundary represents a special case of the above one, with vanishing normal stress on the boundary surface. The two possible cases are shown in Fig. 11.7b.

(c) Where the plastic material is in contact with a rigid solid body having a rough surface so that no relative motion occurs between the particles embedded in the surface of the bodies ("sticking"), the boundary line itself must be either a slip line or an envelope of a family of slip lines. This is a direct consequence of the condition, expressed by Eqs. (11.12), that the linear strain vanishes along directions tangential to the slip lines, as it should along the boundary here considered. Figure 11.7c shows the two alternate possibilities that arise in this case.

(d) In many metal-forming processes the plastic material flows along a rigid "die" while Coulomb's law of friction:

$$\frac{\tau}{\sigma} = f$$

(11.46)

governs the relationship between the shearing stress τ and the normal stress σ acting on the boundary surface. The two distinct cases that may arise are illustrated in Fig. 11.7d.

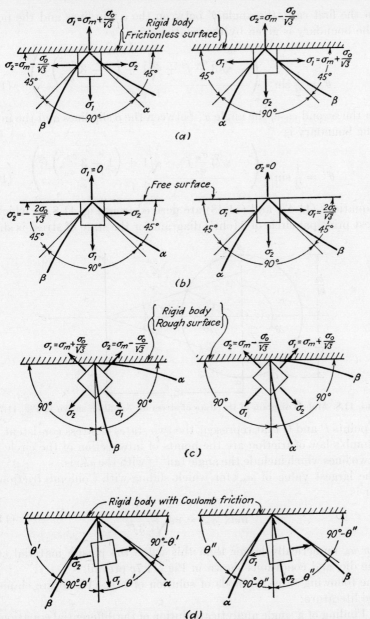

FIG. 11.7. Stresses and slip lines at the boundary of plastic body in plane strain: (a) at surface of contact with smooth rigid body; (b) at stress-free surface; (c) at surface of contact with rough rigid body ("sticking"); (d) at surface of rigid body with Coulomb friction.

In the first case, the angle θ' between the α slip lines and the normal to the boundary is given by the relationship

$$\theta' = \frac{1}{2} \sin^{-1} \left(\frac{-\sqrt{3}\,\frac{\sigma_m}{\sigma_0} f^2 + \sqrt{1 + \left(1 - 3\,\frac{\sigma_m{}^2}{\sigma_0{}^2}\right) f^2}}{1 + f^2} \right) \tag{11.47}$$

In the second case, the angle θ'' between the β slip lines and the normal to the boundary is

$$\theta'' = \frac{1}{2} \sin^{-1} \left(\frac{-\sqrt{3}\,\frac{\sigma_m}{\sigma_0} f^2 - \sqrt{1 + \left(1 - 3\,\frac{\sigma_m{}^2}{\sigma_0{}^2}\right) f^2}}{1 + f^2} \right) \tag{11.48}$$

Equations (11.47) and (11.48) are derived from Fig. 11.8, in which the largest principal circle of Mohr's diagram for the state of stress is shown.

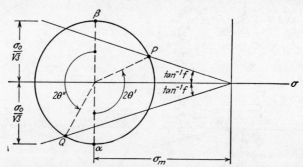

FIG. 11.8. Mohr's diagram of the state of stress for condition shown in Fig. 11.7d.

The points P and Q that represent the two states of stress consistent with Coulomb's law of friction are the points of intersection of the circle with the two lines which include the angle $\tan^{-1} f$ with the σ axis.

The largest value of $|\sigma_m|$ for which sliding with Coulomb friction can occur is

$$\max |\sigma_m| = \sigma_0 \sqrt{\frac{1 + f^2}{3 f^2}} \tag{11.49}$$

For σ_m numerically larger than this value the plastic material sticks to the die, and conditions shown in Fig. 11.7c prevail.

The following three methods of solution of Eqs. (11.45) are employed in the literature:

1. Finding of a single analytical solution of the differential equations for the entire region affected by plastic flow.

2. "Piecing together" of slip-line fields corresponding to solutions valid for different regions. Such an operation, first proposed by Prandtl,

is permissible under the conditions that the boundaries separating the various regions are slip lines common to both adjacent slip-line fields and that the stress components (but not necessarily their space derivatives) are continuous across such boundaries.

3. Numerico-graphical solutions by successive approximations based on geometrical properties of slip-line fields that follow from Eqs. (11.45).

Take the partial derivative of the first equation (11.45) with respect to s_β and that of the second equation with respect to s_α and subtract the second equation thus obtained from the first one to obtain

$$\frac{\partial^2 \theta}{\partial s_\alpha \, \partial s_\beta} = 0 \tag{11.50}$$

from which most of the useful geometrical relationships of slip-line fields originate.

In recent years, Hill and his associates have applied the slip-line method of analysis to a number of problems in two-dimensional plastic flow, such as the yielding of a notched bar under a tension load, drawing and extrusion of plate and tube, etc. No attempt has yet been made to investigate experimentally the validity of the resulting relations.

11.5. The Simplest Slip-line Fields

Prandtl, in several applications of the principle of "piecing together" of slip-line fields, made use of the following two simplest solutions of Eqs. (11.45):

(a) The field of slip lines that are lines of constant cartesian coordinates

(b) The field of slip lines that are lines of constant polar coordinates

These slip-line fields are illustrated in Figs. 11.9, 11.10, and 11.11, and will be discussed briefly as follows:

(a) The assumption that both the α and β slip lines are families of orthogonal straight lines is expressed by the equations

$$\frac{\partial \theta}{\partial s_\alpha} = 0, \qquad \frac{\partial \theta}{\partial s_\beta} = 0 \tag{11.51}$$

which, substituted into Eqs. (11.45), give

$$\frac{\partial \sigma_m}{\partial s_\alpha} = 0, \qquad \frac{\partial \sigma_m}{\partial s_\beta} = 0 \tag{11.52}$$

so that σ_m is constant throughout and is the only unknown quantity to be determined from the boundary conditions of the problem; hence the term "field of uniform stress state" used in the literature for such a condition.

Figure 11.9 shows the stresses acting on volume elements with faces perpendicular to the slip lines and with faces perpendicular to the principal directions.

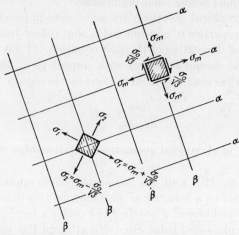

Fig. 11.9. Slip-line field of uniform stress state. Stresses on volume elements.

(b) Assume that the α slip lines are concurrent straight lines and the β slip lines are concentric circles with their center at the point of concurrence of the α lines; then,

$$\frac{\partial \theta}{\partial s_\alpha} = 0 \tag{11.53}$$

and from the first equation (11.45) one has

$$\frac{\partial \sigma_m}{\partial s_\alpha} = 0 \tag{11.54}$$

that is, σ_m is constant along the radial α slip lines.   Along the β lines,

$$s_\beta = r\theta, \qquad \frac{\partial \theta}{\partial s_\beta} = \frac{1}{r}$$

and from the second equation (11.45) one obtains

$$\frac{1}{r}\frac{\partial \sigma_m}{\partial \theta} - \frac{2\sigma_0}{\sqrt{3}}\frac{1}{r} = 0$$

or also

$$\frac{\partial \sigma_m}{\partial \theta} = \frac{2\sigma_0}{\sqrt{3}}$$

and, integrating both sides,

$$\sigma_m = (\sigma_m)_{\theta=0} + \frac{2\sigma_0}{\sqrt{3}}\theta \tag{11.55}$$

This equation indicates that σ_m increases along a circular β slip line by amounts proportional to the angle θ.

Figure 11.10 shows the condition existing throughout the slip-line field described here, for which the term "centered fan" has been used in the literature.

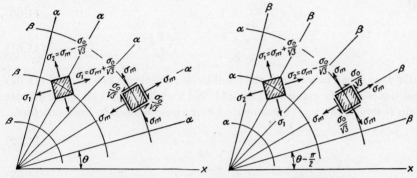

FIG. 11.10   FIG. 11.11
FIGS. 11.10 and 11.11. "Centered fan" type slip-line fields.

(b') Inverting the roles of the two families of slip lines in the case discussed under (b), and labeling α lines the concentric circles and β lines the concurrent straight lines (see Fig. 11.11), one finds

$$\frac{\partial \theta}{\partial s_\beta} = 0 \tag{11.56}$$

and from the second equation (11.45)

$$\frac{\partial \sigma_m}{\partial s_\beta} = 0 \tag{11.57}$$

Along the α lines $s_\alpha = r(\theta - \pi/2)$, $\partial\theta/\partial s_\alpha = 1/r$, and with such values the first Eq. (11.45) becomes

$$\frac{1}{r}\frac{\partial \sigma_m}{\partial \theta} + \frac{2\sigma_0}{\sqrt{3}}\frac{1}{r} = 0 \qquad \text{or} \qquad \frac{\partial \sigma_m}{\partial \theta} = -\frac{2\sigma_0}{\sqrt{3}}$$

Integrating both sides, one finds

$$\sigma_m = (\sigma_m)_{\theta=0} - \frac{2\sigma_0}{\sqrt{3}}\theta \tag{11.58}$$

11.6. First Example: Compression of Sheet between Two Parallel Rough Plates

The following solution was proposed by Prandtl in 1923 to represent the plastic equilibrium in a very extended sheet, of thickness $2a$, compressed between two parallel rough plates in condition of plane strain.   Placing the x axis along the longitudinal plane of symmetry, the y axis in the transverse plane of symmetry of the sheet, the cartesian stress components

$$\sigma_x = \frac{\sigma_0 x}{\sqrt{3}a} + \frac{2\sigma_0}{\sqrt{3}}\sqrt{1 - \frac{y^2}{a^2}} + C \tag{11.59}$$

$$\sigma_y = \frac{\sigma_0 x}{\sqrt{3}a} + C \tag{11.60}$$

$$\tau_{xy} = -\frac{\sigma_0 y}{\sqrt{3}a} \tag{11.61}$$

satisfy, as it can be verified, the equilibrium equations (11.36) and (11.37) and the plasticity condition [Eq. (11.38)] for all points within the infinite strip between the $y = \pm a$ lines.   Along these boundary lines one finds

$$\sigma_x = \frac{\sigma_0 x}{\sqrt{3}a} + C \tag{11.62}$$

$$\sigma_y = \frac{\sigma_0 x}{\sqrt{3}a} + C \tag{11.63}$$

$$\tau_{xy} = \mp \frac{\sigma_0}{\sqrt{3}} \tag{11.64}$$

Substituting these values into Eq. (11.27), one finds

$$\tan 2\theta = \frac{\sigma_y - \sigma_x}{2\tau_{xy}} = 0$$

from which $2\theta = \pm n\pi$ where n can be zero or any integer.   Therefore, one of the slip-line families is tangential to the boundary lines, $y = \pm a$, and the requirement stated in Art. 11.4 for this type of boundary condition is satisfied.

The slip lines corresponding to the stress distribution given above are identical cycloids, with the equation

$$x = a\left(\sin^{-1}\frac{y}{a} - \sqrt{1 - \frac{y^2}{a^2}}\right) + \text{const} \tag{11.65}$$

The plastic flow in the sheet material, consistent with the solution here given, occurs in the $+x$ direction.   The pressure between the sheet and the plates decreases in the $+x$ direction, according to the linear relationship given by Eq. (11.62).   The constant of integration C in Eqs. (11.59) and (11.60) can be expressed in terms of the sheet length L between the points of zero pressure on the sheet surface, from the condition

$$(\sigma_y)_{x=L/2} = 0 = \frac{\sigma_0 L}{2\sqrt{3}a} + C$$

from which

$$C = -\frac{\sigma_0 L}{2\sqrt{3}a}$$

The solution ceases to have physical significance along the $y = \pm a$ lines for values of $x > L/2$, because at $x = L/2$ the forces on the sheet surface change from pressure to tension, according to Eq. (11.62). For the inside of the plastic sheet, the solution ceases to be valid even earlier; indeed, for the transverse plane, $x = L/2$, one finds from Eq. (11.59) σ_x stresses distributed according to the expression

$$\frac{2\sigma_0}{\sqrt{3}}\sqrt{1 - \frac{y^2}{a^2}}$$

i.e., tensile stresses varying from a maximum of $2\sigma_0/\sqrt{3}$ at the mid-plane, $y = 0$, to zero at the boundaries, $y = \pm a$. Such stresses are in

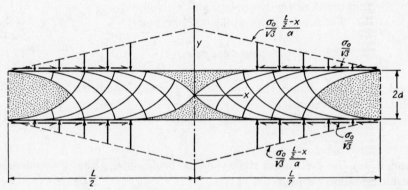

FIG. 11.12. Slip lines and boundary forces for sheet compressed between two parallel rough plates.

conflict with the conditions of a stress-free edge, and it is reasonable to assume that the dotted areas shown in Fig. 11.12 between the slip lines which are tangential to the boundaries at the edge of the sheet represent, approximately, areas of transition from the plastic state of stress represented by Prandtl's solution and the elastic state.

Another incongruity arises at the mid-plane of the sheet, $x = 0$, where the solution cannot be continued into the region of negative x values where it would imply flow in the $+x$ direction, while symmetry requires a flow in the $-x$ direction. This can be remedied by piecing together along the y axis the above-given solution with another one symmetrical to it. But such an operation, if applied to the full slip-line fields, would give rise to inconsistencies in the values of the shearing stresses along the y axis; thus, it is reasonable to assume that the area, dotted in Fig.

11.12, enclosed between the four slip-line arcs intersecting at the origin of the cartesian system, is elastic, or "rigid," as it is often referred to, because of the assumedly negligible magnitude of the elastic deformations. Such an assumption is consistent also with the above-stated principle that "piecing together" of slip-line fields is permissible only along slip lines as boundary lines.

It should be noted that the Prandtl solution does not furnish any information about the stresses in the elastic regions and that the dotted-line extension of the σ_y diagram to the y axis, shown in Fig. 11.12, represents an arbitrary extrapolation from Eq. (11.63).

11.7. Second Example: Strip Load on a Semiinfinite Body

The elastic stress distribution in a semiinfinite solid subjected to an infinitely extended uniform strip loading is well known, and according to it, the largest $\sigma_1 - \sigma_2$ value occurs along a semicircle, having its center at the mid-point of the load strip and a diameter equal to the width of the strip.   For a load p per unit area, one finds

$$\max (\sigma_1 - \sigma_2) = \frac{2p}{\pi} \tag{11.66}$$

and with such value the von Mises–Hencky condition of plasticity [Eq. (11.30)] becomes

$$\frac{2p}{\pi} = \frac{2}{\sqrt{3}} \sigma_0$$

and it can be concluded that yielding begins along the above-defined semicircle under a load

$$p_i = \frac{\pi}{\sqrt{3}} \sigma_0 = 1.81\sigma_0 \tag{11.67}$$

Prandtl proposed in 1920 a solution for the state of unconstrained plastic flow, based on a "mosaic" of five slip-line fields, shown in Fig. 11.13.   The conditions being symmetrical about the center plane of the loaded strip, the following discussion can be limited to the left-hand portion of the composite slip-line configuration.

In the outer right isosceles triangle ECD a state of "uniform stress" is assumed to exist, controlled by the following boundary conditions along the stress-free surface EC: (*a*) the slip lines must intersect this surface under 45°; and (*b*) the principal stress normal to it must vanish.   Assuming that the vanishing principal stress is σ_1, that is, the larger of the two contained in the xy plane, or in other words, assuming that the vertical plane elements are stressed in compression, one finds from Eq. (11.30)

$$\sigma_2 = - \frac{2\sigma_0}{\sqrt{3}} \quad \text{and} \quad \sigma_m = \frac{\sigma_2}{2} = - \frac{\sigma_0}{\sqrt{3}}$$

i.e., constant values throughout the triangular field. Along the slip lines ED and CD the normal stress is equal to the mean stress, $\sigma_m = -\sigma_0/\sqrt{3}$, and the shearing stress is also $\sigma_0/\sqrt{3}$ with direction from E to D and from C to D. Line ED is an α slip line; line CD is a β slip line.

The conditions along the line CD control the conditions throughout the sector CDB, where a "centered fan" type of slip-line field is assumed to exist, with the radial lines being the β lines. The angle θ measured counterclockwise from a horizontal line, is $\theta = \pi/4$ at point D; and

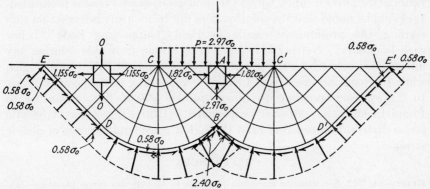

FIG. 11.13. Slip lines and forces on the plastic region for Prandtl's solution of a semi-infinite body with strip load.

$\theta = 3\pi/4$ at point B. The mean stress σ_m, and with it the normal stress acting on the circular arc DB, varies along the latter according to the relationship

$$\sigma_m \Big|_D^B = - \frac{\sigma_0}{\sqrt{3}} \left(1 - \frac{\pi}{2} + 2\theta \right) \tag{11.68}$$

between the values $-\sigma_0/\sqrt{3}$ at D, and $-(\sigma_0/\sqrt{3})(1 + \pi)$ at B. The latter value controls the conditions along CB, which is a β line, and inside the triangular field CBC', which is a field of "uniform stress," with slip lines making 45° with the loaded surface CC'. The lines parallel to CB are the β slip lines; from this it follows that the σ_1 principal stresses are acting on vertical plane elements and the σ_2 stresses are acting on horizontal plane elements. The values of the principal stresses are

$$\sigma_1 = \sigma_m + \frac{\sigma_0}{\sqrt{3}}, \qquad \sigma_2 = \sigma_m - \frac{\sigma_0}{\sqrt{3}}$$

or, considering that $\sigma_m = -(\sigma_0/\sqrt{3})(1 + \pi)$ is constant through the region CBC',

$$\sigma_1 = -\frac{\pi}{\sqrt{3}}\sigma_0, \qquad \sigma_2 = -\frac{\pi + 2}{\sqrt{3}}\sigma_0 \qquad (11.69)$$

In conclusion, the assumption of horizontal compressive stresses in the region ECD yields a compression load of $p = [(\pi + 2)/\sqrt{3}]\sigma_0 = 2.97\sigma_0$ on the loaded surface CC', as being consistent with the state of plastic flow here considered. The opposite assumption for the stresses in the region ECD would yield a tensile load of the same magnitude on CC'.

Figure 11.13 shows the stress states in typical volume elements in the three triangular slip-line fields and the forces distributed along the boundary $EDBD'E'$ upon which the solution discussed here is predicated. It should be noted that the solution does not furnish any information concerning the presumably elastic or rigid "supporting body" below such boundary. Neither is it possible to obtain from this solution any information concerning the progressive development of the plastic region while the load increases from $1.81\sigma_0$, corresponding to incipient yielding, to $2.97\sigma_0$, corresponding to unconstrained plastic flow according to Prandtl's solution. Mesmer's experiments (1930) suggest that the elastic stress distribution remains valid through a considerable range of plastic strains.

REFERENCES

GEIRINGER, H., Fondements mathématiques de la théorie des corps plastiques isotropes, *Memorial sciences mathem.*, Fasc. LXXXVI, Paris, 1937.

HENCKY, H., Ueber einige statisch bestimmte Faelle des Gleichgewichts in plastisch Koerpern, *Z. angew. Math. Mechanik*, Vol. 3, No. 4, pp. 241–251, 1923.

HILL, R., "The Mathematical Theory of Plasticity," Oxford University Press, New York, 1950.

HILL, R., A Theoretical Analysis of the Stresses and Strains in Extrusion and Piercing, *J. Iron Steel Inst. (London)*, Vol. 158, pp. 177–185, 1948.

HILL, R., The Plastic Yielding of Notched Bars under Tension, *Quart. J. Mech. Appl. Math.*, Vol. 1, pp. 40–52, 1949.

MESMER, G., Vergleichende spannungsoptische Untersuchungen und Fliessversuche unter konzentriertem Druck, *Tech. Mitt. Thermodynamik*, Vol. 1, pp. 85–100, 106–112, 1930.

NÁDAI, A., "Theory of Flow and Fracture of Solids," Vol. I, pp. 527–556, McGraw-Hill Book Company, Inc., New York, 1950.

PRANDTL, L., Ueber die Eindringungsfestigkeit (Haerte) plastischer Baustoffe und die Festigkeit von Schneiden, *Z. angew. Math. Mechanik*, Vol. 1, No. 1, pp. 15–20, 1921.

PRANDTL, L., Anwendungsbeispiele zu einem Henckyschen Satz ueber das plastische Gleichgewicht, *Z. angew. Math. Mechanik*, Vol. 3, No. 6, pp. 401–406, 1923.

SACHS, G., Beitrag zum Haerteproblem, *Z. tech. Physik*, Vol. 8, No. 4, pp. 132–141, 1927.

VON MISES, R. Bemerkungen zur Formulierung des mathematischen Problems der Plastizitaetstheorie, *Z. angew. Math. Mechanik*, Vol. 5, No. 2, pp. 147–149, 1925.

Part III

PROBLEMS IN PLASTIC FLOW
OF STRAIN-HARDENING MATERIALS

The problems discussed here will be treated by taking into account the strain-hardening characteristics of the metal during plastic flow. The first two problems, torsion and bending, were already discussed in Part II under the assumption of ideal plastic behavior; here it will be shown that they admit a simple treatment when the effects of strain-hardening are included. The second group of problems, concerned with instability in compression and instability in tension, are peculiar to the strain-hardening behavior of materials, and they do not present themselves, in such a form, in case of ideal plastic behavior.

Consideration of strain-hardening introduces certain complications in the analysis of metal-forming processes without affecting the results substantially. Hence, such problems will be treated later, in Part IV, for ideally plastic materials only.

CHAPTER 12

TORSION AND BENDING IN THE STRAIN-HARDENING RANGE

12.1. Torsion of Cylindrical Bars of Solid Circular Cross Section

The following developments are due to Ludwik (1925) and consist essentially of an extension of the analyses of elastic and ideally plastic torsion (see Art. 10.1). It is assumed that the relations introduced there for the components of the displacement **u** are still valid in the present case

$$
\begin{aligned}
u_r &= 0 \\
u_\theta &= \vartheta z r \\
u_z &= 0
\end{aligned}
\tag{12.1}
$$

where ϑ is the angle of twist per unit length of bar, z the distance measured along the bar axis, r the radial distance in the cross-sectional plane. Consequently, it is found that the tensor of strain can be written as follows:

$$
\mathbf{E} = \begin{pmatrix} 0 & 0 & 0 \\ 0 & 0 & \dfrac{\gamma_{\theta z}}{2} \\ 0 & \dfrac{\gamma_{\theta z}}{2} & 0 \end{pmatrix}
\tag{12.2}
$$

where $\gamma_{\theta z} = \vartheta r$ is the only nonvanishing strain component, with reference to the system of cylindrical coordinates used here. Since the mean strain ϵ_m is zero, and consequently the spherical strain tensor is zero also, $\mathbf{E}'' = 0$, it follows that

$$
\mathbf{E}' = \mathbf{E} = \begin{pmatrix} 0 & 0 & 0 \\ 0 & 0 & \dfrac{\gamma_{\theta z}}{2} \\ 0 & \dfrac{\gamma_{\theta z}}{2} & 0 \end{pmatrix}
\tag{12.3}
$$

Since a single strain component $\gamma_{\theta z}$ suffices to define the state of strain, it can be concluded that "proportional straining" will take place under the above assumptions. Then, Saint-Venant's theory of plastic flow will relate the deviator stress tensor to the deviator strain tensor (instead of the deviator strain-rate tensor as in the general case). The only nonvanishing terms in the deviator stress tensor matrix are the $\tau_{\theta z}$ shearing stress components, so that one obtains

$$\mathbf{S'} = \mathbf{S} = \begin{pmatrix} 0 & 0 & 0 \\ 0 & 0 & \tau_{\theta z} \\ 0 & \tau_{\theta z} & 0 \end{pmatrix} \tag{12.4}$$

The applied torque T can be expressed as the integral of the moment of shearing stresses, which act on the circular cross-sectional area of radius a, as follows:

$$T = \int_0^a 2\pi r\, dr\, \tau_{\theta z} r = 2\pi \int_0^a \tau_{\theta z} r^2\, dr \tag{12.5}$$

In dealing with the present problem, it is convenient to make use of Ludwik's universal stress-strain relation (see Art. 5.2) in its modified form (admissible for comparatively small strains) which relates the maximum shearing stress $\tau_{\max}$ to the maximum conventional shearing strain $\gamma_{\max}$ or, in other words, postulates the existence of the function

$$\tau_{\max} = \tau_{\max}(\gamma_{\max}) \tag{12.6}$$

In the present case, $\tau_{\theta z}$ is the largest shearing stress at any given point; hence, substituting $\tau_{\max}(\gamma_{\max})$ for $\tau_{\theta z}$ and $\gamma_{\max}/\vartheta$ for r in Eq. (12.5), one obtains

$$T = \frac{2\pi}{\vartheta^3} \int_{\gamma_{\max}=0}^{\gamma_{\max}=a\vartheta} \tau_{\max}(\gamma_{\max})\gamma_{\max}^2\, d\gamma_{\max} \tag{12.7}$$

For a given $\tau_{\max}(\gamma_{\max})$ stress-strain relation, this equation permits us to determine T as a function of the angle of twist per unit length ϑ. The inverse problem arises when the $T(\vartheta)$ relationship is obtained from experimental observation and the $\tau_{\max}(\gamma_{\max})$ stress-strain relation is to be derived from it. The relationship between the shearing strain at the surface of the bar, $r = a$, $\gamma_a = a\vartheta$, and the shearing stress at the same point, τ_a, can be conveniently selected for such a purpose. Multiplying both sides of Eq. (12.7) by ϑ^3 and differentiating with respect to ϑ, one has

$$\vartheta^3 \frac{dT}{d\vartheta} + 3\vartheta^2 T = 2\pi \tau_a a^3 \vartheta^2 \tag{12.8}$$

or

$$\tau_a(\gamma_a) = \tau_a(a\vartheta) = \frac{3}{2\pi a^3}\left(\frac{\vartheta}{3}\frac{dT}{d\vartheta} + T\right) \tag{12.9}$$

from which one can calculate the shearing stress which corresponds to any given value of the shearing strain, $\gamma_a = a\vartheta$. Figure 12.1 shows the graphical procedure, suggested by Ludwik, by which from a given $T(\vartheta)$

diagram one can obtain the $\tau_{max}(\gamma_{max})$ stress-strain diagram, plotted to a distorted scale.

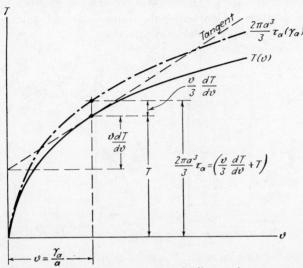

FIG. 12.1. Ludwik's method of deriving stress-strain diagram from torque versus angle-of-twist diagram.

It should be pointed out that the above results, as well as those derived previously for the ideally plastic behavior, have a limited validity, since they are based on the assumption of small strains.

12.2. Bending of Prismatic Bars of Narrow Rectangular Cross Section

The following developments are due to Nádai and are based on the same premises on which the analysis of the elastic and ideally plastic behavior of such structural members, given in Art. 10.2, was based. With reference to the notations adopted there, it is assumed in the present problem also that a uniaxial state of stress exists at all points of the beam with the longitudinal stress σ_z being the only nonvanishing principal stress. It is also assumed that the strain tensor (and, by virtue of the usual volume-constancy assumption, the deviator strain tensor) is defined by the radius of curvature R of the beam centerline (see Fig. 12.2),

$$\mathbf{E} = \mathbf{E}' = \begin{pmatrix} -\dfrac{y}{2R} & 0 & 0 \\ 0 & -\dfrac{y}{2R} & 0 \\ 0 & 0 & \dfrac{y}{R} \end{pmatrix} \qquad (12.10)$$

Under such assumptions, the σ_z stress at any point can be calculated directly from the stress-strain relation $\sigma(\epsilon)$ for the uniaxial stress state, either obtained by direct experimentation or derived from a universal stress-strain relation. Conventional strains are used throughout this analysis which will apply to small strains only.

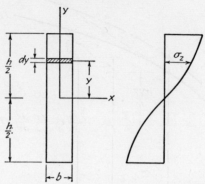

FIG. 12.2. Dimensions and stresses in bending of a prismatic bar.

The applied bending moment M can be expressed as the integral of the moments of the σ_z stresses acting on elementary areas $b\, dy$

$$M = \int_{-h/2}^{+h/2} b\, dy\, \sigma_z y = b \int_{-h/2}^{+h/2} \sigma_z y\, dy \qquad (12.11)$$

By substituting $\sigma(\epsilon)$ for σ_z and ϵR for y, one obtains

$$M = bR^2 \int_{-h/2R}^{+h/2R} \sigma(\epsilon)\epsilon\, d\epsilon \qquad (12.12)$$

Given the stress-strain relation $\sigma(\epsilon)$, the applied bending moment M can be determined from this equation as a function of the curvature $1/R$.

On the other hand, from a given $M(1/R)$ relationship, obtained experimentally, the uniaxial stress-strain relation $\sigma(\epsilon)$ can be derived by expressing, for example, the relationship between the stress $\sigma_{h/2}$ and the strain $\epsilon_{h/2}$ at the outer fibers where $y = h/2$. Dividing both sides of Eq. (12.12) by R^2 and differentiating with respect to $1/R$, one has

$$\frac{1}{R^2}\frac{dM}{d(1/R)} + \frac{2}{R}M = \frac{bh^2}{2}\sigma_{h/2} \qquad (12.13)$$

from which

$$\sigma(\epsilon) = \sigma\left(\frac{h}{2R}\right) = \frac{4}{bh^2}\left[\frac{1}{2R}\frac{dM}{d(1/R)} + M\right] \qquad (12.14)$$

Figure 12.3 shows the procedure of plotting the $\sigma(\epsilon)$ stress-strain diagram (to the distorted scale indicated) from a given $M(1/R)$ diagram.

Equation (12.2) of the present analysis was extended by Nádai to more general types of cross sections.

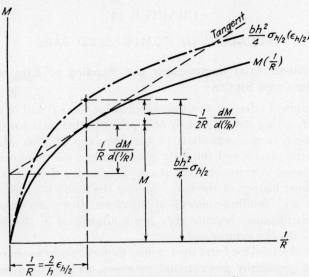

Fig. 12.3. Method of deriving stress-strain diagram from bending moment versus curvature diagram.

REFERENCES

Ludwik, P., and R. Scheu, Vergleichende Zug-, Druck-, Dreh-, und Walzversuche, *Stahl u. Eisen,* Vol. 45, p. 373, 1925.

Nádai, A., "Theory of Flow and Fracture of Solids," Vol. I, pp. 347–370, McGraw-Hill Book Company, Inc., New York, 1950.

CHAPTER 13

BUCKLING OF COMPRESSED BARS

13.1. Combined Axial Compression and Bending of Bars of Narrow Rectangular Cross Section

The combined effect of an axial compressive force P and of a bending moment M, acting simultaneously on a prismatic bar, is uniquely defined in the elastic range, regardless of the sequence of their application. In the elastic-plastic and the fully plastic range, the uniqueness of the solution ceases to exist, and the stress distribution depends essentially upon the load history of the bar. Among the many possible combined axial-force and bending-moment applications, there are two cases of practical significance, because they are fundamental in the analysis of buckling of slender compressed bars.

In case 1 the axial load and the bending moment undergo simultaneous, though not necessarily proportional, increases, and the resulting stresses and strains are monotonically increasing at all points of a cross section.

In case 2 first the axial load is applied up to its final value, and then a bending moment is applied, increasing from zero to its final value. During the second phase of the loading process, strain reversal takes place over a portion of the cross section, and consequently stress reductions occur, governed by the elastic unloading branch of the stress-strain diagram.

The following analysis of these two cases will be carried out under the assumption of a compressive stress-strain diagram made up of two straight-line portions, similar to the tensile stress-strain diagram illustrated in Fig. 5.3, the equation of the strain-hardening portion being

$$\sigma = -A + B\epsilon \qquad (13.1)$$

Case 1. Consider the case of full plasticity, important for later applications, in which stresses due to the gradual simultaneous application of axial load and bending moment are above the initial yield strength σ_0 at all points of a cross section. Both the diagram of stress and that of strain, as functions of the distance y from the mid-plane, consist of sloping straight lines (see Figs. 13.1 and 13.2). The ordinates of the strain diagram depend upon the two parameters of strain, the strain at

142

the center ϵ_c and the curvature $1/R$, so that at distance of y one has

$$\epsilon = \epsilon_c + \frac{y}{R} \tag{13.2}$$

and substituting this expression into Eq. (13.1),

$$\sigma = -A + B\left(\epsilon_c + \frac{y}{R}\right) \tag{13.3}$$

In the above equations, as in the remaining discussion of this chapter, the symbols σ and ϵ are used, for the sake of brevity, instead of σ_z and ϵ_z.

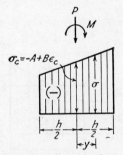

FIG. 13.1. Stresses in combined compression and bending; case 1.

FIG. 13.2. Strains in combined compression and bending; case 1.

The applied axial compressive force P has the expression

$$P = -\int_{-h/2}^{+h/2} \sigma b \, dy = -bh(-A + B\epsilon_c) \tag{13.4}$$

and the applied moment M is

$$M = \int_{-h/2}^{+h/2} \sigma b y \, dy = \frac{bh^3}{12R} B \tag{13.5}$$

Case 2. In this case, first an axial load, which produces a uniform compressive stress of the absolute value $|\sigma_c| = P/bh \geq \sigma_0$, is applied and maintained constant; then a bending moment M is applied gradually. The final stress distribution is shown in Fig. 13.3 and the corresponding strain distribution in Fig. 13.4. In the range of decreasing negative strains the stress decrements are governed by the elastic stress-strain relation, so that one obtains

$$\Delta\sigma = E \, \Delta\epsilon = E \frac{y}{R} \tag{13.6}$$

where y is the distance measured from the zero-stress point rather than from the mid-plane of the cross section. In the range of increasing negative strains the stress increments are given by the expression

$$\Delta\sigma = \frac{d}{d\epsilon}\left(-A + B\epsilon\right)\Delta\epsilon = B\,\Delta\epsilon = -B\frac{y}{R} \tag{13.7}$$

The condition that during the application of the moment M the axial load remains constant is expressed by the equation

$$\Delta P = \int \Delta\sigma\, b\, dy = 0$$

from which

$$\Delta\sigma_1\, y_1 + \Delta\sigma_2\, y_2 = 0 \tag{13.8}$$

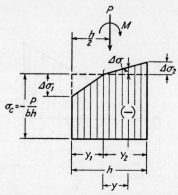
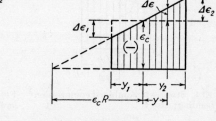

FIG. 13.3. Stresses in combined compression and bending; case 2.

FIG. 13.4. Strains in combined compression and bending; case 2.

The applied moment is expressed in terms of the changes in stress as follows:

$$M = \int_{-h/2}^{+h/2} \Delta\sigma\, by\, dy = \frac{b}{3}\left(\Delta\sigma_1\, y_1{}^2 - \Delta\sigma_2\, y_2{}^2\right) \tag{13.9}$$

From Eqs. (13.6) and (13.7) one has the following expressions for $\Delta\sigma_1$ and $\Delta\sigma_2$:

$$\Delta\sigma_1 = \frac{y_1}{R}E$$

$$\Delta\sigma_2 = -\frac{y_2}{R}B \tag{13.10}$$

Substituting these expressions in Eq. (13.9) and considering that

$$y_1 + y_2 = h,$$

one obtains

$$M = \frac{bh^3}{12R}\frac{4EB}{(\sqrt{E} + \sqrt{B})^2} = \frac{bh^3}{12R}E_r \tag{13.11}$$

where

$$E_r = \frac{4EB}{(\sqrt{E} + \sqrt{B})^2} \tag{13.12}$$

is the expression of the so-called "reduced modulus" for a rectangular cross section. Expressions for arbitrary cross sections are derived in the literature.

13.2. Plastic Buckling of Compressed Bars

As long as the stresses in a compressed bar are within the elastic range, the load which causes instability is accurately predicted by the mathematical theory of elastic stability. As is known, this theory assumes an initially ideally straight and homogenous bar and an exactly axial load application, and postulates that instability occurs when a so-called "bifurcation," or branching of the state of equilibrium, develops, *i.e.*, when, besides the straight configuration, certain laterally deflected equilibrium configurations are also possible.

In the classical example of the two-hinged elastic bar of constant cross section (see Fig. 13.5) equilibrium configurations are characterized by deflections $w(z)$ which satisfy the differential equation

$$\frac{d^2w}{dz^2} + \frac{Pw}{EI} = 0 \tag{13.13}$$

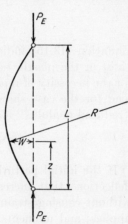

FIG. 13.5. Deflection of buckled two-hinged bar.

where I is the moment of inertia of the cross section with respect to its centroidal axis about which rotations occur during lateral deflection. The smallest value of P for which such equilibrium configurations are possible is the well-known Euler value

$$P_E = \frac{\pi^2 EI}{L^2} \tag{13.14}$$

Small initial perturbances, such as curvature of the bar axis or inaccuracy of loading, are always present in a real column, and they give rise to a gradual development of lateral deflections. As the perturbances decrease, the load at which appreciable deflections begin approaches the Euler load.

In the plastic range, *i.e.*, when the stress in the compressed bar increases beyond the yield point before the Euler load is reached, the buckling load is affected by the lateral deflections caused by initial perturbances. If the column approaches the ideal column, the axial load can be increased to approach the buckling load while the column remains straight; then, lateral deflections, and corresponding bending moments, develop under constant buckling load. This latter phase of loading involves strain reversal on a portion of the cross section, and the results obtained for case 2 of the preceding article apply. Accordingly, the relationship between the moment M and the curvature $1/R$ is governed by Eq. (13.11), which, for an arbitrary cross section with moment of inertia I, can be written as

$$M = \frac{E_r I}{R} \tag{13.15}$$

The differential equation (13.13) for the slightly deflected elastic column is based on the approximate relation

$$\frac{1}{R} \approx - \frac{d^2 w}{dz^2} \tag{13.16}$$

Equation (13.15) indicates that the same differential equation will be valid in the plastic range, under the assumptions above made, except for the necessity of replacing E by E_r and that consequently the buckling load for the case shown in Fig. 13.5 will be expressed by the so-called "reduced modulus" load

$$P_r = \frac{\pi^2 E_r I}{L^2} \tag{13.17}$$

If the initial perturbances of the real column are sufficient to cause deflections that increase gradually with increasing compressive load, without causing strain reversal, the above-discussed case 1 of Art. 13.1 applies; and moments and curvatures will be related by the following equation, obtained by extending Eq. (13.5) to arbitrary cross sections:

$$M = \frac{BI}{R} \tag{13.18}$$

It follows that, both in the differential equation of the deflected column and in the expression for the buckling load, B will replace E. The buckling load, for the case shown in Fig. 13.5, becomes

$$P_t = \frac{\pi^2 BI}{L^2} \tag{13.19}$$

and it is often called the "Engesser load" or "tangent-modulus load." The latter term originates from a frequently followed procedure by which the nonlinear stress-strain relation is approximated by the expression

$$\sigma = -A + E_t \epsilon \tag{13.20}$$

where E_t is the "tangent modulus" or the average slope of the tangent to the stress-strain curve in the range of stresses involved.

The physical significance of the Engesser load was stated recently by Shanley. For an *ideal* column, it is the load at which an increment ΔP gives rise to two alternate equilibrium configurations: that of the straight column and that with finite plastic deflections. A *real* column, having some initial perturbance, will follow the second equilibrium path, and it will buckle under a load P_t, that is always smaller than P_r because $E_t < E_r$. Experimental observations fully confirm this conclusion.

It can be seen that a plastic buckling problem exists only for columns made of strain-hardening materials. The equilibrium of a column made of an ideal plastic material, *i.e.*, for which $B = 0$, becomes unstable suddenly when the compressive stress reaches the yield strength.

REFERENCES

PEARSON, C. E., Bifurcation Criterion and Plastic Buckling of Plates and Columns, *J. Aeronaut. Sci.*, Vol. 17, pp. 417–424, July, 1950.

SHANLEY, F. R., Inelastic Column Theory, *J. Aeronaut. Sci.*, Vol. 14, pp. 261–267, May, 1947.

TIMOSHENKO, S., "Theory of Elastic Stability," pp. 156–165, McGraw-Hill Book Company, Inc., New York, 1936.

VON KÁRMÁN, T., Untersuchungen ueber Knickfestigkeit, *Mitt. Forschungsarb. d. V.d.I.*, Heft 81, Berlin, 1909.

CHAPTER 14

INSTABILITY IN TENSION

The amount of deformation obtainable in forming processes in which ductile metals are subjected to tensile forces is limited either by the cohesive strength of the metal or by so-called "necking" phenomena, consisting in local breakdowns of the uniformity of straining. The practical importance of the problem justifies a detailed analysis of the latter type of forming limit under various conditions of biaxial stress as they occur in forming of plane sheets and shells.

The following analyses are based on the well-established principle that such breakdowns in the uniformity of straining are instability phenomena, similar, in a sense, to the buckling of compressed members discussed in the preceding chapter. In both cases instability is indicated by the "bifurcation" of the state of equilibrium, *i.e.*, by the existence of more than one possible equilibrium configuration under the same applied loading.

The examples offered in this chapter are limited to problems which possess great geometrical simplicity, like plane sheets, spherical and cylindrical shells. The same basic concepts and methods have been extended in the literature to cases of more complex geometry, like bulging of circular and elliptic diaphragms.

14.1. Simplified Universal Stress-Strain Relation

An ideally plastic, *i.e.*, non-strain-hardening metal, when subjected to tensile forces, becomes unstable at the instant of incipient yielding. Finite strains are obtainable before necking only if the metal exhibits strain-hardening. In order to analyze problems of instability under various conditions of biaxial tension, it is necessary to make use of a universal stress-strain relation. Two such relations were discussed in Art. 5.2: (1) Ludwik's proposal of relating the maximum shearing stress to the maximum logarithmic shearing strain, (2) Nádai's proposal of relating the octahedral shearing stress to the logarithmic octahedral shearing strain. Both relations, when used in the present problem, require laborious mathematical work, not consistent with their basically approximate nature. The following analyses will be based on a simplified stress-strain relation, which furnishes sufficiently accurate results when

148

restricted to biaxial tension-stress states. It relates the largest true principal stress σ_I, the so-called "decisive stress," to the largest absolute value of the logarithmic strain $|\bar{\epsilon}|_{max}$, the so-called "decisive strain" [See Sachs and Lubahn (1946)].

For biaxial tension-stress states, with $\sigma_{III} = 0$, the maximum shearing stress is

$$\tau_{max} = \frac{\sigma_I}{2}$$

hence, the "decisive stress" of the simplified stress-strain relation is essentially equivalent to the stress parameter of Ludwik's proposal.

The decisive strain $|\bar{\epsilon}|_{max}$ is either $\bar{\epsilon}_I$ or $-\bar{\epsilon}_{III}$, depending upon the sign of the intermediate principal logarithmic strain $\bar{\epsilon}_{II}$. The volume-constancy relation is, with reference to Art. 2.7, Eq. (2.48),

$$\bar{\epsilon}_I + \bar{\epsilon}_{II} + \bar{\epsilon}_{III} = 0 \tag{14.1}$$

and can be satisfied only if $\bar{\epsilon}_I > 0$ and $\bar{\epsilon}_{III} < 0$, dismissing the trivial case of $\bar{\epsilon}_I = \bar{\epsilon}_{II} = \bar{\epsilon}_{III} = 0$. Solving Eq. (14.1) for $\bar{\epsilon}_I$ one has

$$\bar{\epsilon}_I = -\bar{\epsilon}_{II} - \bar{\epsilon}_{III}$$

which, considering that $\bar{\epsilon}_{III}$ is always negative, can be written also as follows:

$$|\bar{\epsilon}_I| = -\bar{\epsilon}_{II} + |\bar{\epsilon}_{III}| \tag{14.2}$$

From this equation it can be seen that the following three cases can arise:

(1) When $\bar{\epsilon}_{II}$ is negative,

$$|\bar{\epsilon}_I| > |\bar{\epsilon}_{III}|$$

and $|\bar{\epsilon}|_{max} = |\bar{\epsilon}_I| = \bar{\epsilon}_I$ is the decisive strain.

(2) When $\bar{\epsilon}_{II}$ is positive,

$$|\bar{\epsilon}_I| < |\bar{\epsilon}_{III}|$$

and $|\bar{\epsilon}|_{max} = |\bar{\epsilon}_{III}| = -\bar{\epsilon}_{III}$ is the decisive strain.

(3) When $\bar{\epsilon}_{II}$ is zero,

$$|\bar{\epsilon}_I| = |\bar{\epsilon}_{III}|$$

and the common value, $\bar{\epsilon}_I = -\bar{\epsilon}_{III}$, is the decisive strain.

14.2. Necking of a Tensile Test Specimen

The best-known example of localized straining is the so-called "necking" of tensile test specimens of ductile metals. Considère and Ludwik recognized that this phenomenon is the result of a state of instability and is accompanied by a maximum of the applied tensile load.

The concept of "bifurcation" of the equilibrium as a criterion of instability leads to the mathematical formulation of the necking condition. The state of equilibrium can be said to be unstable at a value of the applied tensile load P, for which the state of strain (and stress) can undergo an infinitesimal change, consistent with the governing stress-strain relation, while P remains constant. In a state of uniaxial tension stress, $\sigma_{II} = \sigma_{III} = 0$, one has

$$\bar{\epsilon}_{II} = \bar{\epsilon}_{III} = -\frac{\bar{\epsilon}_I}{2} < 0$$

hence, $\bar{\epsilon}_I$ is to be considered as the decisive strain parameter. The instability criterion can be formulated by postulating that

$$\frac{dP}{d\bar{\epsilon}_I} = 0 \tag{14.3}$$

Expressing P in terms of the axial tensile stress σ_I and the cross-sectional area of the specimen A, one has

$$P = \sigma_I A \tag{14.4}$$

Differentiating both sides with respect to $\bar{\epsilon}_I$ and substituting into Eq. (14.3), one obtains

$$\frac{dP}{d\bar{\epsilon}_I} = \frac{d\sigma_I}{d\bar{\epsilon}_I} A + \frac{dA}{d\bar{\epsilon}_I} \sigma_I = 0 \tag{14.5}$$

The instantaneous value of the cross-sectional area A can be expressed in terms of its initial value A_0 and of the conventional principal strains ϵ_{II} and ϵ_{III} as follows:

$$A = A_0(1 + \epsilon_{II})(1 + \epsilon_{III}) \tag{14.6}$$

or also in terms of the logarithmic principal strains, with reference to Eqs. (2.45), as

$$A = A_0 e^{\bar{\epsilon}_{II} + \bar{\epsilon}_{III}} = A_0 e^{-\bar{\epsilon}_I} \tag{14.7}$$

From this equation it follows by differentiating

$$\frac{dA}{d\bar{\epsilon}_I} = -A_0 e^{-\bar{\epsilon}_I} = -A \tag{14.8}$$

Substituting in Eq. (14.5) and dividing by A, one has

$$\frac{d\sigma_I}{d\bar{\epsilon}_I} = \sigma_I \tag{14.9}$$

This is the condition to be satisfied by the pair of values σ_I and $\bar{\epsilon}_I$ that gives rise to instability. The physical meaning of the instability condition thus formulated can be seen from Eq. (14.5). This equation indicates that besides the state defined by σ_I and $\bar{\epsilon}_I$ there are alternate equilibrium states, defined by $\sigma_I + d\sigma_I$ and $\bar{\epsilon}_I + d\bar{\epsilon}_I$, and such that the decrease in cross-sectional area due to $d\bar{\epsilon}_I$ is exactly compensated by the increase in stress $d\sigma_I$, due to strain-hardening, so that the applied load P remains unchanged. The above mathematical analysis does not indicate the region in the specimen in which the alternate type of straining, with reduced cross-sectional dimensions, takes place. Actually, the increased reduction in cross-sectional area will develop locally, by accentuating a preexisting local dimensional inaccuracy of the specimen or because of a local inhomogeneity of the metal.

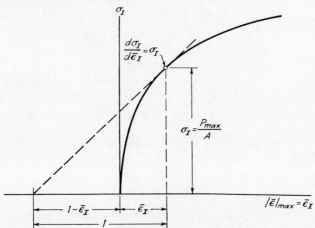

Fig. 14.1. Graphical determination of necking point for axial tension.

Equation (14.9) admits a simple graphical procedure to determine the point of necking (see Fig. 14.1). On the experimentally determined universal stress-strain diagram, with the coordinates σ_I and $|\bar{\epsilon}|_{max} = \bar{\epsilon}_I$, the point of necking is found from the condition that its tangent intersects the negative $|\bar{\epsilon}|_{max}$ axis at the distance $1 - \bar{\epsilon}_I$ from the origin. This graphical procedure has the advantage of being general and flexible and does not require the knowledge of a specific analytical expression for the stress-strain relation. Similar graphical procedures will be developed in the following articles for other more complex cases of tensile loading. Naturally, it is always possible to derive equivalent analytical procedures, based on analytical stress-strain relations.

14.3. Necking of a Plane Sheet under Biaxial Tension

Consider a plane sheet having the dimensions shown in Fig. 14.2, subjected to a state of biaxial tension stress characterized by a stress ratio σ_{II}/σ_I that remains constant during straining. From the initial dimensions of the sheet, a_0, b_0, h_0, and from the instantaneous dimensions a, b, h, the three principal logarithmic strains are expressed as

$$\bar{\epsilon}_I = \ln \frac{a}{a_0}$$

$$\bar{\epsilon}_{II} = \ln \frac{b}{b_0} \tag{14.10}$$

$$\bar{\epsilon}_{III} = \ln \frac{h}{h_0}$$

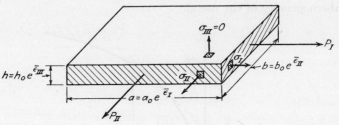

Fig. 14.2. Dimensions, stresses, and stress resultants for plane sheet under biaxial tension.

From equations expressing Saint-Venant's plastic-flow theory, one has, with $\sigma_{III} = 0$,

$$\frac{2\sigma_I - \sigma_{II}}{2\sigma_{II} - \sigma_I} = \frac{d\bar{\epsilon}_I}{d\bar{\epsilon}_{II}}$$

$$\frac{2\sigma_I - \sigma_{II}}{-\sigma_I - \sigma_{II}} = \frac{d\bar{\epsilon}_I}{d\bar{\epsilon}_{III}} \tag{14.11}$$

Eliminating $d\bar{\epsilon}_I$, one has

$$d\bar{\epsilon}_{II} = -\frac{2(\sigma_{II}/\sigma_I) - 1}{\sigma_{II}/\sigma_I + 1} d\bar{\epsilon}_{III} = -m \, d\bar{\epsilon}_{III} \tag{14.12}$$

where $m = \dfrac{2(\sigma_{II}/\sigma_I) - 1}{\sigma_{II}/\sigma_I + 1}$ is a parameter of the biaxiality, which is assumed to remain constant during the process of straining.

Integrating both sides of Eq. (14.12), one has

$$\bar{\epsilon}_{II} + C_1 = -m\bar{\epsilon}_{III} + C_2$$

From the condition that in the unstrained initial state both $\bar{\epsilon}_{II}$ and $\bar{\epsilon}_{III}$ vanish, it follows that the two constants of integration C_1 and C_2 must be equal, and consequently

$$\bar{\epsilon}_{II} = -m\bar{\epsilon}_{III} \tag{14.13}$$

From the volume-constancy relation [Eq. (14.1)], one has

$$\bar{\epsilon}_I = -\bar{\epsilon}_{II} - \bar{\epsilon}_{III}$$

hence,

$$\bar{\epsilon}_I = (m - 1)\bar{\epsilon}_{III} \tag{14.14}$$

From this equation and from Eqs. (14.12) and (14.13) it follows also that

$$\frac{d\bar{\epsilon}_I}{\bar{\epsilon}_I} = \frac{d\bar{\epsilon}_{II}}{\bar{\epsilon}_{II}} = \frac{d\bar{\epsilon}_{III}}{\bar{\epsilon}_{III}} \tag{14.15}$$

and that consequently the problem here considered is an example of the "proportional straining" earlier referred to in Arts. 5.2, 5.5, and 5.6.

Depending upon the values assumed by the stress ratio σ_{II}/σ_I and hence by the parameter of biaxiality m, the following two cases arise:

Case 1:

$$\frac{1}{2} \geq \frac{\sigma_{II}}{\sigma_I} > 0 \qquad \text{and} \qquad 0 \geq m \geq -1$$

Since $\bar{\epsilon}_{III}$ is always negative, Eq. (14.14) indicates that $\bar{\epsilon}_{II}$ is also negative in the present case, and consequently $\bar{\epsilon}_I$ is the decisive strain. The condition of instability can now be formulated, in analogy to the criterion developed in the preceding article for the case of uniaxial tension, by postulating that the total force P_I, applied in direction of the major tensile stress σ_I, has a maximum

$$\frac{dP_I}{d\bar{\epsilon}_I} = 0 \tag{14.16}$$

The instantaneous dimensions of the sheet can be expressed from Eqs. (14.10) as

$$\begin{aligned} a &= a_0 e^{\bar{\epsilon}_I} \\ b &= b_0 e^{\bar{\epsilon}_{II}} \\ h &= h_0 e^{\bar{\epsilon}_{III}} \end{aligned} \tag{14.17}$$

and with these values the expression for the force P_I becomes

$$P = bh\sigma_I = b_0 h_0 e^{\bar{\epsilon}_{II} + \bar{\epsilon}_{III}} \sigma_I = b_0 h_0 e^{-\bar{\epsilon}_I} \sigma_I \tag{14.18}$$

Differentiating both sides with respect to $\bar{\epsilon}_I$ and simplifying, one has

$$\frac{d\sigma_I}{d\bar{\epsilon}_I} = \sigma_I \tag{14.19}$$

This is identical with Eq. (14.9) previously obtained for uniaxial tension, which indeed is one of the limits of the present case, with $\sigma_{II}/\sigma_I = 0$, $m = -1$. The other limiting case, for which the same equation (14.19) applies, is that of plane strain, with $\epsilon_{II} = 0$, $\sigma_{II}/\sigma_I = \frac{1}{2}$, and $m = 0$; for this case Baransky has observed experimentally that necking occurs for practically the same value of the $\bar{\epsilon}_I$ strain as in uniaxial tension.

Case 2:

$$1 \geq \frac{\sigma_{II}}{\sigma_{I}} \geq \frac{1}{2} \quad \text{and} \quad \frac{1}{2} \geq m \geq 0$$

In this case $\bar{\epsilon}_{II}$ is negative and $|\bar{\epsilon}_{III}| = -\bar{\epsilon}_{III}$ becomes the decisive strain, and the condition of instability [Eq. (14.16)] must be restated in terms of

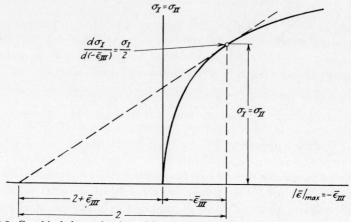

FIG. 14.3. Graphical determination of instability condition for plane sheet in balanced biaxial tension.

the latter as the strain parameter.   From Eq. (14.14) one has

$$d\bar{\epsilon}_{I} = (m - 1)\, d\bar{\epsilon}_{III}$$

and consequently

$$\frac{d\sigma_{I}}{d\bar{\epsilon}_{I}} = \frac{d\sigma_{I}}{d(-\bar{\epsilon}_{III})} \frac{1}{1 - m}$$

which substituted in Eq. (14.19) yields

$$\frac{d\sigma_{I}}{d(-\bar{\epsilon}_{III})} = (1 - m)\sigma_{I} \tag{14.20}$$

In the limiting case of balanced biaxial tension, with $\sigma_{II}/\sigma_{I} = 1$, $m = \frac{1}{2}$, the above equation becomes

$$\frac{d\sigma_{I}}{d(-\bar{\epsilon}_{III})} = \frac{\sigma_{I}}{2} \tag{14.21}$$

The graphical procedure of determining the critical $\bar{\epsilon}_{III}$ strain for this particular case is due to Gensamer and is shown in Fig. 14.3.

14.4. Instability of Thin-walled Spherical Shells Subjected to Internal Pressure

Consider a thin-walled spherical shell having an instantaneous diameter $2R$ and an instantaneous wall thickness h and being subjected to an internal pressure p. From symmetry it can be concluded that at all points there is a balanced biaxial state of stress, with the same principal stress:

$$\sigma_\theta = \frac{pR}{2h} \tag{14.22}$$

on all radial planes and with the third principal stress:

$$\sigma_r \approx 0 \tag{14.23}$$

on planes tangential to the spherical surface. It can be seen that

$$\sigma_I = \sigma_{II} = \sigma_\theta \quad \text{and} \quad \sigma_{III} = \sigma_r.$$

The logarithmic principal strains are expressed by means of the initial values R_0 and h_0 of R and h, respectively, as follows. The principal strain in all directions tangential to the spherical surface is

$$\bar{\epsilon}_\theta = \bar{\epsilon}_I = \bar{\epsilon}_{II} = \ln \frac{R}{R_0} \tag{14.24}$$

and the radial strain

$$\bar{\epsilon}_r = \bar{\epsilon}_{III} = \ln \frac{h}{h_0} \tag{14.25}$$

From the volume-constancy relation, $\epsilon_I + \epsilon_{II} + \epsilon_{III} = 0$, it follows that

$$\bar{\epsilon}_r = -2\bar{\epsilon}_\theta \tag{14.26}$$

Hence, $|\bar{\epsilon}_r|$ is the decisive strain.

Solving Eqs. (14.24) and (14.25) for R and h, one has

$$R = R_0 e^{\bar{\epsilon}_\theta} \tag{14.27}$$
$$h = h_0 e^{\bar{\epsilon}_r}$$

Substituting into Eq. (14.22), one obtains

$$\sigma_\theta = \frac{pR_0}{2h_0} e^{\bar{\epsilon}_\theta - \bar{\epsilon}_r} = \frac{pR_0}{2h_0} e^{-\frac{3}{2}\bar{\epsilon}_r} \tag{14.28}$$

It appears to be consistent with the concepts developed in the preceding articles to postulate that instability will occur when the internal pressure, expressed as a function of the decisive strain $|\bar{\epsilon}_{III}|$, reaches a maximum, or

$$\frac{dp}{d|\bar{\epsilon}_{III}|} = 0 \tag{14.29}$$

From Eq. (14.28) one has

$$p = \frac{2h_0}{R_0} e^{\frac{3}{2}\bar{\epsilon}_r} \sigma_\theta = \frac{2h_0}{R_0} e^{\frac{3}{2}\bar{\epsilon}_{III}} \sigma_I \tag{14.30}$$

Differentiating both sides with respect to $|\bar{\epsilon}_{III}| = -\bar{\epsilon}_{III}$, one obtains

$$\frac{dp}{d(-\bar{\epsilon}_{III})} = -\frac{2h_0}{R_0}\frac{3}{2}e^{\frac{3}{2}\bar{\epsilon}_{III}}\sigma_I + \frac{2h_0}{R_0}e^{\frac{3}{2}\bar{\epsilon}_{III}}\frac{d\sigma_I}{d(-\bar{\epsilon}_{III})}$$

Substituting in Eq. (14.29) and simplifying, one obtains finally the condition of instability:

$$\frac{d\sigma_I}{d(-\bar{\epsilon}_{III})} = \frac{3}{2}\sigma_I \tag{14.31}$$

Figure 14.4 shows the graphical procedure based on this equation.

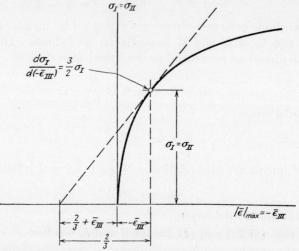

FIG. 14.4. Graphical determination of instability condition for spherical shell subjected to internal pressure.

14.5. Instability of Thin-walled Tubes Subjected to Internal Pressure

Various cases can arise when a thin-walled tube is subjected to a longitudinal load in addition to internal pressure p, so that the ratio of the two nonvanishing principal stresses, the tangential stress σ_θ and the longitudinal stress σ_z, remains constant. For the smallest value of the stress ratio here considered, $\sigma_z/\sigma_\theta = 0$, one has the pure tangential stress condition; for the largest value, $\sigma_z/\sigma_\theta = 1$, one has the case of balanced biaxial stress condition. In all these cases, the internal pressure p is the governing load parameter, and the tangential stress is the decisive stress.

Consider a thin-walled tube, having an instantaneous diameter $2R$ and an instantaneous wall thickness h, subjected to an internal pressure p and to a longitudinal tension loading. At all points of the cylindrical wall (with the exception of a limited region at each end) the same state of stress exists, with the tangential principal stress

$$\sigma_\theta = \frac{pR}{h} \tag{14.32}$$

acting on radial planes. The other principal stress, the longitudinal stress σ_z, is acting on planes normal to the tube axis, its magnitude depending on the longitudinal load. The third principal stress, the radial stress, is $\sigma_r \approx 0$. For all the states of stress here considered $\sigma_\theta \geq \sigma_z \geq \sigma_r$, and hence $\sigma_I = \sigma_\theta$, $\sigma_{II} = \sigma_z$, $\sigma_{III} = \sigma_r$.

The logarithmic tangential strain is

$$\bar{\epsilon}_\theta = \bar{\epsilon}_I = \ln \frac{R}{R_0} \tag{14.33}$$

the logarithmic radial strain is

$$\bar{\epsilon}_r = \bar{\epsilon}_{III} = \ln \frac{h}{h_0} \tag{14.34}$$

and the logarithmic longitudinal strain is obtained from the volume-constancy condition, $\bar{\epsilon}_\theta + \bar{\epsilon}_z + \bar{\epsilon}_r = 0$, as

$$\bar{\epsilon}_z = \bar{\epsilon}_{II} = -\bar{\epsilon}_\theta - \bar{\epsilon}_r \tag{14.35}$$

Solving Eq. (14.33) for R and Eq. (14.34) for h and substituting in Eq. (14.32), one has

$$\sigma_\theta = \frac{pR_0}{h_0} e^{\bar{\epsilon}_\theta - \bar{\epsilon}_r} \tag{14.36}$$

As in the preceding problem, instability will be expected to occur when the internal pressure, expressed in terms of the decisive strain $|\bar{\epsilon}|_{max}$, reaches a maximum. In order to establish relationships between the stress ratio and the ratio of the logarithmic principal strains, reference should be made to Saint-Venant's plastic-flow relations [Eqs. (5.23)], which in the present case become

$$\begin{aligned} \frac{2\sigma_\theta - \sigma_z}{2\sigma_z - \sigma_\theta} &= \frac{d\bar{\epsilon}_\theta}{d\bar{\epsilon}_z} \\ \frac{2\sigma_\theta - \sigma_z}{-\sigma_\theta - \sigma_z} &= \frac{d\bar{\epsilon}_\theta}{d\bar{\epsilon}_r} \end{aligned} \tag{14.37}$$

From the first of these equations one obtains

$$d\bar{\epsilon}_z = -\frac{2(\sigma_z/\sigma_\theta) - 1}{\sigma_z/\sigma_\theta - 2} d\bar{\epsilon}_\theta = -n\, d\bar{\epsilon}_\theta \tag{14.38}$$

where $n = \dfrac{2(\sigma_z/\sigma_\theta) - 1}{\sigma_z/\sigma_\theta - 2}$ is the parameter of biaxiality, constant during straining, because of the assumed constancy of the stress ratio σ_z/σ_θ.

Adopting the line of reasoning which yielded Eqs. (14.13) and (14.15), one can conclude that the present case is also one of "proportional straining" and that

$$\bar{\epsilon}_z = -n\bar{\epsilon}_\theta \tag{14.39}$$

and

$$\bar{\epsilon}_r = -\bar{\epsilon}_\theta - \bar{\epsilon}_z = (n-1)\bar{\epsilon}_\theta \tag{14.40}$$

The decisive strain will be either $\bar{\epsilon}_I = \bar{\epsilon}_\theta$ or $-\bar{\epsilon}_{III} = -\bar{\epsilon}_r$, depending upon the sign of $\bar{\epsilon}_{II} = \bar{\epsilon}_z$ and, according to Eq. (14.39), upon the sign of the parameter n. Two cases arise:

Case 1:

$$\frac{1}{2} \geq \frac{\sigma_z}{\sigma_\theta} \geq 0 \qquad \text{and} \qquad 0 \leq n \leq \frac{1}{2}$$

Since $\bar{\epsilon}_\theta$ is always positive, $\bar{\epsilon}_z$ is negative in this case, and $\bar{\epsilon}_\theta = \bar{\epsilon}_I$ is the decisive strain.   The condition of instability is then

$$\frac{dp}{d\bar{\epsilon}_\theta} = 0 \tag{14.41}$$

Solving Eq. (14.36) for p and substituting the expression for $\bar{\epsilon}_r$ from Eq. (14.40), one has

$$p = \frac{\sigma_0 h_0}{R_0} e^{(2-n)\bar{\epsilon}_\theta} \tag{14.42}$$

and Eq. (14.41) becomes

$$\frac{d}{d\bar{\epsilon}_\theta}\left(\frac{\sigma_\theta h_0}{R_0} e^{(2-n)\bar{\epsilon}_\theta}\right) = \frac{d\sigma_\theta}{d\bar{\epsilon}_\theta} \frac{h_0}{R_0} e^{(n-2)\bar{\epsilon}_\theta} + \sigma_0 \frac{h_0}{R_0} (n-2)e^{(n-2)\bar{\epsilon}_\theta} = 0 \tag{14.43}$$

This equation simplifies to

$$\frac{d\sigma_\theta}{d\bar{\epsilon}_\theta} = (2-n)\sigma_\theta \qquad \text{or} \qquad \frac{d\sigma_I}{d\bar{\epsilon}_I} = (2-n)\sigma_I \tag{14.44}$$

which is the instability condition sought.

This case comprises the two limiting states: the state of pure tangential tension stress, in which $\sigma_z = 0$, $n = \frac{1}{2}$, $\bar{\epsilon}_r = \bar{\epsilon}_z = -\bar{\epsilon}_\theta/2$, and

$$\frac{d\sigma_I}{d\bar{\epsilon}_I} = \frac{3}{2}\sigma_I \tag{14.45}$$

and the state of plane strain in which $\sigma_z = \sigma_\theta/2$, $n = 0$, $\bar{\epsilon}_z = 0$, $\bar{\epsilon}_r = -\bar{\epsilon}_\theta$, and

$$\frac{d\sigma_I}{d\bar{\epsilon}_I} = 2\sigma_I \tag{14.46}$$

Case 2:

$$1 \geq \frac{\sigma_z}{\sigma_\theta} \geq \frac{1}{2} \qquad -1 \leq n \leq 0$$

In this case $\bar{\epsilon}_z$ is positive and $|\bar{\epsilon}_r| = |\bar{\epsilon}_{III}| = -\bar{\epsilon}_r$ becomes the decisive strain. From Eq. (14.40) it follows that

$$d\bar{\epsilon}_\theta = \frac{d\bar{\epsilon}_r}{n - 1} \quad \text{or} \quad d\bar{\epsilon}_I = \frac{-d\bar{\epsilon}_{III}}{1 - n} \tag{14.47}$$

which, substituted in Eq. (14.46), yields the instability condition

$$\frac{d\sigma_I}{d(-\bar{\epsilon}_{III})} = \frac{2n}{1 - n}\sigma_I \tag{14.48}$$

The limiting condition of this case is the state of balanced biaxial tension in which $\sigma_z = \sigma_\theta$, $n = 1$, $\bar{\epsilon}_\theta = \bar{\epsilon}_z = -\bar{\epsilon}_r/2$ and for which the instability condition becomes

$$\frac{d\sigma_I}{d(-\bar{\epsilon}_{III})} = \frac{3}{2}\sigma_I \tag{14.49}$$

Figure 14.5 shows the graphical procedure which applies to the various stress states of thin-walled tubes.

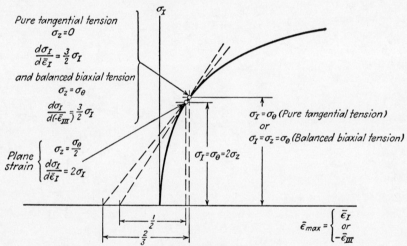

Fig. 14.5. Graphical determination of instability condition for tubes in various stress states.

REFERENCES

BARANSKI, G., Zerreissversuche bei ebener plastischer Verformung, *Z. Metallkunde*, Vol. 26, No. 8, pp. 173–180, August, 1934.

BROWN, W. F. JR., and G. SACHS, Strength and Failure Characteristics of Metal Membranes, *Trans. ASME*, Vol. 70, p. 241, 1948.

CHOW, C. C., A. W. DANA, and G. SACHS, Stress and Strain States in Elliptical Bulges, *Metals Trans.*, pp. 49–58, January, 1949.

CONSIDÈRE, A., "Mémoire sur l'emploi du fer et de l'acier dans les constructions," Paris, 1886.

GENSAMER, M., Flow and Fracture of Sheet under Combined Tensile Stresses, *Modern Industrial Press*, pp. 36–38 and 43, September, 1942.

HILL, R., A Theory of the Plastic Bulging of a Metal Diaphragm by Lateral Pressure, *Phil. Mag.*, Series 7, Vol. 51, p. 1133, November, 1950.

LUDWIK, P., "Elemente der technologischen Mechanik," Springer-Verlag, Berlin, 1909.

SACHS, G., and G. FIEK, "Der Zugversuch," Akademische Verlagsgesellschaft m.b.H., Leipzig, 1926.

SACHS, G., and J. D. LUBAHN, Failure of Ductile Metals in Tension, *Trans. ASME*, Vol. 68, pp. 271–276, 1946.

PART IV

THEORY OF METAL-FORMING PROCESSES

The problems herein discussed deal with the stress distribution in ductile metals subjected to large plastic deformations during forming processes. It is a common feature of these processes that they impose certain geometrical conditions upon the deformations, and hence upon the stress distribution, such as, for example, the "plane-strain" condition or the condition of axial symmetry, which make the problems more easily accessible to analysis. Moreover, in this class of problems certain dimensions of the plastic metal body prevail over certain other dimensions, a circumstance that gives rise to methods of solution based on simple approximate assumptions concerning the stress distribution on certain surfaces ("sections"). The use of such assumptions is the common philosophy of these "elementary" solutions; their justification lies not only in the relative simplicity of the mathematical methods required and the results obtained but above all in the agreement with experimental results that characterizes the analyses.

Rigorous analyses of general three-dimensional or axially symmetrical forming processes are not available at present, although certain two-dimensional (plane-strain) solutions have been adapted to represent, by analogy, axially symmetrical conditions. Hill and his associates have analyzed a number of two-dimensional forming processes; however, some features of these analyses are not supported by experimental evidence. This refers particularly to the assumed existence of undeformed ("dead") regions surrounded by or adjacent to the plastic regions, as exemplified by the cases discussed in Arts. 11.6 and 11.7. Experiments indicate that such areas do not exist and that a sudden change from elasticity to plasticity never occurs. The problem needs further investigation, both theoretical and experimental.

Undoubtedly, rigorous solutions should improve considerably upon the elementary analyses presented here. On the other hand, available rigorous results indicate that elementary methods yield surprisingly good results whenever the actual conditions are closely represented by the assumptions of the analysis.

CHAPTER 15

DRAWING AND EXTRUDING WITHOUT FRICTION

15.1. Scope of Problem

This chapter is devoted to the analysis of the simplest problems which arise in connection with plastic flow of metal through dies when friction between the metal and dies is neglected. Two fundamental cases will be considered. In the first case a circular cylindrical body (rod or wire) is transformed into another circular cylindrical body of smaller diameter by means of a cone-shaped die. In the second case a wide strip of metal is transformed into a thinner strip by means of a wedge-shaped die.

The forming process is called "drawing" when the metal is forced through the die by a tensile force applied to the metal at the exit or "in front" of the die; it is called "extruding" when a compressive force is applied at the entry or "in back" of the die.

Besides the distribution of stresses and strains and the amount of work consumed, important information gained from the analysis of forming processes consists in the "limit" of the obtainable plastic deformation, usually expressed in terms of reduction of cross-sectional area. For ideal plastic metals and the frictionless processes here considered it will be found that such a limit is independent of the mechanical properties of the metal, except for the condition that its strength should be adequate to carry the load, required for the forming, to the section where plastic flow commences.

15.2. Three-dimensional Radial Plastic Flow

The flow of a plastic metal through a smooth conical die will be analyzed herein under the assumption that it can be regarded as a radial flow toward the apex of the conical die surface. The problem of strains and stresses in spherical shells, discussed in Chap. 7, has several features in common with the present problem, and certain results of that chapter will be utilized here, with proper modifications. The analysis of strains in spherical shells was based on *small* displacements, for which initial and instantaneous values of the radial distance r of a particle from the sphere center are interchangeable. In the present problem, involving large displacement, the symbol r will indicate the instantaneous radius,

163

to be distinguished from r_0, the initial radius, at the point where the particle enters the plastic region.   A steady state of flow will be assumed, for which the state of strain remains unchanged at a given point; this assumption implies that the spherical surfaces with radius r_0, at which plastic flow begins (the entry section of the die), remain stationary. Symmetry will require that the radial direction and all tangential directions be principal directions both for strain and for stress.   The conventional tangential strain for small radial displacements u_r, as given by Eq. (7.2), is

$$\epsilon_\theta = \frac{u_r}{r}$$

In the present problem, this equation is to be modified by putting $u_r = r - r_0$ and by replacing in the denominator r by its initial value r_0 to obtain

$$\epsilon_\theta = \frac{r - r_0}{r_0} = \frac{r}{r_0} - 1 \tag{15.1}$$

The logarithmic tangential strain is then [see Eq. (2.40)]

$$\bar{\epsilon}_\theta = \ln (1 + \epsilon_\theta) = \ln \frac{r}{r_0} \tag{15.2}$$

and its increment corresponding to a displacement dr

$$d\bar{\epsilon}_\theta = \frac{d\epsilon_\theta}{1 + \epsilon_\theta} = \frac{dr}{r} \tag{15.3}$$

From the volume-constancy equation, $\bar{\epsilon}_r + 2\bar{\epsilon}_\theta = 0$, one has for the radial strain

$$\bar{\epsilon}_r = - 2\bar{\epsilon}_\theta = -2 \ln \frac{r}{r_0} = 2 \ln \frac{r_0}{r} \tag{15.4}$$

and also

$$d\bar{\epsilon}_r = -2 \, d\bar{\epsilon}_\theta = -2 \frac{dr}{r} \tag{15.5}$$

and it can be concluded that $d\bar{\epsilon}_r/\bar{\epsilon}_r = d\bar{\epsilon}_\theta/\bar{\epsilon}_\theta$ and that a condition of "proportional straining" exists.   Saint-Venant's plastic-flow relation [Eq. (5.21)]

$$\mathbf{S}' = \left(\frac{2\lambda}{dt}\right) d\mathbf{E}$$

becomes, when written in matrix form,

$$
\begin{pmatrix} \frac{2}{3}(\sigma_\theta - \sigma_r) & 0 & 0 \\ 0 & \frac{1}{3}(\sigma_\theta - \sigma_r) & 0 \\ 0 & 0 & \frac{1}{3}(\sigma_\theta - \sigma_r) \end{pmatrix} = \frac{2\lambda}{dt} \begin{pmatrix} d\bar{\epsilon}_r & 0 & 0 \\ 0 & d\bar{\epsilon}_\theta & 0 \\ 0 & 0 & d\bar{\epsilon}_\theta \end{pmatrix} \quad (15.6)
$$

where σ_r is the radial principal stress and σ_θ the tangential principal stress. Expansion of this equation furnishes the relation

$$
\sigma_\theta - \sigma_r = \frac{6\lambda}{dt} d\bar{\epsilon}_\theta = \frac{6\lambda}{dt} \frac{dr}{r} \quad (15.7)
$$

Since λ is an essentially positive number, $\sigma_\theta - \sigma_r$ and dr will have the same sign. According to the sign of dr, distinction should be made between the following two cases:

Case 1. *Outward Radial Flow*:

$$
dr > 0 \qquad \text{and} \qquad \sigma_\theta - \sigma_r > 0
$$

As it was shown in Art. 7.4 for the present case of "cylindrical" state of stress, both the Tresca–Saint-Venant, or maximum-shearing-stress, criterion and the von Mises–Hencky, or distortion-energy, criterion of plasticity furnish the same relation

$$
\sigma_\theta - \sigma_r = \sigma_0 \quad (15.8)
$$

Substituting this expression into the differential equation of equilibrium, Eq. (7.10), one has

$$
\frac{d\sigma_r}{dr} - \frac{2\sigma_0}{r} = 0 \quad (15.9)
$$

Integrating, one obtains the following expressions for the principal stresses:

$$
\sigma_r = C + \sigma_0 \ln r^2
$$
$$
\sigma_\theta = C + \sigma_0(1 + \ln r^2) \quad (15.10)
$$

Case 2. *Inward Radial Flow*:

$$
dr < 0 \qquad \text{and} \qquad \sigma_\theta - \sigma_r < 0
$$

In this case the yield condition becomes

$$
\sigma_r - \sigma_\theta = \sigma_0 \quad (15.11)
$$

The differential equation of equilibrium takes the form

$$
\frac{d\sigma_r}{dr} + \frac{2\sigma_0}{r} = 0 \quad (15.12)
$$

and the principal stresses are

$$\sigma_r = C - \sigma_0 \ln r^2$$
$$\sigma_\theta = C - \sigma_0(1 + \ln r^2) \tag{15.13}$$

15.3. Stresses in Wire Drawing

A simple theory of wire drawing can be developed on the assumption that the state of strain in the metal flowing inside the conical die can be represented with sufficient accuracy by the above-discussed inward radial

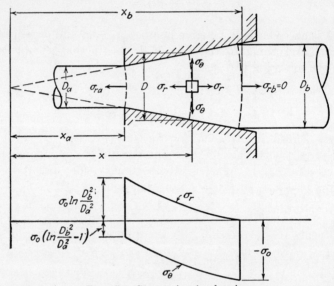

FIG. 15.1. Stresses in wire drawing.

plastic flow. Introducing the notations shown in Fig. 15.1, that is, x for the distance from the die apex to a concentric spherical surface, x_b for the distance to the entry section, Eqs. (15.2) and (15.4) become

$$\bar{\epsilon}_\theta = \ln \frac{x}{x_b}$$
$$\bar{\epsilon}_r = \ln \frac{x_b^2}{x^2} \tag{15.14}$$

The constant of integration in Eqs. (15.13) is determined from the condition that at the entry section

$$x = x_b, \qquad \sigma_r = 0, \qquad \text{or} \qquad C - \sigma_0 \ln x_b^2 = 0$$

from which

$$C = \sigma_0 \ln x_b^2$$

and the expressions for the principal stresses become

$$\sigma_r = \sigma_0 \ln \frac{x_b{}^2}{x^2}$$

$$\sigma_\theta = \sigma_0 \left(\ln \frac{x_b{}^2}{x^2} - 1 \right)$$

(15.15)

Introducing the variable wire diameter D and considering that

$$\frac{x_b}{x} = \frac{D_b}{D}$$

one obtains the alternate expressions

$$\sigma_r = \sigma_0 \ln \frac{D_b{}^2}{D^2}$$

$$\sigma_\theta = \sigma_0 \left(\ln \frac{D_b{}^2}{D^2} - 1 \right)$$

(15.16)

In the lower part of Fig. 15.1 the principal stresses σ_r and σ_θ are plotted against the distance x.

The solution presented here is consistent with the physical conditions of the drawing process along the smooth die surface where displacements are directed along the generatrix of the surface and pressures are normal to the surface. Deviations from the calculated strains and stresses are expected to occur locally at the sections of entrance and exit and to taper off with increasing distance from such sections. When the die angle is small, the concentric spherical surfaces can be approximated by planes normal to the die axis, and an analysis can be based on the assumption of uniform states of strain and stress over such planes yielding end results which are equivalent to those obtained here. Similar assumptions will prove to be highly useful in the analysis of more complex metal-forming processes to be discussed in later chapters.

15.4. Maximum Reduction in Wire Drawing

The drawing process is limited by the magnitude of the draw stress σ_{ra}, which for an ideally plastic material cannot become larger than the yield stress σ_0. The reduction in area R, expressed by

$$R = 1 - \frac{D_a{}^2}{D_b{}^2}$$

is often considered as the measure of the reduction obtained in a passage of the wire through the die; its maximum value results then from the condition that $(\sigma_r)_{x=x_a} = \sigma_0$ or

$$\sigma_0 \ln \frac{D_b{}^2}{D_a{}^2} = \sigma_0$$

(15.17)

Solving for $D_a{}^2/D_b{}^2$, one has

$$\frac{D_a{}^2}{D_b{}^2} = \frac{1}{e} = 0.37 \qquad (15.18)$$

and

$$R_{max} = 1 - \frac{1}{e} = 0.63 \qquad (15.19)$$

In other words, in drawing without friction a rod or wire can be reduced in cross section by a maximum value of 63 percent.

15.5. Stresses in Extruding Cylindrical Rods

The following simple analysis follows closely the pattern of that given in Art. 15.3 for wire drawing on the assumption of inward radial plastic

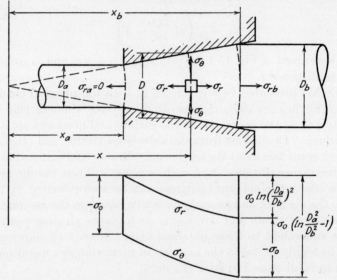

Fig. 15.2. Stresses in extruding a rod.

flow. The expressions for the principal strains remain the same as for wire drawing [Eqs. (15.14)]. The constant of integration in Eqs. (15.13) is determined from the condition at the exit section, $x = x_a$, where $\sigma_r = 0$, or

$$C - \sigma_0 \ln x_a{}^2 = 0$$

from which

$$C = \sigma_0 \ln x_a{}^2$$

and the principal stresses are expressed by

$$\sigma_r = \sigma_0 \ln \frac{x_a{}^2}{x^2}$$

$$\sigma_\theta = \sigma_0 \left(\ln \frac{x_a{}^2}{x^2} - 1 \right) \qquad (15.20)$$

or, in terms of the variable rod diameter D,

$$\sigma_r = \sigma_0 \ln \frac{D_a{}^2}{D^2}$$
$$\sigma_\theta = \sigma_0 \left(\ln \frac{D_a{}^2}{D^2} - 1 \right)$$

(15.21)

Figure 15.2 shows the plot of σ_r and σ_θ versus x.

15.6. Maximum Reduction in Extruding a Rod

The process of extrusion is limited by the largest value of the compressive stress that can be applied to the rod to be extruded. If this compressive stress is the yield stress σ_0 of the material, the condition, $(\sigma_r)_{x=x_b} = -\sigma_0$, furnishes

$$\sigma_0 \ln \frac{D_a{}^2}{D_b{}^2} = -\sigma_0$$

(15.22)

and the expression for the maximum reduction in area R_{max} is

$$R_{max} = 1 - \frac{1}{e} = 0.63$$

(15.23)

identical with the corresponding expression for wire drawing [Eq. (15.19)].

This result is predicated on the assumption that the entering rod is free to expand laterally, so that when a pressure equal to the yield stress σ_0 is applied to it, it will upset rather than push the metal through the die. However, by confining the compressed rod within a tube, compressive stresses much higher than σ_0 can be carried, and reductions greater than 63 per cent can be achieved. On the other hand, if the rod is not properly prevented from buckling, the obtainable reduction may be lower than the above value, depending upon the slenderness of the rod.

15.7. Two-dimensional Radial Plastic Flow

The flow of a wide strip through a smooth tapered die will be regarded as a two-dimensional radial flow toward the line of intersection of the two plane die surfaces. Reference will be made to results obtained in Chap. 8 for strains and stresses in a thick-walled tube in plane strain, $\epsilon_z = 0$, with the proper modifications required for large displacements. As in Art. 15.2, the symbol r will now indicate the instantaneous radial distance of the particle and r_0 its initial radial distance. Steady flow with constant r_0 and constant state of strain at a given r will be considered. Owing to symmetry, radial, tangential, and longitudinal directions are principal directions of strain and stress. For the tangential strain, Eqs. (15.1) to (15.3) apply here also.

$$\epsilon_\theta = \frac{r}{r_0} - 1$$

$$\bar{\epsilon}_\theta = \ln \frac{r}{r_0} \tag{15.24}$$

$$d\bar{\epsilon}_\theta = \frac{dr}{r}$$

From the volume-constancy equation, $\bar{\epsilon}_r + \bar{\epsilon}_\theta + \bar{\epsilon}_z = 0$, and from the plane-strain condition, $\bar{\epsilon}_z = 0$, one has for the radial strain

$$\bar{\epsilon}_r = -\bar{\epsilon}_\theta = \ln \frac{r_0}{r} \tag{15.25}$$

and also

$$d\bar{\epsilon}_r = -d\bar{\epsilon}_\theta = -\frac{dr}{r} \tag{15.26}$$

Saint-Venant's plastic-flow relation, written in matrix form, becomes

$$
\begin{pmatrix}
\dfrac{2\sigma_r - \sigma_\theta - \sigma_z}{3} & 0 & 0 \\[2ex]
0 & \dfrac{2\sigma_\theta - \sigma_z - \sigma_r}{3} & 0 \\[2ex]
0 & 0 & \dfrac{2\sigma_z - \sigma_r - \sigma_\theta}{3}
\end{pmatrix}
$$
$$
= \frac{2\lambda}{dt}
\begin{pmatrix}
d\bar{\epsilon}_r & 0 & 0 \\
0 & d\bar{\epsilon}_\theta & 0 \\
0 & 0 & d\bar{\epsilon}_z = 0
\end{pmatrix} \tag{15.27}
$$

where σ_r, σ_θ, and σ_z are the radial, tangential, and longitudinal principal stresses, respectively. Expanding the above equation and considering Eqs. (15.25) and (15.26), one obtains the two relations:

$$\sigma_z = \frac{\sigma_r + \sigma_\theta}{2} \tag{15.28}$$

$$\sigma_\theta - \sigma_r = \frac{4\lambda}{dt}\frac{dr}{r} \tag{15.29}$$

The von Mises–Hencky condition of yielding is stated in this case as

$$(\sigma_r - \sigma_\theta)^2 + (\sigma_\theta - \sigma_z)^2 + (\sigma_z - \sigma_r)^2 = 2\sigma_0{}^2$$

Substituting σ_z from Eq. (15.28), it becomes

$$\sigma_\theta - \sigma_r = \pm \frac{2}{\sqrt{3}}\sigma_0 \tag{15.30}$$

or, by introducing the notation $\sigma_0' = \dfrac{2}{\sqrt{3}}\sigma_0$,

$$\sigma_\theta - \sigma_r = \pm\sigma_0' \qquad (15.31)$$

The upper sign applies when $dr > 0$, that is, in case of *outward* radial flow; the same rule governs in the following Eqs. (15.32) and (15.33). Substituting the expression for $\sigma_\theta - \sigma_r$ from Eq. (15.30) into the differential equation of equilibrium, Eq. (8.11), one has

$$\frac{d\sigma_r}{dr} \mp \frac{\sigma_0'}{r} = 0 \qquad (15.32)$$

Integrating, one has the following expressions for the principal stresses:

$$\begin{aligned}
\sigma_r &= C \pm \sigma_0' \ln r \\
\sigma_\theta &= C \pm \sigma_0'(1 + \ln r) \\
\sigma_z &= C \pm \sigma_0'(\tfrac{1}{2} + \ln r)
\end{aligned} \qquad (15.33)$$

15.8. Stresses in Drawing and Extruding a Strip

The following simple analysis will be developed by considering the metal inside the wedge-shaped die as being in a state of two-dimensional

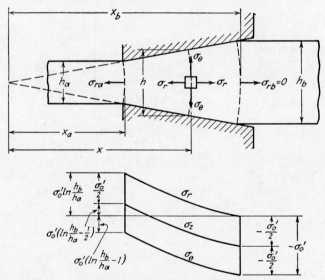

FIG. 15.3. Stresses in drawing a strip.

inward radial flow. The discussion of the approximations involved by the similar procedure used above for the problem of drawing and extruding of cylindrical bars applies to the present analysis also. With the notations of Figs. 15.3 and 15.4, the expressions for the principal strains become

$$\bar{\epsilon}_\theta = \ln \frac{x}{x_b}$$

$$\bar{\epsilon}_r = \ln \frac{x_b}{x}$$

(15.34)

The constant of integration in Eqs. (15.33) is determined from the condition that the radial stress vanishes at the entry section (in case of drawing) or at the exit section (in case of extruding).

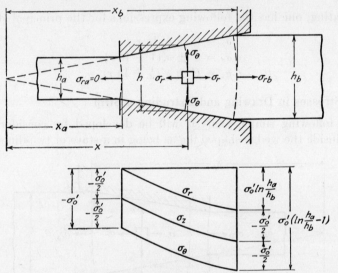

FIG. 15.4. Stresses in extruding a strip.

For *strip drawing* (Fig. 15.3), one has $(\sigma_r)_{x=x_b} = 0$ or

$$C - \sigma_0' \ln x_b = 0$$

from which $C = \sigma_0' \ln x_b$ and the expressions for the principal stresses become

$$\sigma_r = \sigma_0' \ln \frac{x_b}{x}$$

$$\sigma_\theta = \sigma_0' \left(\ln \frac{x_b}{x} - 1 \right)$$

$$\sigma_z = \sigma_0' \left(\ln \frac{x_b}{x} - \frac{1}{2} \right)$$

(15.35)

or also, in terms of the variable strip thickness h,

$$\sigma_r = \sigma_0' \ln \frac{h_b}{h}$$

$$\sigma_\theta = \sigma_0' \left(\ln \frac{h_b}{h} - 1 \right) \qquad (15.36)$$

$$\sigma_z = \sigma_0' \left(\ln \frac{h_b}{h} - \frac{1}{2} \right)$$

For *strip extruding* (Fig. 15.4), the boundary condition is $(\sigma_r)_{x=x_a} = 0$ or

$$C - \sigma_0' \ln x_a = 0 \qquad \text{and} \qquad C = \sigma_0' \ln x_a$$

The principal stresses are then

$$\sigma_r = \sigma_0' \ln \frac{x_a}{x} = \sigma_0' \ln \frac{h_a}{h}$$

$$\sigma_\theta = \sigma_0' \left(\ln \frac{x_a}{x} - 1 \right) = \sigma_0' \left(\ln \frac{h_a}{h} - 1 \right) \qquad (15.37)$$

$$\sigma_z = \sigma_0' \left(\ln \frac{x_a}{x} - \frac{1}{2} \right) = \sigma_0' \left(\ln \frac{h_a}{h} - \frac{1}{2} \right)$$

15.9. Maximum Reduction in Drawing or Extruding a Strip

The reduction in area for a strip, $R = 1 - h_a/h_b$, reaches its upper limit when the σ_r stress in the strip immediately outside the die becomes equal to the uniaxial yield strength of the metal σ_0. The conditions to be satisfied are then

$$(\sigma_r)_{x=x_a} = +\sigma_0 \qquad \text{for drawing}$$
$$(\sigma_r)_{x=x_b} = -\sigma_0 \qquad \text{for extruding}$$

In both cases the same equation is obtained:

$$\frac{2}{\sqrt{3}} \sigma_0 \ln \frac{h_b}{h_a} = \sigma_0$$

from which

$$R_{\max} = 1 - e^{\sqrt{3}/2} = 0.58 \qquad (15.38)$$

15.10. Work Consumption in Drawing and Extruding

The work consumed in plastic deformation of a unit volume of metal is the basis for the estimate of the minimal energy requirement (excluding friction losses) in a metal-forming process. Equation (5.43) furnishes the expression for the plastic work

$$W = \frac{2}{\sqrt{3}} \sigma_0 \sqrt{\bar{\epsilon}_1{}^2 + \bar{\epsilon}_1\bar{\epsilon}_2 + \bar{\epsilon}_2{}^2} \qquad (15.39)$$

where $\bar{\epsilon}_1$ and $\bar{\epsilon}_2$ are any two of the three logarithmic principal strains. This expression was derived in Chap. 5 under the assumption of "proportional straining" and applies to the processes here discussed. For *wire drawing or rod extruding*, Eq. (15.39) becomes, with $\bar{\epsilon}_1 = \bar{\epsilon}_2 = \bar{\epsilon}_\theta$,

$$W = 2\sigma_0|\bar{\epsilon}_\theta| \qquad (15.40)$$

The logarithmic tangential strain of a particle at the instant of reaching the exit section is calculated from the first of Eqs. (15.14) by putting $x = x_a$.

$$|\bar{\epsilon}_\theta| = \ln \frac{x_b}{x_a} \qquad (15.41)$$

The work per unit volume becomes

$$W = \sigma_0 \ln \frac{x_b{}^2}{x_a{}^2} = \sigma_0 \ln \frac{D_b{}^2}{D_a{}^2} \qquad (15.42)$$

For *strip drawing or extruding*, Eq. (15.39) furnishes with $\bar{\epsilon}_1 = \bar{\epsilon}_\theta$ and $\bar{\epsilon}_2 = \bar{\epsilon}_z = 0$ and with reference to Eq. (15.41), applicable to these processes,

$$W = \sigma_0'\bar{\epsilon}_\theta = \sigma_0' \ln \frac{x_b}{x_a} = \sigma_0' \ln \frac{h_b}{h_a} \qquad (15.43)$$

15.11. Draw Stress Determined from Work Consumption

In a slow steady plastic flow the total work of the external forces during a time interval is dissipated by the plastic straining of the volume of material which passes during that interval through the section where the plastic deformation terminates. This relationship follows directly from the principle of conservation of energy, and it can be shown that in simple cases it furnishes a method of calculating the external forces needed to maintain the state of steady plastic flow.

The example of the calculation of the "draw stress" in wire drawing, *i.e.*, the stress acting on the reduced wire section, will illustrate the procedure. The draw force F, that is, the resultant of the draw stresses on the wire section, is the only external force doing work in a drawing process in absence of friction. Its work during a displacement δ_a of the exit section is

$$F\delta_a = \sigma_{ra} \frac{\pi D_a{}^2}{4} \delta_a \qquad (15.44)$$

During the same time interval a reduced wire of length δ_a and of volume $(\pi D_a{}^2/4)\delta_a$ leaves the exit section of the die; and its plastic deformation consumes the total work [see Eq. (15.42)]

$$W \frac{\pi D_a{}^2}{4} \delta_a = \sigma_0 \ln \frac{D_b{}^2}{D_a{}^2} \frac{\pi}{4} D_a{}^2 \delta_a \qquad (15.45)$$

Equating the expressions on the right sides of Eqs. (15.44) and (15.45), one has for the draw stress

$$\sigma_{ra} = \sigma_0 \ln \frac{D_b{}^2}{D_a{}^2} \qquad (15.46)$$

in agreement with the results obtained in Art. 15.3.

CHAPTER 16

DRAWING AND EXTRUDING OF CYLINDRICAL BODIES

16.1. Scope of Problem

This chapter deals with one of the simplest plastic-forming processes in which a cylindrical body is deformed into another one of smaller diameter by drawing or extruding through a conical die. In Chap. 15 such processes were analyzed under the assumption of absence of friction along the die-metal interface; in the present chapter the effect of friction will be included in the analysis.

For sake of greater generality, another factor will be included, the so-called "backpull," a tensile force applied to the metal rod at the entry in addition to that acting at the exit. Experimental evidence indicates that even without an externally applied force a certain amount of backpull is generally present in wire drawing owing to the existence of an elastic region inside the die adjacent to the entry section. The resultant of the die pressure in this elastic region is an axial force directed against the direction of metal flow and is the so-called elastic backpull. In absence of a satisfactory analytical method of determining this backpull, experimental data can be utilized by plotting the observed drawing force versus the reduction in area and extrapolating to find the draw force corresponding to zero reduction.

16.2. Wire Drawing

The frictional forces acting between the wire metal and the rough die will be assumed to obey Coulomb's law of sliding friction. According to this law, the tangential force at a point is proportional to the normal pressure p between the two bodies at that point, and it is directed to oppose the relative motion. The coefficient of friction f is regarded as constant for a given die and wire material and for given surface conditions and temperature and is considered independent of the speed of sliding motion.

The following analysis, due to Sachs (1927), is based on the assumption of a uniform state of stress at all points of a plane normal to the die axis. A "cylindrical" state of stress is assumed throughout, with the axial or x direction being one of the principal directions and the (tensile)

176

stress σ_x the corresponding principal stress; and all directions perpendicular to the x axis being principal directions with the (compressive) principal stress equal to the pressure between wire and die, $-p$. The physical significance of these assumptions can be best appreciated with

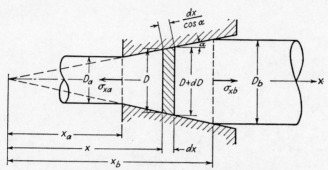

FIG. 16.1. Dimensions in wire drawing.

reference to the analysis of frictionless drawing in Chap. 15, where a similar uniform stress state over concentric spherical surfaces was found from the assumption that the metal inside the die can be regarded as a portion of a thick-walled spherical shell. The present assumptions imply the existence of a similar "arching" effect; furthermore, they replace the spherical surfaces by tangential planes. The smaller the die angle and the smaller the coefficient of friction, the better the approximation afforded by this procedure.

Consider the equilibrium of a volume element bounded by two planes perpendicular to the x axis at distances x and $x + dx$ from the apex of the conical die (see Fig. 16.1). The following groups of forces, acting on the volume element, are axial-symmetrically distributed; hence, their resultants are acting along the x axis.

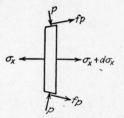

FIG. 16.2. Stresses acting on wire element.

(*a*) The σ_x stresses on the two transverse planes yield the resultant, neglecting infinitesimals of higher order (see Fig. 16.2),

$$(\sigma_x + d\sigma_x) \frac{\pi}{4} (D + dD)^2 - \sigma_x \frac{\pi}{4} D^2 = \frac{\pi D}{4} (D\, d\sigma_x + 2\sigma_x\, dD) \quad (16.1)$$

(*b*) The resultant of the normal pressures on the surface in contact with the die is determined by considering a surface element, shown in Fig. 16.3, obtained by intersecting the conical die surface with two radial planes including the angle $d\theta$. The total normal pressure on the surface element is

$$\left(p\,\frac{dx}{\cos\,\alpha}\right)\left(\frac{D}{2}\,d\theta\right)$$

which yields the axial component

$$\left(p\,\frac{dx}{\cos\,\alpha}\right)\left(\frac{D}{2}\,d\theta\right)\sin\,\alpha = p\,\frac{D}{2}\,\tan\,\alpha\,dx\,d\theta$$

Integrating this expression from $\theta = 0$ to $\theta = 2\pi$, one obtains the resultant of the normal pressures on the volume element

$$\int_0^{2\pi} p\,\frac{D}{2}\,\tan\,\alpha\,dx\,d\theta = p\pi D\,\tan\,\alpha\,dx = \frac{p\pi}{2}\,D\,dD \qquad (16.2)$$

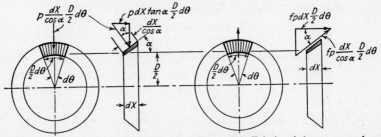

FIG. 16.3. Normal pressure on surface element. FIG. 16.4. Frictional force on surface element.

(c) The resultant of the frictional forces is obtained similarly by considering a surface element with the dimensions $dx/\cos\,\alpha$ and $\left(\dfrac{D}{2}\right)d\theta$ (see Fig. 16.4). The total frictional force on the surface element is

$$\left(fp\,\frac{dx}{\cos\,\alpha}\right)\left(\frac{D}{2}\,d\theta\right)$$

with the axial component

$$\left(fp\,\frac{dx}{\cos\,\alpha}\right)\left(\frac{D}{2}\,d\theta\right)\cos\,\alpha = fp\,\frac{D}{2}\,dx\,d\theta$$

Integrating this expression from $\theta = 0$ to $\theta = 2\pi$, the resultant of the frictional forces on the wire element becomes

$$\int_0^{2\pi} fp\,\frac{D}{2}\,dx\,d\theta = fp\pi D\,dx = \frac{fp\pi D}{2\,\tan\,\alpha}\,dD \qquad (16.3)$$

The equilibrium equation expresses that the sum of the forces given by Eqs. (16.1) to (16.3) vanishes, or

$$\frac{\pi D}{4} (D \, d\sigma_x + 2\sigma_x \, dD) + \frac{p\pi}{2} D \, dD + fp \frac{\pi}{2 \tan \alpha} D \, dD = 0$$

Simplifying, one obtains the following differential equation:

$$D \, d\sigma_x + 2\sigma_x \, dD + 2p \, dD \left(1 + \frac{f}{\tan \alpha}\right) = 0 \qquad (16.4)$$

In the "cylindrical" stress state here assumed, both the maximum-shearing-stress criterion and the distortion-energy criterion of plasticity are expressed by the same relation between the principal stresses:

$$\sigma_{\text{I}} - \sigma_{\text{III}} = \sigma_0$$

which in this case, with $\sigma_{\text{I}} = \sigma_x$ and $\sigma_{\text{III}} = -p$, becomes

$$\sigma_x + p = \sigma_0 \qquad (16.5)$$

With such a relationship and with the notation

$$B = \frac{f}{\tan \alpha} \qquad (16.6)$$

the differential equation governing the variation of the axial stress σ_x as a function of the wire diameter D becomes

$$\frac{d\sigma_x}{\sigma_x B - \sigma_0(1 + B)} = \frac{2 \, dD}{D} \qquad (16.7)$$

Integrating both sides of Eq. (16.7) and simplifying, one obtains

$$\frac{1}{B} \ln [\sigma_x B - \sigma_0(1 + B)] = 2 \ln D + C$$

where C is a constant of integration. Solving this equation for the axial stress σ_x, the following expression is obtained:

$$\sigma_x = C' \frac{D^{2B}}{B} + \sigma_0 \frac{1 + B}{B}$$

where C' is a new constant of integration related to C by the expression

$$C' = e^{CB}$$

This constant, C', is to be determined from the condition at the die entry section, $D = D_b$, where, in case of a given backpull stress $\sigma_x = \sigma_{xb}$, the following condition is to be satisfied:

$$\sigma_{xb} = \frac{C' D_b^{2B}}{B} + \sigma_0 \frac{1 + B}{B}$$

This equation yields the following value of C':

$$C' = \left(\sigma_{xb} - \sigma_0 \frac{1 + B}{B} \right) \frac{B}{D_b^{2B}}$$

Finally, with this value of the constant of integration the following expressions are obtained for the stress ratios:

$$\frac{\sigma_x}{\sigma_0} = \frac{1 + B}{B} \left[1 - \left(\frac{D^2}{D_b^2} \right)^B \right] + \frac{\sigma_{xb}}{\sigma_0} \left(\frac{D^2}{D_b^2} \right)^B$$

$$\frac{p}{\sigma_0} = 1 - \frac{\sigma_x}{\sigma_0} = \frac{1}{B} \left[1 + (1 + B) \left(\frac{D^2}{D_b^2} \right)^B \right] - \frac{\sigma_{xb}}{\sigma_0} \left(\frac{D^2}{D_b^2} \right)^B \qquad (16.8)$$

The "draw stress" is defined as the axial stress σ_{xa} at the exit where $D = D_a$. It is expressed by the ratio

$$\frac{\sigma_{xa}}{\sigma_0} = \frac{1 + B}{B} \left[1 - \left(\frac{D_a^2}{D_b^2} \right)^B \right] + \frac{\sigma_{xb}}{\sigma_0} \left(\frac{D_a^2}{D_b^2} \right)^B \qquad (16.9)$$

With zero backpull, $\sigma_{xb} = 0$, Eq. (16.9) reduces to

$$\frac{\sigma_{xa}}{\sigma_0} = \frac{1 + B}{B} \left[1 - \left(\frac{D_a^2}{D_b^2} \right)^B \right] \qquad (16.10)$$

In Fig. 16.5 the values of σ_{xa}/σ_0 from Eq. (16.10) are plotted against the parameter D_a^2/D_b^2, for various values of the constant B.

It is to be noted that the solution derived here is valid only for $B \neq 0$. Therefore, in Fig. 16.5 the curve representing frictionless drawing, $B = 0$, was plotted on the basis of the relationships developed in Chap. 15 [Eq. (15.15)] for such a condition.

16.3. Effects of Backpull

Draw-stress values can be computed either from Eq. (16.9) or with the aid of Fig. 16.5. Values of σ_{xa}/σ_0 thus obtained for the case of $B = 1$, selected as an arbitrary example, are plotted in Fig. 16.6 for backpulls σ_{xb}/σ_0 varying from 0 to 1. Experimentally determined values of the draw stress σ_{xa}, for steel, obtained by Lueg and Pomp (1943), are plotted in a similar manner in Fig. 16.7. It can be seen from a comparison of Figs. 16.6 and 16.7 that the trend of these experimental data agrees closely with that of the theoretical data for $B = 1$, indicating the existence of an elastic backpull, to be discussed in Art. 16.4.

According to Eq. (16.9), the draw stress increases with increasing back-pull, though by an amount less than the backpull itself.   The larger the reduction and the constant B become, the smaller becomes the contribution of the backpull to the draw stress.   As a consequence of this fact,

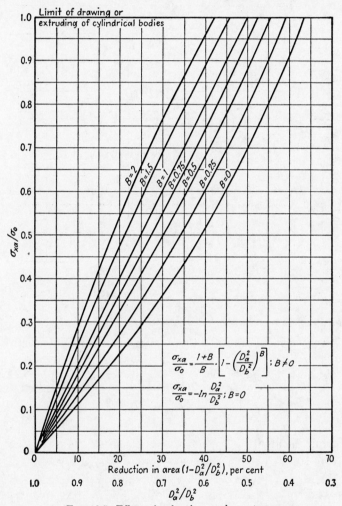

Fig. 16.5. Effect of reduction on draw stress.

the work consumption decreases with increasing backpull, other conditions being constant, provided that the work done by the backpull can be recuperated, *e.g.*, by operating a generator.   This reduction in work consumption is due to the reduction in frictional losses as a consequence of the decrease in die pressure.   The practical advantages achieved by applying backpull have been recognized commercially; die life is increased and lost time in drawing is correspondingly reduced.

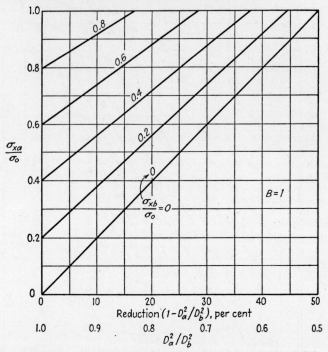

FIG. 16.6. Effect of reduction on draw stress for various backpull values.

On the other hand, the maximum possible reduction decreases with increasing backpull. This reduction at which the draw stress reaches the metal strength, that is,

$$\frac{\sigma_{xa}}{\sigma_0} = 1$$

is obtained as a function of σ_{xb}/σ_0 from the theoretical curves shown in Fig. 16.6 and from the experimental data in Fig. 16.7. The agreement between theoretical and experimental values can be improved according to Fig. 16.8 by assuming that the average flow stress, shown as a dashed line in Fig. 16.7, is the limit in actual drawing rather than the yield stress. This average flow stress is taken as the average of the yield stress values before and after drawing, provided that the strain-hardening effect is small. Also, the draw stresses for $D_a{}^2/D_b{}^2 = 0$ in Fig. 16.7 are taken as backpull.

16.4. Elastic Backpull

The above-developed analysis does not account for the experimental fact that, for a given *applied* backpull σ_{xb}'', the draw stress extrapolates for

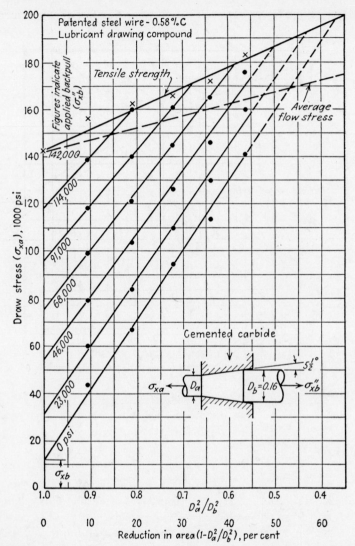

FIG. 16.7. Effect of backpull on draw stress and reductions according to tests by **Lueg** and **Pomp** (1943).

$D_a{}^2/D_b{}^2 = 1$, that is, for zero permanent reduction, to a value

$$\sigma_{xb} > \sigma''_{xb}$$

The difference

$$\sigma'_{xb} = \sigma_{xb} - \sigma''_{xb} \tag{16.11}$$

can be best interpreted as that axial stress which corresponds to the die pressure acting in the elastic regions adjacent to the die openings. The

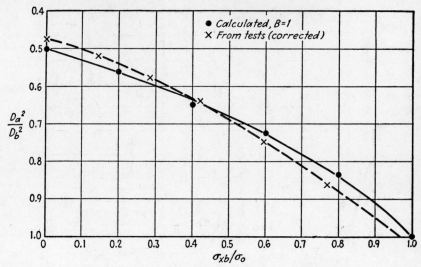

FIG. 16.8. Effect of backpull on maximum reduction.

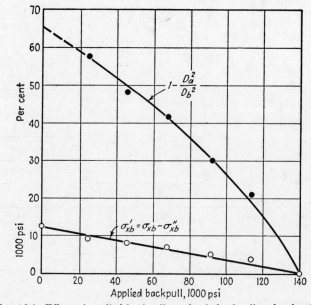

FIG. 16.9. Effect of applied backpull on elastic backpull and reduction.

experimental data, plotted in Fig. 16.7, yield for σ'_{xb} values of about 8 per cent of the flow stress of the metal, if $\sigma''_{xb} = 0$. Plotting the values of the elastic backpull σ'_{xb} against the applied backpull σ''_{xb}, as it is done in Fig. 16.9, the existence of a linear relationship of the following form can be recognized:

$$\sigma'_{xb} = a(\sigma_0 - \sigma''_{xb}) \tag{16.12}$$

Here, a is a constant to be determined from a series of tests without applied backpull, for which $\sigma''_{xb} = 0$; hence,

$$\sigma'_{xb} = \sigma_{xb} = a\sigma_0$$

The value σ_{xb}/σ_0 in Eq. (16.11) can be expressed then as follows:

$$\frac{\sigma_{xb}}{\sigma_0} = \frac{\sigma'_{xb}}{\sigma_0} + \frac{\sigma''_{xb}}{\sigma_0} = a + \frac{\sigma''_{xb}}{\sigma_0}(1 - a) \tag{16.13}$$

16.5. Extruding

The differential equation that governs wire drawing, *e.g.*, Eq. (16.7), applies to the extruding of a cylindrical rod also. However, the constant of integration C' is now determined from the condition at the die exit, $D = D_a$, where the axial stress is equal to the given front pressure σ_{xa}, that is,

$$\sigma_{xa} = \frac{C'D_a{}^{2B}}{B} + \sigma_0 \frac{1 + B}{B}$$

Then, one obtains

$$C' = \left(\sigma_{xa} - \sigma_0 \frac{1 + B}{B}\right)\frac{D}{D_a{}^{2B}}$$

With this value for the constant of integration, the expressions for the stresses become

$$\frac{\sigma_x}{\sigma_0} = \frac{1 + B}{B}\left[1 - \left(\frac{D^2}{D_a{}^2}\right)^B\right] + \frac{\sigma_{xa}}{\sigma_0}\left(\frac{D^2}{D_a{}^2}\right)^B$$

$$\frac{p}{\sigma_0} = 1 - \frac{\sigma_x}{\sigma_0} = \frac{1}{B}\left[1 + (1 + B)\left(\frac{D^2}{D_a{}^2}\right)^B\right] - \frac{\sigma_{xa}}{\sigma_0}\left(\frac{D^2}{D_a{}^2}\right)^B \tag{16.14}$$

The "extrusion pressure" σ_{xb} results from the first of these equations by letting $D = D_b$.

$$\frac{\sigma_{xb}}{\sigma_0} = \frac{1 + B}{B}\left[1 - \left(\frac{D_b{}^2}{D_a{}^2}\right)^B\right] + \frac{\sigma_{xa}}{\sigma_0}\left(\frac{D_b{}^2}{D_a{}^2}\right)^B \tag{16.15}$$

With zero front pressure, this equation becomes

$$\frac{\sigma_{xb}}{\sigma_0} = \frac{1 + B}{B}\left[1 - \left(\frac{D_b{}^2}{D_a{}^2}\right)^B\right] \tag{16.16}$$

16.6. Consideration of Strain-Hardening

The analyses of metal-forming processes presented in Chaps. 15 through 23 apply to an ideally plastic material. However, as shown in Art. 16.3, the procedure followed in such analyses can be readily applied to actual metals which are strain-hardened by plastic deformation. If this effect is small, as in the case of metals strengthened by cold work or heat treating, the usual process needs two modifications. First, the average of the flow stresses at the outset and at the termination of the plastic flow is to be used in place of the (initial) yield stress σ_0. Second, the maximum reduction is calculated from the actual strength of the metal rather than from its average strength. Thus the high values of actual maximum reduction (see Figs. 16.7 and 16.9) can be readily explained.

If the strain-hardening is large, the flow stress should be expressed as a function of the strain, and such function is to be introduced in the analysis. Davis and Dokos (1944) gave an example of such a treatment of the wire-drawing problem based on a power-function type of stress-strain relation.

REFERENCES

Davis, E. A., and S. J. Dokos, Theory of Wire Drawing, *J. Appl. Mechanics*, Vol. 11, pp. 193–198, 1944.

Lueg, W., and A. Pomp, Der Einfluss des Gegenzuges beim Ziehen von Stahldraht, *Stahl u. Eisen*, Vol. 63, No. 12, pp. 229–236, 1943.

MacLellan, G.D.S., A Critical Survey of Wire-Drawing Theory, *J. Iron Steel Inst.*, Vol. 158, pp. 347–356, 1948.

MacLellan, G.D.S., Some Friction Effects in Wire Drawing, *J. Inst. Metals*, Vol. 81, 1952.

Poeschl, T., Ueber die Berechnung der Ziehkraefte und des Spannungszustandes beim Drahtziehen, *Metallwirtschaft*, Vol. 22, pp. 428–434, 1943; Vol. 23, pp. 245–249, 1944.

Sachs, G., Beitrag zur Theorie des Ziehvorganges, *Z. angew. Math. Mechanik*, Vol. 7, pp. 235–236, 1927.

Sachs, G., "Spanlose Formung der Metalle," Springer-Verlag, Berlin, 1931.

CHAPTER 17

DRAWING AND EXTRUDING THROUGH TAPERED DIES IN CONDITION OF PLANE STRAIN

17.1. Scope of Problem

This chapter is devoted to the analysis of a group of metal-forming processes characterized by steady two-dimensional plastic flow of metal between rough die or tool surfaces. Two cases of practical significance will be handled: (1) drawing and extruding of a wide strip; (2) forming of a thin-walled tube with negligible changes in diameter.

In case 1, a wide strip is pushed or pulled through a wedge-shaped die and it is assumed that frictional forces of adequate magnitude acting in a direction parallel to the edge of the die prevent any change in width of the strip, so that a state of plane strain is present, with zero strain in the direction parallel to the width of the strip.

In case 2, a thin-walled cylindrical tube is forced through a gap between two concentric conical tools. Because of axial symmetry, a sector of an annular element of the tube, bounded by two radial planes, continues to be bounded by the same planes during the forming process. Then, considering the assumption of negligible changes in tube diameter, it can be concluded that the tangential (or circumferential) strain is zero or negligible in comparison with the longitudinal and radial strains and that a state of plane strain can be assumed in the analysis of this forming process.

Assumptions concerning the stress state will be formulated separately for the two cases; they will be found to be similar to those used in the preceding chapter. In general, the discussion presented in this chapter follows that given by Sachs, Lubahn, and Tracy (1944).

17.2. Differential Equation for Strip Drawing

Reference will be made to a cartesian coordinate system having its x and y axes oriented as shown in Fig. 17.1 and its z axis perpendicular to the plane of the figure, which is the plane of the two-dimensional plastic flow here assumed. The same state of stress is assumed to exist at all points of a plane normal to the x axis, with principal axes oriented parallel to the x, y, z axes and with $\sigma_y = -p$ throughout, where p denotes the die pressure at the intersection of the transverse plane with the die surface.

Consider the equilibrium of a volume element of unit width bounded by the two plane die surfaces, each making a dihedral angle α with the

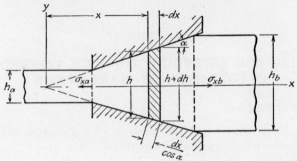

FIG. 17.1. Dimensions in strip drawing.

xz plane, and by two planes parallel to the yz plane, located at distances x and $x + dx$ from the origin. Because of symmetry of the volume element and of the forces acting on it, the only significant equilibrium equation relates the following x components of the forces (see Fig. 17.2).

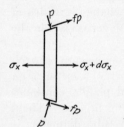

FIG. 17.2. Stresses on strip element.

(a) The resultant of the σ_x stresses on transverse planes is, neglecting infinitesimals of higher order,

$$(\sigma_x + d\sigma_x)(h + dh) - \sigma_x h = \sigma_x\,dh + h\,dx \quad (17.1)$$

(b) The normal pressures on the die surfaces yield the x component

$$2p \tan \alpha\, dx = p\, dh \qquad (17.2)$$

(c) The frictional forces along the die surfaces yield the x component

$$2fp\, dx = fp\, \frac{dh}{\tan \alpha} \qquad (17.3)$$

Equilibrium requires that the sum of the forces expressed by Eqs. (17.1) to (17.3) vanishes, or

$$\sigma_x\, dh + h\, d\sigma_x + p\, dh + fp\, \frac{dh}{\tan \alpha} = 0$$

Introducing the constant B, defined as

$$B = \frac{f}{\tan \alpha} \qquad (17.4)$$

and regrouping, the equilibrium equation becomes

$$h\, d\sigma_x + [\sigma_x + p(1 + B)] = 0 \qquad (17.5)$$

It was shown in Art. 11.2 that the von Mises–Hencky (distortion-energy) criterion of plasticity is expressed, in case of plane strain, by the relationship

$$\sigma_I - \sigma_{III} = \frac{2}{\sqrt{3}}\sigma_0 = \sigma_0'$$

or in the present case, with $\sigma_I = \sigma_x$ and $\sigma_{III} = \sigma_y = -p$, by

$$\sigma_x + p = \sigma_0' \tag{17.6}$$

Solving for p, one obtains

$$p = \sigma_0' - \sigma_x \tag{17.7}$$

and substituting this expression in Eq. (17.5), the differential equation of strip drawing becomes

$$\frac{d\sigma_x}{\sigma_x B - \sigma_0'(1 + B)} = \frac{dh}{h} \tag{17.8}$$

17.3. Stresses in Strip Drawing

A comparison of Eq. (17.8) with Eq. (16.7) of the preceding chapter shows that the former can be obtained from the latter by replacing σ_0 by $(2/\sqrt{3})\sigma_0$, D by h, and by omitting the factor 2 on the right side. Equations (16.8) can be therefore utilized here with the appropriate changes to obtain the following expressions:

$$
\begin{aligned}
\frac{\sigma_x}{\sigma_0'} &= \frac{1+B}{B}\left[1 - \left(\frac{h}{h_b}\right)^B\right] + \frac{\sigma_{xb}}{\sigma_0'}\left(\frac{h}{h_b}\right)^B \\
\frac{p}{\sigma_0'} &= 1 - \frac{\sigma_x}{\sigma_0'} = \frac{1}{B}\left[1 + (1 + B)\left(\frac{h}{h_b}\right)^B\right] - \frac{\sigma_{xb}}{\sigma_0'}\left(\frac{h}{h_b}\right)^B
\end{aligned}
\tag{17.9}
$$

σ_{xb} is the backpull stress at the entry section where $h = h_b$. From the known relationship for plane strain, the σ_z principal stress has the expression

$$\sigma_z = \frac{\sigma_x + \sigma_y}{2} = \frac{\sigma_x - p}{2}$$

The draw stress, *i.e.*, the σ_x stress at the exit section, where $h = h_a$, is

$$\frac{\sigma_{xa}}{\sigma_0'} = \frac{1+B}{B}\left[1 - \left(\frac{h_a}{h_b}\right)^B\right] + \frac{\sigma_{xb}}{\sigma_0'}\left(\frac{h_a}{h_b}\right)^B \tag{17.10}$$

With zero backpull, $\sigma_{xb} = 0$, this equation becomes

$$\frac{\sigma_{xa}}{\sigma_0'} = \frac{1+B}{B}\left[1 - \left(\frac{h_a}{h_b}\right)^B\right] \tag{17.11}$$

Similar expressions for stresses in strip extruding can be derived by following the pattern of the analysis given here for drawing.

17.4. Differential Equation for Tube Drawing with a Mandrel

A uniform state of stress is assumed to exist at all points of a plane normal to the x axis, *i.e.*, the tube axis (see Fig. 17.3) with σ_x being one of

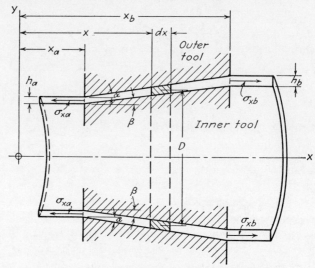

FIG. 17.3. Dimensions in tube drawing.

the principal stresses. The die pressure p is assumed to be the same on both the inner and the outer tube surfaces at points having a given x coordinate; the radial stress in the tube is assumed to be $\sigma_r = -p$ across the tube wall.

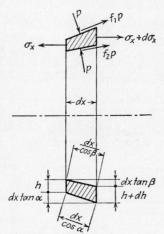

FIG. 17.4. Stresses on tube element.

Consider the equilibrium of an annular element cut from the tube by two transverse planes at x and $x + dx$ from the origin. The following groups of forces acting on the ring are axial-symmetrically distributed and yield resultants directed along the x axis (see Fig. 17.4):

(a) The stresses σ_x on the two transverse planes furnish the resultant, neglecting infinitesimals of higher order,

$$(\sigma_x + d\sigma_x)(h + dh)\pi D - \sigma_x h\pi D = (\sigma_x\, dh + h\, d\sigma_x)\pi D \quad (17.12)$$

(b) The resultant of the normal pressure on the outer tool (die) surface is [see Eq. (16.2)]

$$\int_0^{2\pi} p\, \frac{D}{2} \tan\alpha\, dx\, d\theta = p\pi D \tan\alpha\, dx \quad (17.13)$$

(c) The resultant of the normal pressure on the inner tool (mandrel) surface is

$$- \int_0^{2\pi} p \frac{D}{2} \tan \beta \, dx \, d\theta = -p\pi D \tan \beta \, dx \qquad (17.14)$$

(d) The resultant of the frictional forces on the outer tool surface is

$$\int_0^{2\pi} f_1 p \frac{D}{2} \, dx \, d\theta = f_1 p \pi D \, dx \qquad (17.15)$$

(e) The resultant of the frictional forces on the inner tool surface is

$$\int_0^{2\pi} f_2 p \frac{D}{2} \, dx \, d\theta = f_2 p \pi D \, dx \qquad (17.16)$$

In the above expressions, D is the mean diameter of the tube, assumed to undergo negligible changes during the drawing process here considered, h is the (variable) tube-wall thickness, 2α and 2β are respectively the apex angles of the outer and inner conical tool surfaces, f_1 and f_2 are respectively the coefficients of friction at the outer and inner tool surfaces. The equilibrium equation expresses that the sum of the forces given by Eqs. (17.12) through (17.16) vanishes, or

$$(\sigma_x \, dh + h \, d\sigma_x)\pi D + p\pi D \, dx(\tan \alpha - \tan \beta) + (f_1 + f_2)p\pi D \, dx = 0$$

Simplifying and considering that $dh = (\tan \alpha - \tan \beta) \, dx$ (see Fig. 17.4), one obtains

$$\sigma_x \, dh + h \, d\sigma_x + p \, dh \left(1 + \frac{f_1 + f_2}{\tan \alpha - \tan \beta}\right) = 0 \qquad (17.17)$$

or by introducing the notation

$$B = \frac{f_1 + f_2}{\tan \alpha - \tan \beta} \qquad (17.18)$$

one has

$$\sigma_x \, dh + h \, d\sigma_x + p \, dh(1 + B) = 0 \qquad (17.19)$$

As in the case discussed in the previous article [see Eqs. (17.6) and (17.7)], the von Mises–Hencky condition of plasticity furnishes the relation

$$p = \sigma_0' - \sigma_x$$

which, substituted in Eq. (17.19), furnishes the differential equation

$$\frac{d\sigma_x}{\sigma_x B - \sigma_0'(1 + B)} = \frac{dh}{h} \qquad (17.20)$$

This equation is identical with Eq. (17.8), except for the different definition given by Eq. (17.18) for the constant B; therefore, Eqs. (17.9) to (17.11) furnish the values of the stresses in tube drawing with a mandrel, provided that the constant B is calculated from Eq. (17.18).

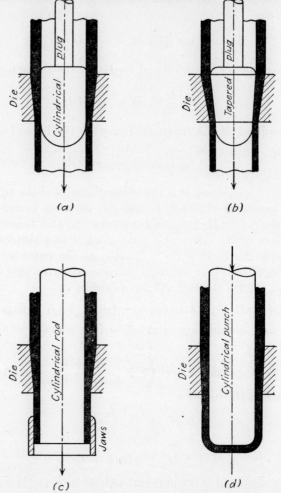

Fɪɢ. 17.5. (*a*) Tube drawing with cylindrical stationary mandrel or plug.   (*b*) Tube drawing with conical stationary mandrel or plug.   (*c*) Tube drawing with pulled moving mandrel or rod.   (*d*) Tube drawing with pushed moving mandrel or punch.

17.5. The Constant *B* for Various Tube-drawing Processes

The constant *B* is determined by the specific type of drawing process. Strip drawing is included here as a special case in which $\beta = -\alpha$ and in addition $f_2 = f_1 = f$. Consequently,

$$B = \frac{f}{\tan \alpha}$$

in agreement with Eq. (17.4).

Several typical tube-drawing processes are illustrated in Fig. 17.5. In tube drawing with a stationary mandrel or "plug" usually one has $f_2 = f_1 = f$, yielding

$$B = \frac{2f}{\tan \alpha - \tan \beta} \tag{17.21}$$

Often the stationary mandrel has a cylindrical shape, or $\beta = 0$; hence,

$$B = \frac{2f}{\tan \alpha} \tag{17.22}$$

If the inner cylindrical tool is of a different material than the die, $f_2 \neq f_1$, the expression for B becomes, in the case of a cylindrical plug,

$$B = \frac{f_1 + f_2}{\tan \alpha} \tag{17.23}$$

17.6. Drawing without Friction

Interesting conditions defining tube drawing with a moving mandrel or "rod" are obtained if the frictional forces between the mandrel and the metal reverse their directions, as it will be discussed later in detail. Under such conditions, if the mandrel is cylindrical, B is zero; and if the two coefficients of friction have the same value, the relationship $f_2 = -f_1$ is to be substituted into the expression for B. Then, the numerator of B and therefore B itself will become zero, and the differential equation (17.20) reduces to the following:

$$\frac{d\sigma_x}{\sigma_0'} = \frac{dh}{h} \tag{17.24}$$

which is the equivalent of Eq. (15.32) governing frictionless forming of a strip.

Integration of this equation, satisfying the condition that at the entry where $h = h_b$ the longitudinal stress equals the backpull, $\sigma_x = \sigma_{xb}$, furnishes the following expression for the stresses:

$$\frac{\sigma_x}{\sigma_0'} = \ln \frac{h_b}{h} + \frac{\sigma_{xb}}{\sigma_0'}$$
$$\frac{p}{\sigma_0'} = 1 - \ln \frac{h_b}{h} - \frac{\sigma_{xb}}{\sigma_0'} \tag{17.25}$$

17.7. Maximum Reductions in Strip Drawing and Tube Drawing with a Plug

In Fig. 17.6 values of the quantity σ_{xa}/σ_0', calculated from Eq. (17.11), are plotted versus the reduction in thickness for various values of the constant B. For strip drawing and for tube drawing with a plug, B is always positive.

The tensile strength of the metal at the exit sets the limit for the draw stress and, therefore, for the maximum possible reduction, $1 - h_a/h_b$. The metal at the exit is in a state of uniaxial stress rather than of plane strain, because it is free to undergo transverse or circumferential strains.

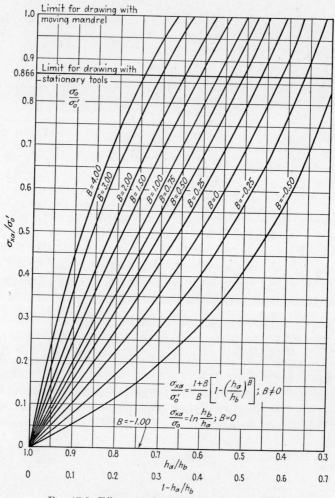

FIG. 17.6. Effect of reduction on drawing stresses.

Its strength in such a state is given by the flow stress σ_0, and thus the following condition equation can be written:

$$\frac{\sigma_{xa}}{\sigma_0'} = \frac{\sigma_0}{\sigma_0'} = 0.866 \qquad \text{or} \qquad \frac{1+B}{B}\left[1 - \left(\frac{h_a}{h_b}\right)^B\right] = 0.866$$

from which the maximum reduction is obtained as follows:

$$R_{max} = 1 - \frac{h_a}{h_b} = 1 - \left(\frac{1 + 0.133B}{1 + B}\right)^{1/B} \tag{17.26}$$

In Fig. 17.7 this equation was used in plotting curve a as a function of B; it can be seen that the larger B becomes, the smaller the maximum reduction is, the highest reduction of about 58 per cent being obtained for $B = 0$, that is, for drawing without friction. This value is the same as that obtained in Chap. 15 for frictionless strip drawing.

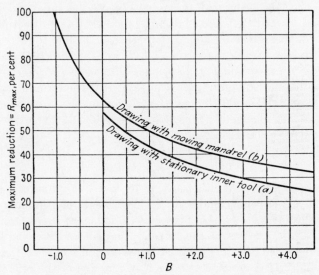

FIG. 17.7. Maximum reductions in tube drawing.

It is to be noted that the above analysis applies for an ideal plastic metal, for which the flow stress σ_0 is assumed to be constant and equal to the tensile strength. Strain-hardening increases the possible reduction because of the possibility of applying a higher tensile stress to the metal at the exit.

17.8. Tube Drawing with a Moving Mandrel

Drawing a tube with a moving mandrel is performed according to one of the two schemes indicated in Figs. 17.5c and 17.5d. In the first process the tube at the front end is pulled together with the mandrel or "rod"; in the second process the mandrel or "punch" is in compression and pushes against the closed front end of the tube. In either case the drawing force is transferred to the metal in part by pull on the exit section, similarly to the previously discussed drawing processes, and in part by friction along the mandrel surface. The frictional forces acting on the inner and outer tube surfaces always oppose the relative motion of the metal with respect to the adjacent tool. At the outer tube surface, the metal is moving toward the front end of the die with respect to the stationary outer tool (die); hence, the frictional forces are directed toward the back end, or in the positive x direction in Fig. 17.3. At the inner tube surface, a relative motion between the mandrel and the tube is set up by the longitudinal deformation of the metal, by virtue of which each particle gains velocity in moving from the entry to the exit section, while the mandrel undergoes only elastic changes in length of a negligible magnitude. Hence, the frictional forces acting on the inner tube surface are directed toward the front end, or in the negative x direction in Fig. 17.3, thus opposing the tendency of the metal to slide toward the back end with respect to the mandrel. Therefore, the direction of the frictional forces $f_2 p$ shown in Fig. 17.4 must be reversed in the case of tube drawing with a moving mandrel. Consequently, the term in the equilibrium equation (17.17) affected by the friction on the inner tube surface will have its sign changed. This yields the following new expression for the constant B, to be used here:

$$B = \frac{f_1 - f_2}{\tan \alpha - \tan \beta} \qquad (17.27)$$

This expression may yield either positive or negative values of B, depending on the relative magnitudes of the coefficients of friction f_1 and f_2.

Again, Eqs. (17.9) to (17.11) furnish, with values of B determined from Eq. (17.27), the stresses in the metal. The curves given in Fig. 17.6 thus also represent the longitudinal stress in the metal at the exit for tube drawing with a moving mandrel as a function of the reduction and of B. It can be seen that this maximum longitudinal stress σ_{za} increases with increasing B for the range of values shown in Fig. 17.6, that is, $B > -1$; for $B = -1$ it becomes zero; and for $B < -1$ the stress in the metal at the exit becomes a compression; hence, the process has the characteristics of extruding rather than of drawing.

It is to be noted that the condition described here is possible only if a compression can be applied at the exit, as may be the case in the process shown in Fig. 17.5c. In the case shown in Fig. 17.5d no such compression can be realized; therefore equilibrium can exist only if the metal at the exit moves faster than the mandrel, reversing the direction of the friction near the exit and giving rise to a so-called "no-slip" point between the regions of forward- and backward-directed friction.

17.9. Maximum Reduction in Tube Drawing with a Moving Mandrel

The theoretical maximum reduction in drawing with a moving mandrel is determined by a different condition than for drawing processes with stationary tools. Owing to the presence of the mandrel, the metal at the exit cannot undergo any circumferential strain; hence, it is in the condition of plane strain. As it was shown previously, the metal is expected to fail under such a condition when the longitudinal stress reaches the value σ_0'. This limit furnishes the relationship

$$\frac{\sigma_{xa}}{\sigma_0'} = 1 = \frac{1+B}{B}\left[1 - \left(\frac{h_a}{h_b}\right)^B\right]$$

from which the following expression for the maximum reduction is obtained:

$$R_{max} = 1 - \frac{h_a}{h_b} = 1 - \left(\frac{1}{1+B}\right)^{1/B}$$

Curve b in Fig. 17.7 represents the maximum reduction as a function of B according to this equation. For $B = 0$, the maximum reduction becomes about 63 per cent, and such a value corresponds to all cases with $f_1 = f_2$, including the case of frictionless drawing, $f_1 = f_2 = 0$.

For negative values of B, reductions in excess of 63 per cent are indicated by the analysis and confirmed by experimental results (Espey and Sachs, 1947).

As already mentioned, for $B < -1$ the metal is not subjected to any tension, but it is extruded by means of the frictional forces developed between the mandrel and the inner tube surface. The factors governing the limit of drawing in such cases are not well identified. Some observations indicate that either tool breakage occurs, owing to the resulting high pressures, or the metal fractures in an unpredictable fashion, possibly because of some defect.

17.10. Draw Force for Tube Drawing with a Moving Mandrel

As previously mentioned, the total draw force F consists of two parts (see Fig. 17.8):

1. The resultant of the tensile stresses acting on the metal at the exit section:

$$F_1 = \pi D_a h_a \sigma_{xa} = \pi D_a h_a \left\{\sigma_0' \frac{1+B}{B}\left[1 - \left(\frac{h_a}{h_b}\right)^B\right] + \sigma_{xb}\left(\frac{h_a}{h_b}\right)^B\right\} \quad (17.28)$$

2. The force carried by the mandrel, equal to the x component of the resultant of the normal pressures p, and of the frictional forces acting between the metal and the mandrel:

$$F_2 = \int_{x_a}^{x_b} \pi D p \tan \beta \, dx + \int_{x_a}^{x_b} \pi D f_2 p \, dx$$

Assuming, as it has been done throughout the present chapter, that the changes in tube diameter are negligible, one can substitute $D = D_a$ and obtain

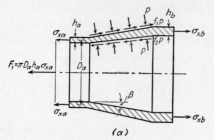

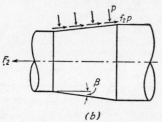

FIG. 17.8. (a) Forces acting on tube in drawing. (b) Forces acting on mandrel in drawing.

$$F_2 = \pi D_a(\tan \beta + f_2) \int_{x_a}^{x_b} p \, dx$$

Substituting

$$dx = \frac{dh}{\tan \alpha - \tan \beta}$$

and introducing the notation

$$C = \frac{\tan \beta + f_2}{\tan \alpha - \tan \beta}$$

the final expression for F_2 becomes

$$F_2 = \pi D_a C \int_{h_a}^{h_b} p \, dh \qquad (17.29)$$

An explicit expression for the total draw force

$$F = F_1 + F_2$$

will be developed here for the simplest, though practically important, case of a cylindrical mandrel and of identical coefficients of friction along the inner and outer tool surfaces. In such a case, the following values are to be used:

$$\beta = 0, \qquad f_1 = f_2 = f$$

and consequently

$$B = 0 \qquad \text{and} \qquad C = \frac{f}{\tan \alpha}$$

The longitudinal stress σ_x and the tool pressure p are given by Eq. (17.25); the stress at the exit is obtained by substituting $h = h_a$ into the expression for σ_x

$$\frac{\sigma_{xa}}{\sigma_0'} = \ln \frac{h_b}{h_a} + \frac{\sigma_{xb}}{\sigma_0'}$$

Then the total draw force becomes

$$F = F_1 + F_2 = \pi D_a h_a \sigma_{xa} + \pi D_a C \int_{h_a}^{h_b} p \, dh$$

$$= \pi D_a h_a \left[\sigma_0' \ln \frac{h_b}{h_a} + \sigma_{xb} + C \int_{h_a}^{h_b} \left(\sigma_0' - \sigma_0' \ln \frac{h_b}{h} - \sigma_{xb} \right) dh \right]$$

$$= \pi D h_a \left\{ \sigma_0'(1 + C) \ln \frac{h_b}{h_a} + \sigma_{xb} \left[1 - C \left(\frac{h_b}{h_a} - 1 \right) \right] \right\} \qquad (17.30)$$

It is convenient to refer to a "unit draw force," obtained by dividing the total draw force F by the cross-sectional area of the tube at the exit $\pi D_a h_a$:

$$\frac{F}{\pi D_a h_a} = \sigma_0'(1 + C) \ln \frac{h_b}{h_a} + \sigma_{xb} \left[1 - C \left(\ln \frac{h_b}{h_a} - 1 \right) \right] \quad (17.31)$$

This quantity, which has the dimension of a stress but does not represent the true stress at any point of the tube, has been used in plotting the experimental curves discussed in the next section and shown in Fig. 17.10. The term "draw stress" is sometimes used for this quantity, but should be reserved for those cases where the metal carries the total load.

17.11. Experimental Results

Espey and Sachs (1947) investigated experimentally the process of tube drawing with a moving mandrel. The best agreement with calcu-

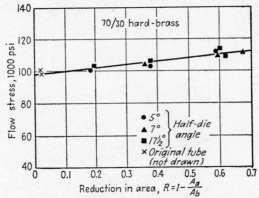

FIG. 17.9. Flow stress values for hard-drawn 70/30 brass tube subjected to various reductions by drawing with a moving mandrel.

lated values can be expected when using a cold-worked metal exhibiting a nearly constant flow stress. Figure 17.9 shows the flow-stress values obtained with hard-drawn 70/30 brass tube subjected to various reductions. From this graph it can be concluded that an average value of $\sigma_0 = 104,000$ psi and of $\sigma_0' = 120,000$ psi can be used in comparative calculations, neglecting the slight increase with reduction.

In order to include the effect of the changes in diameter of the tube during the forming process, the reduction R must express the reduction of cross-sectional area rather than that of the wall thickness of the tube.

$$R = 1 - \frac{A_a}{A_b} = 1 - \frac{h_a D_a}{h_b D_b}$$

where A_b and A_a are the initial and final cross-sectional areas, D_b and D_a the initial and final mean diameters of the tube. In Fig. 17.10, the experimentally determined values of the unit draw force F/A_a are plotted against the reductions in area to which the tube samples were subjected

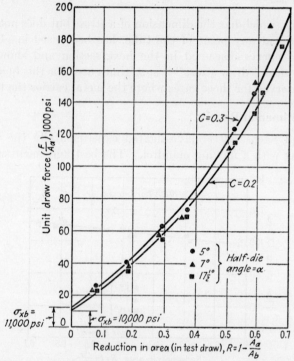

Fig. 17.10. Effects of reduction and die angle on draw stresses for hard-drawn 70/30 brass tube.

in test draws. In the same figure, two theoretical curves are plotted assuming $B = 0$; the lower one was calculated with the value of

$$C = \frac{f}{\tan \alpha} = 0.2$$

and with a hypothetical backpull of $\sigma_{xb} = 10,000$ psi. It appears to represent closely the experimental points obtained with dies having a half die angle $\alpha = 17\frac{1}{2}°$. The upper curve was calculated with $C = 0.3$ and $\sigma_{xb} = 11,000$ psi and fits closely the experimental points both for $\alpha = 5°$ and for $\alpha = 7°$.

The corresponding values of the coefficient of friction f can be calculated as follows:

$\alpha =$	$5°$	$7°$	$17\frac{1}{2}°$
$\tan \alpha =$	0.087	0.123	0.315
$C =$	0.3	0.3	0.2
$f = C \tan \alpha =$	0.026	0.037	0.063

On the average, a value of $f = 0.05$ appears to be consistent with the experimental results discussed here.

The physical significance of the assumed backpull is that a longitudinal stress is built up in the metal in the elastic region near the die openings, as discussed previously in Chap. 16.

The experiments also confirm the theoretical considerations regarding the maximum reduction. As discussed in Art. 17.9, the theoretical maximum reduction is obtained when the stress in the metal at the exit reaches the strength of the metal under the condition of plane strain, that is, σ'_0. For the experiments discussed here, this stress is calculated as 1.15 times the strength of the tubes subjected to the largest reductions, approximately 125,000 psi.

The maximum theoretical reduction for equal coefficients of friction, $f_1 = f_2$, was calculated in Art. 17.9 as 63 per cent; actually, slightly larger reductions were observed. This is a peculiarity of the process of drawing with a moving mandrel; differences in the coefficients of friction may allow raising the maximum reduction. On the contrary, in other drawing operations practical conditions, except strain-hardening, lower the maximum reduction as compared with the theoretical value.

17.12. Tandem Drawing

In drawing processes with stationary tools no improvement can be expected from replacing a single die by two dies in tandem. In such processes the force required for the total reduction has to be transferred through the metal and a given reduction requires, as a rule, a higher total force if performed in two dies than if performed in a single die.

However, in drawing tubular parts with a moving mandrel, two dies in tandem are often used with advantage (see Fig. 17.11). Such an arrangement permits greater reductions in a single operation than a single die. This fact can be explained as follows (Sachs and Espey, 1947): In drawing processes with a moving mandrel the force required to perform the reduction of the wall thickness is partially transferred by tension on the metal at the die exit and partially by friction along the contact area between metal and mandrel. Therefore, an increase of this area of contact may permit the transfer of an increased portion of the force by friction; and this should correspondingly relieve the tension load which may cause the metal to break. Such relieving effect may be expected to increase with the increasing spacing S (see Fig. 17.11) between the two dies. The spacing is hereby defined as the axial distance between the contact area of the larger or first die at the exit and the contact area of the smaller or second die at the entrance.

Let A_c be the initial cross-sectional area of the tube, A_b the area after passing through the second die, A_a the final area. Then the various

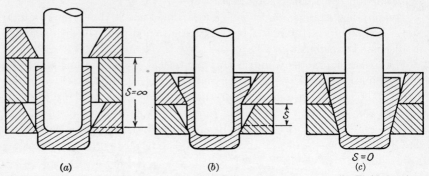

FIG. 17.11. Tandem die arrangement. (*a*) Infinite spacing, $S = \infty$. (*b*) Finite spacing, S. (*c*) Zero spacing, $S = 0$.

reductions in area performed in the drawing process can be defined as follows:

$$R_1 = 1 - \frac{A_b}{A_c} = \text{first reduction}$$

$$R_2 = 1 - \frac{A_a}{A_b} = \text{second reduction}$$

$$R = 1 - \frac{A_a}{A_c} = R_1 + (1 - R_1)R_2 = \text{total reduction}$$

In representing experimental results, it is convenient to select the first reduction R_1 and the spacing S as independent variables and to plot the values of the second reduction R_2 and of the total reduction R as their functions (see Figs. 17.12 and 17.13).

Maximum possible reduction values are selected from experimental data by the criterion that they would yield 50 per cent successful draws and 50 per cent breakage.

Consider first the limiting case of a very large spacing, $S \to \infty$; then, the second reduction $(R_2)_\infty$, performable in drawing through tandem dies, should be the same as that for a draw in a second operation subsequent to the first draw. Because of the strain-hardening of the metal, $(R_2)_\infty$ will depend slightly upon the first reduction, R_1.

Let R' be the maximum possible first reduction of the soft annealed metal, R'' the maximum possible reduction of the metal strain-hardened by being previously subjected to the reduction R'.

Then it can be stated that for a very large spacing S the second reduction $(R_2)_\infty$ and the total reduction $(R)_\infty$ vary between the following limits,

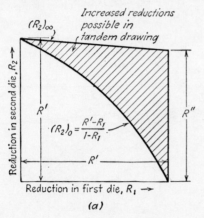

(a)

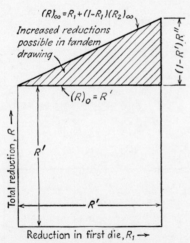

Fig. 17.12. (a) Diagrammatic representation of relation between reductions in partial draws of a tandem die arrangement. (b) Diagrammatic representation of relation between total reduction and first reduction in a two-die tandem arrangement.

depending upon the magnitude of the first reduction R_1:

$$R_1 = 0 \qquad (R_2)_\infty = R' \qquad (R)_\infty = R' \qquad (17.32)$$

and

$$R_1 = R' \qquad (R_2)_\infty = R'' \qquad (R)_\infty = R' + (1 - R')R'' \quad (17.33)$$

In the second limiting case of zero spacing, $S = 0$, the two dies actually act as a single die; hence, the maximum total reduction is that of the soft annealed metal:

$$(R)_0 = R' \quad \text{or} \quad R_1 + (1 - R_1)(R_2)_0 = R' \qquad (17.34)$$

from which

$$(R_2)_0 = \frac{R' - R_1}{1 - R_1} \qquad (17.35)$$

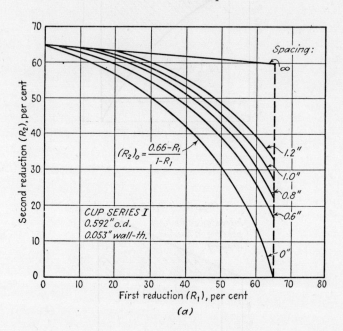

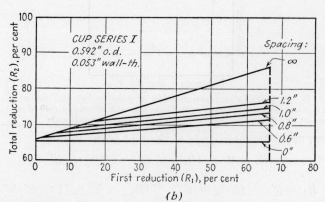

FIG. 17.13. (*a*) Possible maximum reductions in tandem die arrangement for various spacings. (*b*) Possible maximum total reduction in tandem die arrangement for various spacings.

In Fig. 17.12 limiting curves for the maximum possible second reductions R_2 and the total reductions R are plotted versus the first reduction R_1, according to Eqs. (17.32) through (17.35). Curves representing relationships for any finite spacing should fall into the shaded areas enclosed by the limiting curves.

Figures 17.13a and 17.13b show such relationships for tandem drawing of SAE 1030 steel tubes, determined experimentally by Sachs and Espey (1947). For a tube having a thin wall, the curves were found to approach the relationship for infinite spacing more rapidly than for a tube having a heavy wall.

REFERENCES

ESPEY, G., and G. SACHS, Experimentation on Tube Drawing with a Moving Mandrel, *J. Applied Mechanics*, Vol. 14, pp. 81–87, 1947.

SACHS, G., and G. ESPEY, Effect of Spacing between Dies in the Tandem Drawing of Tubular Parts, *Trans. ASME*, Vol. 69, pp. 139–143, 1947.

SACHS, G., J. D. LUBAHN, and D. P. TRACY, Drawing Thinwalled Tubing with a Moving Mandrel through a Single Stationary Die, *J. Applied Mechanics*, Vol. 11, pp. 199–210, 1944.

CHAPTER 18

DRAWING AND EXTRUDING THROUGH STATIONARY TOOLS OF CIRCULAR CONTOUR IN CONDITION OF PLANE STRAIN

18.1. Scope of Problem

In this chapter drawing and extruding of a metal strip between two stationary cylindrical tools will be analyzed, a problem which has a somewhat limited practical application in itself but which affords an introduction to Chap. 19 on strip rolling. It will be assumed that the two cylindrical tool surfaces have the same radius and that the pulling or pushing forces are applied to the metal strip so as to assure a condition of symmetry about the mid-plane of the strip. Furthermore, two-dimensional plastic deformation in planes parallel to the xy plane (see Fig. 18.1) will be assumed. In strip forming with cylindrical tools, this condition is assumed to be maintained by frictional forces of adequate magnitude acting in the z direction. The analysis will apply also to tube-forming processes with stationary tools of cylindrical contour in which the condition of plane strain is assured by the geometry of the process.

18.2. Differential Equation of the Problem

It is assumed that the same state of stress exists at all points of a transverse plane, the x, y, and z directions being the principal directions. The σ_y principal stress is assumed to be $-p$, for all points of the transverse plane, where p denotes the normal pressure on the die surface.

Consider the equilibrium of a volume element of unit width bounded by two transverse planes at distances x and $x + dx$ from the origin (see Figs. 18.1 and 18.2). The equation of equilibrium expresses that the sum of the x components of all forces acting on the element is zero, or

$$h \, d\sigma_x + \sigma_x \, dh + 2p \, dx(\tan \alpha + f) = 0 \qquad (18.1)$$

The distortion-energy condition of plasticity is expressed, in the case of plane strain, by the relationship

$$\sigma_{\mathrm{I}} - \sigma_{\mathrm{III}} = \frac{2}{\sqrt{3}} \sigma_0 = \sigma_0'$$

or in the present case, with $\sigma_{\mathrm{I}} = \sigma_x$ and $\sigma_{\mathrm{III}} = \sigma_y = -p$, by

$$\sigma_x + p = \sigma_0'$$

206

from which

$$\sigma_x = \sigma_0' - p \quad \text{and} \quad d\sigma_x = -dp \tag{18.2}$$

Substituting in Eq. (18.1), one has

$$-h\,dp + (\sigma_0' - p)\,dh + 2p\,dx\,(\tan\alpha + f) = 0 \tag{18.3}$$

or, by considering that

$$dx = \frac{dh}{2\tan\alpha} \tag{18.4}$$

one obtains

$$h\,dp - \left(\frac{pf}{\tan\alpha} + \sigma_0'\right)dh = 0 \tag{18.5}$$

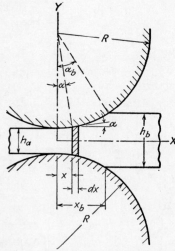

FIG. 18.1. Dimensions in strip forming with stationary tools of circular contour.

FIG. 18.2. Stresses on strip element.

To integrate this differential equation, the relationship between the thickness h and the angle α is to be introduced. In the following analysis the relationship valid for a circular contour

$$h = h_a + 2R(1 - \cos\alpha) \tag{18.6}$$

will be replaced, for sake of simpler computations, by

$$h = h_a + \frac{x^2}{R} \tag{18.7}$$

This is the equation of a parabola of second order which approximates the circle very closely, since it has the same tangent and the same curvature at the exit section ($x = 0$); actually it gives a tool contour slightly flatter than the circular.   The projected contact length between strip and tool is expressed by

$$x_b = \sqrt{(h_b - h_a)R - \left(\frac{h_b - h_a}{2}\right)^2} \qquad \text{for the circle} \qquad (18.8)$$

$$x_b = \sqrt{(h_b - h_a)R} \qquad\qquad\qquad \text{for the parabola}$$

In terms of the angle α and with reference to Eq. (18.4), Eq. (18.7) becomes

$$h = h_a + R \tan^2 \alpha \qquad (18.9)$$

and, introducing the new parameter w, defined by the equation

$$\tan w = \sqrt{\frac{R}{h_a}} \tan \alpha \qquad (18.10)$$

Eq. (18.9) becomes

$$h = h_a(1 + \tan^2 w) \qquad (18.11)$$

Its derivative with respect to the parameter w is

$$\frac{dh}{dw} = 2h_a \tan w(1 + \tan^2 w) \qquad (18.12)$$

Substituting the expressions from Eqs. (18.11) and (18.12) into Eq. (18.5) and introducing the constant

$$A = 2f \sqrt{\frac{R}{h_a}} \qquad (18.13)$$

one has the differential equation

$$dp - (pA + 2\sigma_0' \tan w)\, dw = 0 \qquad (18.14)$$

A differential equation equivalent to Eq. (18.3) was first given by von Kármán (1925) in connection with the problem of rolling.   Nádai (1939) developed further the theory of rolling and suggested the method of solution for Eq. (18.14) to be discussed in the next article.

18.3. General Solution of the Differential Equation

To apply the "integrating-factor" method to solving the differential equation (18.14), the equation is rearranged as follows:

$$dp - pA\, dw = 2\sigma_0' \tan w\, dw$$

Multiplying both sides by e^{-Aw} yields

$$e^{-Aw}\, dp - e^{-Aw}pA\, dw = e^{-Aw}2\sigma_0' \tan w\, dw$$

The left side of this equation is the differential of the product $(e^{-Aw}p)$; hence, the equation can be rewritten as follows:

$$d(e^{-Aw}p) = e^{-Aw}2\sigma_0' \tan w \, dw$$

Integrating both sides and solving for p, one has

$$p = e^{Aw}(2\sigma_0' \int e^{-Aw} \tan w \, dw + C_1) \qquad (18.15)$$

where C_1 is a constant of integration. According to Nádai, the integral appearing in this equation can be calculated with sufficient approximation by putting

$$\tan w \approx w \qquad (18.16)$$

to obtain

$$\int e^{-Aw} \tan w \, dw \approx \int e^{-Aw}w \, dw = - \frac{e^{-Aw}(1 + Aw)}{A^2}$$

Substituting in Eq. (18.15), dividing both sides by σ_0', and putting $C = C_1/\sigma_0'$, one obtains

$$\frac{p}{\sigma_0'} = Ce^{Aw} - \frac{2}{A^2}(1 + Aw) \qquad (18.17)$$

This general solution of the problem contains the constant C to be determined in the following articles separately for drawing and extruding.

Bland and Ford (1948) proposed a simplified version of Eq. (18.14), essentially by putting $\sigma_0' \approx p$ and thus obtaining the differential equation

$$dp - p(A + 2 \tan w) \, dw = 0 \qquad (18.18)$$

This can be integrated without resorting to the approximation involved in Eq. (18.16) and yields the general solution

$$\frac{p}{\sigma_0'} = C \frac{e^{Aw}}{\cos^2 w} \qquad (18.19)$$

It appears that the final accuracy of the solution is somewhat improved by this procedure.

18.4. Drawing with Stationary Dies

For zero or negligible backpull, the constant of integration is determined from the boundary condition at the entry section, $h = h_b$, where the longitudinal stress σ_{xb} vanishes. Dividing both sides of Eq. (18.2) by σ_0' and substituting p/σ_0' from Eq. (18.17), one has

$$\frac{\sigma_x}{\sigma_0'} = 1 - \frac{p}{\sigma_0'} = 1 - Ce^{Aw} + \frac{2}{A^2}(1 + Aw) \qquad (18.20)$$

The condition equation then becomes, with the notation

$$w_b = (w)_{h=h_b} = \tan^{-1} \sqrt{\frac{h_b}{h_a} - 1} \qquad (18.21)$$

$$\left(\frac{\sigma_x}{\sigma_0'}\right)_{w=w_b} = \frac{\sigma_{xb}}{\sigma_0'} = 1 - Ce^{-Aw_b} + \frac{2}{A^2}(1 + Aw_b) = 0$$

Solving for the constant C, one obtains

$$C = e^{-Aw_b}\left[1 + \frac{2}{A^2}(1 + Aw_b)\right]$$

and, substituting this expression in Eqs. (18.20) and (18.17), one has the following expressions for the stresses:

$$\frac{\sigma_x}{\sigma_0'} = 1 - e^{A(w-w_b)}\left[1 + \frac{2}{A^2}(1 + Aw_b)\right] + \frac{2}{A^2}(1 + Aw) \quad (18.22)$$

$$\frac{p}{\sigma_0'} = e^{A(w-w_b)}\left[1 + \frac{2}{A^2}(1 + Aw_b)\right] - \frac{2}{A^2}(1 + Aw) \quad (18.23)$$

An example of the distribution of stresses is represented in Fig. 18.3 for the values $f = 0.224$, $h_a/h_b = 0.7$, $R/h_a = 80$, $\sigma_{xb} = 0$.

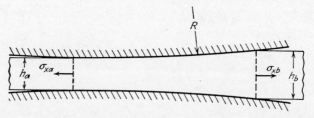

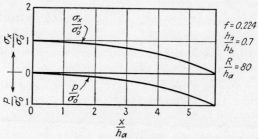

Fig. 18.3. Example of stress distribution for drawing through stationary dies of circular contour.

It should be noted that a limit is set for the drawing process here analyzed by the value of the maximum axial stress at the exit section, which cannot be greater than the yield stress in uniaxial tension σ_0.

From the definition of σ'_0 it follows that $(\sigma_x/\sigma'_0)_{x=0}$ cannot be greater than $\sqrt{3/2} = 0.866$ without producing tension failure of the strip in front of the die.

In the example used here as an illustration one obtains $\sigma_x/\sigma'_0 = 0.986$; since this value exceeds the limiting value of 0.866, the process illustrated in Fig. 18.3 should be considered as an academic example, and it does not represent a physically possible process.

18.5. Extruding with Stationary Dies

The problem of extruding a strip through stationary dies is particularly interesting because the solution has to satisfy the same boundary condition at the exit as that for the problem of rolling without frontpull, *i.e.*, the vanishing of the σ_x stress, or

$$\left(\frac{\sigma_x}{\sigma'_0}\right)_{x=0} = \left(\frac{\sigma_x}{\sigma'_0}\right)_{w=0} = \frac{\sigma_{xa}}{\sigma'_0} = 1 - C + \frac{2}{A^2} = 0$$

Solving for C, one obtains

$$C = 1 + \frac{2}{A^2}$$

and, substituting this expression in Eqs. (18.20) and (18.17), one has

$$\frac{\sigma_x}{\sigma'_0} = 1 - e^{Aw}\left(1 + \frac{2}{A^2}\right) + \frac{2}{A^2}(1 + Aw) \qquad (18.24)$$

$$\frac{p}{\sigma'_0} = e^{Aw}\left(1 + \frac{2}{A^2}\right) - \frac{2}{A^2}(1 + Aw) \qquad (18.25)$$

Figure 18.4 shows the stress distribution for the same values ($f = 0.224$, $h_a/h_b = 0.7$, $R/h_a = 0.80$) used in Fig. 18.3, except for $\sigma_{xa} = 0$.

A limiting condition exists for the extrusion process, similar to that previously discussed for drawing. The compressive stress applied to the metal at the entry section cannot exceed the yield stress in the uniaxial stress state σ_0 without causing the metal to upset and preventing it from entering the die. In the example chosen here one has $(\sigma_x/\sigma'_0)_{x=x_b} = 10.03$, and therefore it does not yield a physically possible solution unless special measures are taken to prevent the transverse expansion of the strip, *e.g.*, by enclosing it in a channel with plane parallel surfaces.

18.6. Effect of Elastic Flattening of Tools

The original radius R of the cylindrical tools undergoes an increase due to elastic deformation, so that, rigorously speaking, in Eqs. (18.6) through (18.13) the increased radius R' should be used. Hitchcock (1935) suggested making use of Hertz's theory of elastic compression of two cylindrical bodies with equal diameter, which furnishes the following expression for the change in curvature due to a contact pressure per unit width P:

$$\frac{1}{R} - \frac{1}{R'} = \frac{16(1 - \nu^2)P}{\pi E x_b^2} \tag{18.26}$$

where ν is Poisson's ratio, E Young's modulus for the tool material, and x_b the projected length of the arc of contact between the strip and the

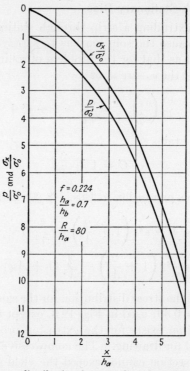

FIG. 18.4. Example of stress distribution for extruding through stationary dies of circular contour.

tools. Substituting $x_b = \sqrt{(h_b - h_a)R'}$ from the second equation (18.8) and solving for R', one has

$$R' = R\left[1 + \frac{16(1 - \nu^2)P}{\pi E(h_a - h_b)}\right] \tag{18.27}$$

To calculate R' from this equation, one must know the tool pressure per unit width P, which itself is a function of R' and which is furnished with sufficient approximation by the expression

$$P = R' \int_0^{\alpha_b} p\, d\alpha \tag{18.28}$$

where p should be taken from Eq. (18.23) or (18.25). The integration can be best performed numerically for given values of f, R, and h_a. R' is obtained from a trial-and-error procedure which can start with assuming a value of P, and calculating R' from Eq. (18.27). The assumed value of P should be checked then from Eq. (18.28), and, if necessary, the cycle should be repeated.

REFERENCES

BLAND, D. R., and H. FORD, The Calculation of Roll Force and Torque in Cold Strip Rolling with Tensions, *Inst. Mech. Engrs. (London), J. & Proc.*, Vol. 150, p. 144, 1948.

HITCHCOCK, J. H., "Roll Neck Bearings," Report of ASME Special Research Committee on Heavy-duty Anti-friction Bearings, 1935.

NÁDAI, A., The Forces Required for Rolling Steel Strip under Tension, *J. Applied Mechanics*, Vol. 6, pp. 54–62, 1939.

SACHS, G., and L. J. KLINGLER, The Flow of Metals through Tools of Circular Contour, *J. Applied Mechanics*, Vol. 14, pp. 88–98, 1947.

VON KÁRMÁN, T., Beitrag zur Theorie des Walzvorganges, *Z. angew. Math. Mechanik*, Vol. 5, pp. 139–142, 1925.

CHAPTER 19

ROLLING OF SHEET AND STRIP
IN CONDITION OF PLANE STRAIN

19.1. Scope of Problem

In this chapter the stresses developed in a metal sheet or strip during rolling will be investigated. It will be assumed that the metal sheet or strip is prevented from spreading in the direction perpendicular to the direction of rolling, so that plastic flow takes place in the condition of "plane strain." The frictional forces have an important part in the rolling process; in the following analysis the coefficient of friction will be considered as independent of both pressure and relative speed between metal and tool surfaces, *i.e.*, the validity of Coulomb's law (see Art. 16.2) will be assumed. The relative motion of metal with respect to the rolls is directed from a point of relative rest, the so-called "no-slip point," toward the entry and exit sections. The two distinct solutions of the differential equation of the problem, obtained for the two regions, are predicated upon the two directions which the frictional forces can assume. Back and front tension forces are included in the solution without any additional analytical difficulty. In addition to the forming process with driven rolls, the problem of drawing through idle rolls, or rolling with a mill driven by tension on the delivered strip only, will be discussed in this chapter.

19.2. Rolling without Tensions

The differential equation derived in Art. 18.2, Eq. (18.5),

$$h \, dp - \left(\frac{pf}{\tan \alpha} + \sigma'_0 \right) dh = 0 \tag{19.1}$$

applies to the present case with the proper consideration of the direction of the frictional forces pf. As the thickness of the metal changes from h_b at $x = x_b$ to h_a at $x = 0$, its speed varies from its smallest value at the entry section to its largest value at the exit section. The rolls have an intermediate velocity; at an intermediate point, the so-called no-slip point, the metal moves with the same velocity as the roll perimeter. Between the no-slip point and the exit section the metal moves faster than the rolls, and the frictional forces, opposing the relative motion,

214

are directed against the direction of rolling. In this region, Eq. (19.1) applies without modification, and the boundary condition to be satisfied is that of zero longitudinal stress at the exit section, the same as for extruding with stationary circular tools, discussed in Art. 18.5. The roll pressure distribution is given by Eq. (18.25) as

$$\frac{p}{\sigma_0'} = e^{Aw}\left(1 + \frac{2}{A^2}\right) - \frac{2}{A^2}(1 + Aw) \tag{19.2}$$

Between the no-slip point and the entry section the metal moves more slowly than the rolls and is acted upon by frictional forces directed toward the exit which build up the longitudinal compression force needed for equilibrium. The differential equation for this region is obtained from Eq. (19.1) by changing the sign of the frictional forces pf to obtain

$$h\,dp - \left(\sigma_0' - \frac{pf}{\tan \alpha}\right)dh = 0 \tag{19.3}$$

The general solution of this equation is

$$\frac{p}{\sigma_0'} = Ce^{-Aw} - \frac{2}{A^2}(1 - Aw) \tag{19.4}$$

The constant of integration C is determined from the condition of zero longitudinal stress at the entry section

$$(\sigma_x)_{x=b} = 0$$

From $\sigma_x = \sigma_0' - p$ one has

$$\frac{\sigma_x}{\sigma_0'} = 1 - \frac{p}{\sigma_0'} = 1 - Ce^{-Aw} + \frac{2}{A^2}(1 - Aw) \tag{19.5}$$

and the boundary condition is expressed as follows:

$$\left(\frac{\sigma_x}{\sigma_0'}\right)_{w=w_b} = 1 - Ce^{-Aw_b} + \frac{2}{A^2}(1 - Aw_b) = 0$$

and furnishes the expression for the constant of integration

$$C = e^{Aw_b}\left[1 + \frac{2}{A^2}(1 - Aw_b)\right]$$

Substituting in Eqs. (19.4) and (19.5), one has the expressions

$$\frac{\sigma_x}{\sigma_0'} = 1 - e^{A(w_b-w)}\left[1 + \frac{2}{A^2}(1 - Aw_b)\right] + \frac{2}{A^2}(1 - Aw) \tag{19.6}$$

$$\frac{p}{\sigma_0'} = e^{A(w_b-w)}\left[1 + \frac{2}{A^2}(1 - Aw_b)\right] - \frac{2}{A^2}(1 - Aw) \tag{19.7}$$

The roll pressure diagram (called also the "pressure hill" or the "friction hill") is made up of two curvilinear portions, intersecting at the no-slip point. Equation (18.25) furnishes the pressure values in the so-called "extrusion region," between the no-slip point and the exit section; and Eq. (19.7) furnishes the pressure values in the "compression region," between the entry section and the no-slip point. The position of the latter is defined by the value w_0 of the parameter w for which Eqs. (18.25) and (19.7) furnish the same roll pressure, or

$$1 - e^{Aw_0}\left(1 + \frac{2}{A^2}\right) + \frac{2}{A^2}\left(1 + Aw_0\right)$$
$$= 1 - e^{A(w_b - w_0)}\left[1 + \frac{2}{A^2}\left(1 - Aw_0\right)\right] + \frac{2}{A^2}\left(1 - Aw_0\right)$$

This equation can be simplified to obtain

$$e^{A(w_b - w_0)}\left(\frac{2w_0}{A} - \frac{2}{A^2} - 1\right) - \left(1 + \frac{2}{A^2}\right)e^{Aw_0} - \frac{4w_0}{A} = 0 \qquad (19.8)$$

a transcendental equation in the unknown w_0, to be solved for a given A and w_b by trial-and-error procedure.

The effects of the elastic flattening of the rolls require a treatment analogous to that indicated in Art. 18.6. In calculating the parameters w and A, the modified radius R' determined from Eq. (18.27) is to be used. The value of the roll force P is to be evaluated from Eq. (18.28) by numerical integration. Inasmuch as P itself is a function of R', a trial-and-error procedure must be followed, based on solving alternately Eqs. (18.27) and (18.28).

Hill (1950) gave the following empirical formula for the roll force per unit width which fits very closely the values calculated from Bland and Ford's theory (1948):

$$P = \sigma_0'\sqrt{R'(h_b - h_a)}\left[1.08 + 1.79\left(1 - \frac{h_a}{h_b}\right)f\sqrt{\frac{R'}{h_b}} - 1.02\left(1 - \frac{h_a}{h_b}\right)\right]$$
$$(19.9)$$

19.3. Limit of Rolling without Tensions

When the no-slip point is at the exit section, the "extrusion region" vanishes; on the other hand, a "compression region" cannot exist without an "extrusion region," as it can be seen from Eq. (19.6) which furnishes the value of the longitudinal stress that must exist in the sheet in order to have equilibrium. Hence, the limit of rolling is reached when w_0, the parameter value which defines the location of the no-slip point, vanishes or

$$1 - e^{Aw_b} \left(1 + 2 \frac{1 - Aw_b}{A^2} \right) + \frac{2}{A^2} = 0 \qquad (19.10)$$

This is a transcendental equation in w_b, an approximate solution of which is

$$w_b \approx A \qquad (19.11)$$

from which one finds

$$\alpha_b \approx \frac{2f}{A} w_b \approx 2f \qquad (19.12)$$

the well-known condition for the rolling limit, at which the rolls slip over the entire surface of contact with the metal sheet.

19.4. Rolling with Front and Back Tensions

The effects of front and back tensions are determined from the previously obtained solutions of the differential equations (18.5) and (19.1) by modifying adequately the boundary conditions.

A front tension σ_{xa} acting on the exit section modifies the roll pressures in the "extrusion region." The integration constant C in Eq. (18.17), which is the solution of Eq. (18.5), is determined from the condition [see Eq. (18.20)]

$$\left(\frac{\sigma_x}{\sigma_0'} \right)_{x=0} = \left(\frac{\sigma_x}{\sigma_0'} \right)_{w=0} = 1 - C + \frac{2}{A^2} = \frac{\sigma_{xa}}{\sigma_0'}$$

from which

$$C = 1 + \frac{2}{A^2} - \frac{\sigma_{xa}}{\sigma_0'}$$

Substituting this value into Eq. (18.17), one obtains the pressure distribution between the no-slip point and the exit section:

$$\frac{p}{\sigma_0'} = e^{Aw} \left(1 + \frac{2}{A^2} - \frac{\sigma_{xa}}{\sigma_0'} \right) - \frac{2}{A^2} (1 + Aw) \qquad (19.13)$$

By a similar procedure the integration constant in Eq. (19.5) is determined from the condition

$$\left(\frac{\sigma_x}{\sigma_0'} \right)_{w=w_b} = 1 - Ce^{-Aw_b} + \frac{2}{A^2} (1 - Aw_b) = \frac{\sigma_{xb}}{\sigma_0'}$$

from which one obtains

$$C = e^{Aw_b} \left[1 + \frac{2}{A^2} (1 - Aw_b) - \frac{\sigma_{xb}}{\sigma_0'} \right]$$

Substitution of this expression into Eq. (19.4) furnishes the following expression for the pressure distribution in the compression region between the entry section and the no-slip point:

$$\frac{p}{\sigma_0'} = e^{A(w_b - w)} \left[1 + \frac{2}{A^2} (1 - A w_b) - \frac{\sigma_{xb}}{\sigma_0'} \right] - \frac{2}{A^2} (1 - A w) \quad (19.14)$$

Figure 19.1 illustrates the pressure distributions obtained by assuming various combinations of front and back tensions, taken from examples

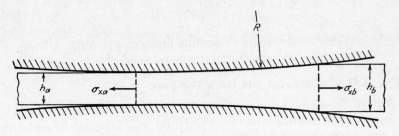

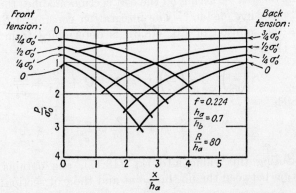

Fig. 19.1. Examples of stress distribution for rolling with front and/or back tensions of 0, $\frac{1}{4}\sigma_0'$, $\frac{1}{2}\sigma_0'$, and $\frac{3}{4}\sigma_0'$.

calculated by Nádai (1939). It can be seen that a given value of back tension has a much greater effect in reducing the roll pressure than a front tension of the same value. The limit of rolling is of course modified by the presence of front and back tensions, although it is determined by the same criterion as for rolling without tensions.

19.5. Drawing through Idle Rolls

The process of rolling a strip in a mill driven solely by tension on the delivered strip is closely related to the rolling of a strip with front tension. Between the entry section and the no-slip point the same equation (19.7)

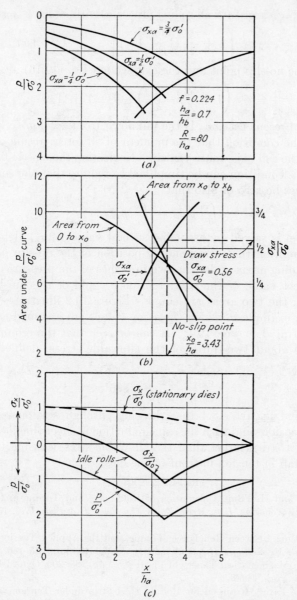

FIG. 19.2. (a) Examples of stress distributions for rolling with various values of draw stress. (b) Graphical determination of no-slip point and draw stress for drawing through idle rolls. (c) Comparison of stress distributions for drawing through stationary dies and through idle rolls or roller dies.

furnishes roll pressure as for all rolling processes without back tension, *i.e.*,

$$\frac{p}{\sigma_0'} = e^{A(w_b - w)} \left[1 + \frac{2}{A^2} (1 - Aw_b) \right] - \frac{2}{A^2} (1 - Aw)$$

Between the no-slip point and the exit section Eq. (19.13) applies

$$\frac{p}{\sigma_0'} = e^{Aw} \left(1 + \frac{2}{A^2} - \frac{\sigma_{xa}}{\sigma_0'} \right) - \frac{2}{A^2} (1 + Aw)$$

where, in the present case, σ_{xa} is the unknown front tension to be determined from the condition that the moment of all forces acting on a roll, taken about the roll axis, must vanish. Neglecting the elastic flattening of the roll, this condition can be simplified to require that the sum of the frictional forces be zero or also that

$$\int_0^{x_0} p \, dx = \int_{x_0}^{x_b} p \, dx \tag{19.15}$$

The problem is solved by assuming several values of σ_{xa}, determining for each assumption the corresponding position of the no-slip point and the corresponding areas under the two branches of the pressure diagram. For the correct value of the front tension σ_{xa} and of the no-slip point coordinate x_0, the two areas are equal. Figure 19.2 illustrates the procedure for an example in which the same values are assumed as for the example illustrated in Fig. 19.1. It can be seen that the required draw stress is only about two-thirds of the allowable stress, defined by the relationship

$$\frac{\sigma_x}{\sigma_0'} = \frac{\sqrt{3}}{2} = 0.866$$

It was found in Art. 18.4 that drawing through stationary dies of identical dimensions and with the same reduction in sheet thickness would require a draw stress larger than the allowable stress causing the sheet (or strip) to fail in tension in front of the dies.

REFERENCES

BLAND, D. R., and H. FORD, Calculation of Roll Force and Torque in Cold Strip Rolling with Tensions, *Inst. Mech. Engrs. (London), J. & Proc.*, Vol. 150, p. 144, 1948.

HILL, R., Relations between Roll Force, Torque, and the Applied Tension in Strip-rolling, *Inst. Mech. Engrs. (London), J. & Proc.*, Vol. 163, pp. 135–140, 1950.

HILL, R., "The Mathematical Theory of Plasticity," pp. 188–206, Oxford University Press, New York, 1950.

NÁDAI, A., The Forces Required for Rolling Steel Strip under Tension, *J. Applied Mechanics*, Vol. 6, pp. 54–62, 1939.

OROWAN, E., The Calculation of Roll Pressure in Hot and Cold Flat Rolling, *Inst. Mech. Engrs. (London), J. & Proc.*, Vol. 150, pp. 140–167, 1942.

SACHS, G., and L. J. KLINGLER, The Flow of Metals through Tools of Circular Contour, *J. Applied Mechanics*, Vol. 14, pp. 88–98, 1947.

SIEBEL, E., Kraefte und Materialfluss bei der bildsamen Formgebung, *Stahl. u. Eisen*, Vol. 45, pp. 1563–1566, 1925.

CHAPTER 20

NONSYMMETRIC PLASTIC FLOW
THROUGH CIRCULAR-CONTOUR TOOLS IN PLANE STRAIN

20.1. Scope of Problem

Figure 20.1 shows diagrams of various forming processes in which tools of circular contour are used. Several of these processes are symmetrical and were covered in Chap. 18 and 19. Several others are nonsymmetrical, and this lack of symmetry may be in three different respects. First, the direction of the frictional forces may be different at the two opposite tool surfaces, as occurs over a certain length of the surface of contact in processes of forming with differently restrained tools. Second, the tools may have different radii of curvature, a condition which is encountered particularly in tube drawing, where the gap through which the metal flows may be bounded by a roll on the outside and by a plane or slightly curved tool surface on the inside. Third, the friction coefficients on the two surfaces may be different.

The treatment of these problems requires slight modifications to the analysis of symmetrical problems presented in the preceding chapters.

20.2. Flow of Metal through a Gap Bordered by Differently Restrained Tools

When the two tools have different perimetral speeds and hence different relative speeds with respect to the metal sheet, the direction of frictional forces will not be everywhere necessarily the same at opposite points of the tool metal interfaces. Consequently, in these cases two distinct conditions will develop. There will be regions where the frictional forces at the two opposite points of the tool surfaces have the same direction, because both tools are slower or both tools are faster than the metal. Then, there will be a region where the frictional forces have opposite directions at the two faces, because one of the tools is faster and the other one is slower than the metal. The equilibrium equation for this latter type of condition becomes particularly simple; indeed, under the same assumptions as those used in deriving the basic differential equation, Eq. (18.1), one has now

$$h \, d\sigma_x + \sigma_x \, dh + p \, dx \, (2 \tan \alpha + f - f) = 0$$

or

$$h \, d\sigma_x + \sigma_x \, dh + 2p \tan \alpha \, dx = 0 \qquad (20.1)$$

221

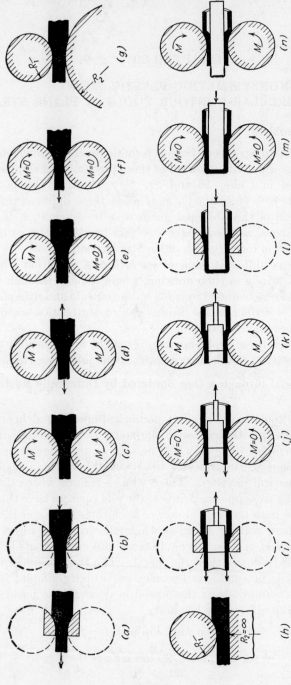

Fig. 20.1. Diagrammatic representation of a number of forming processes with tools of circular contour. (a) Drawing strip through stationary dies. (b) Extruding strip through stationary dies. (c) Ordinary rolling. (d) Rolling with front and back tension. (e) Rolling with one driven and one idle roll. (f) Drawing through stationary dies. (g) Forming processes with rolls of different diameters. (h) Forming processes with one roll and a plate. (i) Tube drawing through stationary dies with a stationary mandrel (plug). (j) Tube drawing through roller dies with a stationary mandrel (plug). (k) Tube rolling with a stationary mandrel (plug). (l) Tube drawing through stationary dies with a moving mandrel (rod). (m) Tube drawing through roller dies with a moving mandrel (rod). (n) Tube reducing (with driven rolls) with a moving mandrel (rod).

Introducing the plasticity condition [Eq. (18.2)]

$$\sigma_x = \sigma_0' - p$$

and the geometrical relationship [Eq. (18.4)]

$$dx = \frac{dh}{2 \tan \alpha}$$

one obtains

$$h\, dp - \sigma_0'\, dh = 0 \qquad (20.2)$$

By separating the variables, one has

$$\frac{dp}{\sigma_0'} = \frac{dh}{h} \qquad (20.3)$$

and, integrating both sides,

$$\frac{p}{\sigma_0'} = \ln h + C \qquad (20.4)$$

where the integration constant C is to be determined from the boundary conditions of the problem. Equations (20.3) and (20.4) do not contain the angle α, which depends on the tool radius; hence, they apply generally to all forming processes in condition of plane strain, regardless of the tool contours; and, indeed, they are consistent with the results obtained in Art. 15.8 for drawing and extruding of strips through smooth tapered dies. It can be concluded that in a region where the frictional forces on opposite faces have opposite directions their effects cancel and that the forming process is governed by the same relation [Eq. (20.4)] which is valid when the coefficient of friction f vanishes.

20.3. Rolling with One Driven and One Idle Roll

The most common condition in which the two tools forming the gap through which the metal flows are restrained differently is rolling of strip with one driven and one idle roll. To conform to the different equilibrium conditions for the two rolls, they must have different speeds. Consequently, there will be an intermediate region, extending from x_c to x_d, in which the pressure distribution is governed by Eq. (20.4). In the two outer regions, between the exit, $x = 0$, and x_c and between x_d and the entrance, $x = x_b$, the pressure distributions are the same as those for the two branches of the pressure diagram for the rolling process with two driven rolls.

The extension of the intermediate region and the corresponding pressures are obtained by the following procedure (see Fig. 20.2). Various p/σ_0' curves are drawn from Eq. (20.4) by assuming arbitrary values at

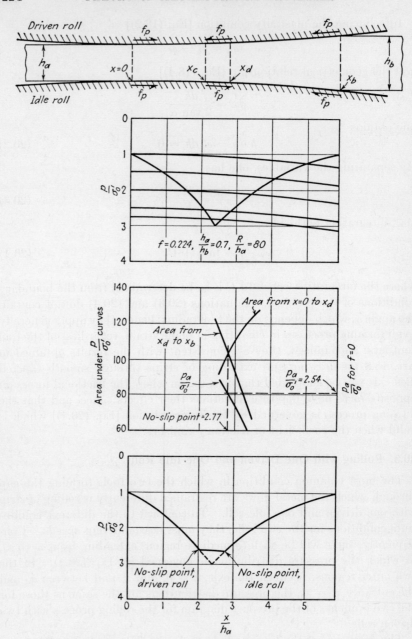

FIG. 20.2. Graphical solution for rolling with one driven and one idle roll.

the exit p_a/σ'_0, for example, from 1.0 to 2.75. For a given p_a/σ'_0, the integration constant C is determined from the condition

$$\frac{p_a}{\sigma'_0} = \ln h_a + C$$

from which

$$C = \frac{p_a}{\sigma'_0} - \ln h_a \quad \text{and} \quad \frac{p}{\sigma'_0} - \frac{p_a}{\sigma'_0} = \ln \frac{h}{h_a} \quad (20.5)$$

The curves representing this equation cut off the pressure peak formed by the other two branches, by varying amounts. The actual pressure distribution must then satisfy the condition developed for drawing through idle rolls (Art. 19.5); *i.e.*, the sum of the frictional forces along the perimeter of the idle roll must be zero, or, as expressed by Eq. (19.15), the total pressure, between the metal and the idle roll, over the contact area in which the frictional forces are directed forward is equal to that in the contact area in which the frictional forces are directed backward. This condition can be fulfilled if the region of backward friction on the idle roll extends from $x = 0$ to x_d, where the idle roll moves more slowly than the metal, and if the region of forward friction on the idle roll extends from x_d to x_b, where the idle roll moves faster than the metal. It can be seen that the perimetral speed of the idle roll is lower than that of the driven roll. The position x_d of the no-slip point on the idle roll and the particular value of p_a/σ'_0, which satisfies the equilibrium condition for the idle roll, are then obtained by the trial-and-error method discussed previously in Art. 19.5 and illustrated in Fig. 20.2.

It can be concluded that replacing two driven rolls by one driven and one idle roll modifies the pressure diagram by cutting off its peak and introducing two breaks. The break closer to the entry section is the no-slip point of the idle roll; the break closer to the exit is the no-slip point of the driven roll. The reduction in peak pressure and the displacements of the no-slip points become larger as the reduction nears the maximum reduction point. The limiting condition, *i.e.*, the no-slip point of the driven roll being at the exit, is reached considerably earlier, probably at a roll angle of three-quarters or an estimated reduction of less than one-half of that for both rolls driven. This is illustrated in Fig. 20.3, which compares pressure distributions for various friction coefficients ($f = 0.224, 0.112$,

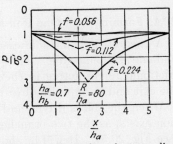

Fig. 20.3. Examples of stress distribution for rolling with one driven and one idle roll for various values of friction coefficient f.

0.056), roll diameter and per cent reduction remaining constant $(h_a/h_b = 0.7, R/h_a = 80)$. According to Fig. 20.4, derived from Fig. 20.3, at an estimated value of $f = 0.06$ the no-slip point for one roll driven reaches the exit, whereas this limit for both rolls driven occurs at $f = 0.0375$. It can be concluded that for a friction coefficient intermediate to these two limits, $0.037 < f < 0.060$, rolling with one driven and one idle roll is possible only if a front tension is added. For $f = 0.056$, a front tension of approximately $\sigma_{xa} = 0.1\sigma_0'$ is required.

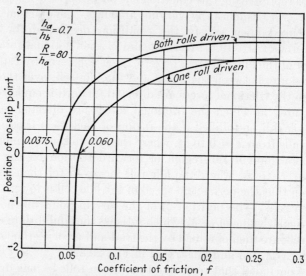

Fig. 20.4. Position of no-slip point, x_c/h_a, versus coefficient of friction for driven rolls and for one driven and one idle roll.

20.4. Forming with One Roll and One Stationary Die

A theoretically possible case is that of forming a strip with one roll and one stationary die. The solution again consists of two branches, the frictional forces acting in the same direction in the region adjacent to the exit and in opposite directions in the region near the entrance.

When the roll is driven and no tensions are applied, no possible solution exists, as the two branches of the pressure diagram do not intersect (see Fig. 20.5). It will be shown later in Art. 20.14 that such a process becomes a possibility if the friction coefficients between the metal and the two tools are different.

To obtain another possible solution, a front tension must be applied; the minimum tension is that which moves the no-slip point on the driven roll to the exit (see Fig. 20.5).

When the roll is idle, the front tension is obtained from the condition that Eq. (19.15) be satisfied. This draw stress is only slightly less than that required for drawing through stationary dies, while it is considerably higher than that for two idle rolls (see Figs. 19.2 and 20.5).

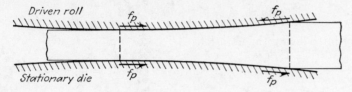

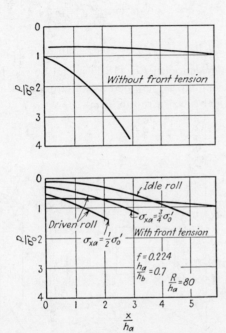

Fig. 20.5. Examples of stress distribution for forming with one roll and one stationary die.

The draw stress required for forming with one idle roll, under the conditions selected in the example shown in Fig. 20.5, still exceeds the limiting value, $\sigma_{xa}/\sigma_0' = 0.866$. Therefore, it is impossible to reduce a strip as much as 30 per cent in thickness by this process if $f = 0.224$ and $R/h_a = 80$.

20.5. Basic Equations for Tools Having Different Contour Radii

If the two surfaces between which the metal is formed have the different contour radii R_1 and R_2 (see Fig. 20.6), the basic differential equation,

Eq. (18.1), becomes

$$h \, d\sigma_x + \sigma_x \, dh + p \, dx \, (\tan \alpha_1 + \tan \alpha_2 + 2f) = 0 \qquad (20.6)$$

For small values of α_1 and α_2 one can write the approximate relations

$$\tan \alpha_1 \approx \frac{x}{R_1} \qquad \text{and} \qquad \tan \alpha_2 \approx \frac{x}{R_2}$$

and by introducing the notations

$$\tan \alpha' = \frac{1}{2} \, (\tan \alpha_1 - \tan \alpha_2) = \frac{x}{R'} \qquad (20.7)$$

and

$$R' = \frac{2R_1R_2}{R_1 + R_2} \qquad (20.8)$$

one finds

$$h \, d\sigma_x + \sigma_x \, dh + 2p \, dx \, (\tan \alpha' + f) = 0 \qquad (20.9)$$

From a comparison with Eq. (18.1) it can be concluded that this type of forming process can be handled as an equivalent symmetrical process with two identical tools of radius R'.

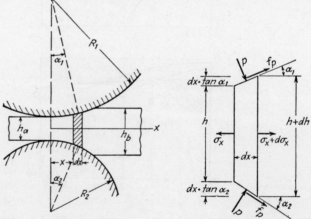

Fig. 20.6. Flow of metal through gap formed by tools of circular contour of different radii R_1 and R_2.

20.6. Processes Using Tools with Different Contour Radii

Figure 20.7 includes several practically significant examples of forming processes with tools having different contour radii. Rolling is performed frequently with rolls of different diameter, the three-high mill being an example.

Figure 20.7a shows a symmetrical process with the ratio $R/h_a = 80$; the results for this example, discussed in the preceding chapters, may be applied, other conditions being equal, to describe processes of the type shown in Fig. 20.7b where $R_1/h_a = 60$ and $R_2/h_a = 120$. The same would apply to any process other than rolling.

If one of the two radii is very small, for example, $R_1/h_a = 30$, Eq. (20.8) may require a negative R_2 value, in this example $R_2/h_b = -120$. This condition would occur in the hypothetical case of rolling of a tubular section by means of a roll on the inside and a large-diameter rotating ring on the outside (see Fig. 20.7c). So far, this type of forming apparently has not yet found an application.

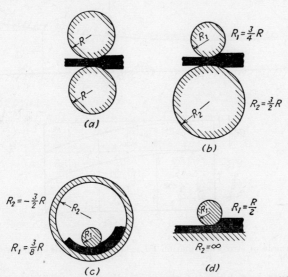

FIG. 20.7. Examples of flow of metal through gap formed by tools of different contour radii with identical $R' = 2R_1R_2/(R_1 + R_2)$ values.

If one of the radii is very large (infinite), a group of processes result which are represented by a variety of forming operations performed on tubes and tubular parts. In such processes, the tube is formed with an external tool, which frequently has a circular contour, while its inside is supported by a cylindrical or almost cylindrical (tapered) mandrel. If the wall thickness of the tube is small in relation to its diameter, it can be assumed that the condition of plane strain applies. The metal then flows through a gap bounded by a small-radius contour and an almost straight contour (see Fig. 20.7d). Many of the previously discussed boundary conditions actually occur in various tube-drawing processes. The previous example with $R'/h_a = 80$ can be used here with $R_1/h_a = 40$ and $R_2/h_a = \infty$. Various processes of this type are analyzed in the following articles, both for stationary and for moving straight tools.

20.7. Tube Drawing with Stationary Dies and a Stationary Mandrel

The condition where both tools are stationary, the one possessing circular and the other straight contour, is represented by tube drawing with a stationary mandrel. The solutions for this process are identical with those for drawing a strip through dies of circular contour, the contour radii of which are twice that of the die in tube drawing (Fig. 20.8).

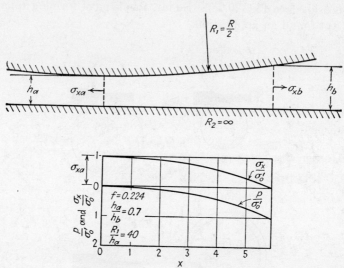

Fig. 20.8. Example of stress distribution for tube drawing with stationary dies and stationary mandrel.

This process is subject to the same limiting condition as drawing a strip through stationary dies, namely, that the draw stress σ_x/σ_0' cannot exceed a value of 0.866. For the example chosen, Fig. 20.8, the required stress is larger than this limit; therefore, a tube cannot be reduced with a stationary mandrel as much as 30 per cent in wall thickness for the conditions $R_1/h_a = 40$ and $f = 0.224$.

20.8. Tube Drawing with Roller Dies and a Stationary Mandrel

The condition where one tool is an idle roll of circular contour and the other is a stationary tool of straight contour is represented by tube drawing with a stationary mandrel through roller dies. The solutions for this process are identical with those for drawing strip through one idle roll and a stationary die, both having circular contours, with contour radii twice that of the roller dies in tube drawing (Fig. 20.9).

This process is subject to the same limitation as any other drawing process. For the example given, Fig. 20.9, the draw stress σ_{xa}/σ_0' required exceeds the limiting value 0.866; therefore, a tube wall thickness cannot be reduced as much as 30 per cent for the conditions $f = 0.224$ and $R_1/h_a = 40$. From Figs. 20.8 and 20.9 it can be concluded that replacing a stationary die by a roller die, in tube drawing with a stationary mandrel, changes the stress distributions, reduces the draw stress, and increases

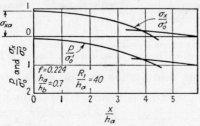

Fig. 20.9. Example of stress distribution for tube drawing with roller dies and stationary mandrel.

the possible reduction only slightly. Similar effects were discussed previously for the change from two stationary dies to one idle roll and one stationary die (Fig. 20.5).

20.9. Tube Rolling with a Stationary Mandrel

The condition where one tool is a driven roll of circular contour and the other is a stationary tool of straight contour is represented by tube

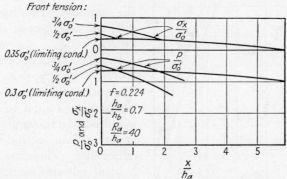

Fig. 20.10. Examples of stress distribution for tube rolling with stationary mandrel.

rolling with a stationary mandrel and driven rolls. The solutions for this process are identical with those for forming strip with one driven roll and one stationary die, the contour radii of which are twice that of the driven rolls in tube rolling.

As with a driven roll and a stationary die, if no front tension is applied, there is no solution. There are two methods by which this process can be made possible: (*a*) the addition of sufficient front tension to shift the no-slip point back into the deforming area (Fig. 20.10); and (*b*) the use of rough rolls in connection with a smooth mandrel, resulting in higher friction between the metal and the roll than between the metal and the mandrel, as discussed later.

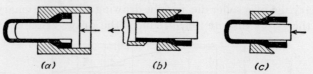

(a)   **(b)**   **(c)**

Fig. 20.11. Tube-forming processes with stationary dies and driven mandrel: (*a*) Hooker process; (*b*) tube drawing; (*c*) ironing (deep drawing) a tubular part.

20.10. Tube Drawing with Stationary Dies and a Moving Mandrel

Of the various tube-forming processes where the inner tool or mandrel is moving, the most common is drawing through stationary dies of circular contour. This process is similar to the previously discussed rolling of tube with a stationary mandrel where the rolls are the driven tool. To make the tube-drawing process definite, another condition must be added, namely, the position of the no-slip point on the mandrel. Two fundamentally different processes of this type are known.

In the Hooker process (Fig. 20.11*a*) a tubular part is extruded. The speed of the metal at the entry is, therefore, equal to that of the mandrel. In this process the metal at all points moves faster than either tool. Therefore, the process is identical with extruding a strip through stationary dies, the contour radii of which are twice that of the dies used in the Hooker process (see Fig. 20.12).

On the other hand, in tube drawing with a moving mandrel (Fig. 20.11*b*) or in ironing a tubular part with an inserted punch (Fig. 20.11*c*), the metal at the exit is usually forced to assume the same speed as the mandrel. These two processes

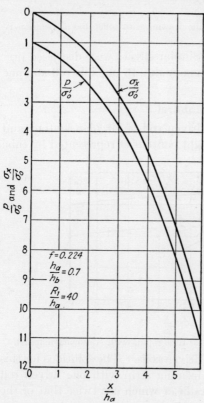

Fig. 20.12. Example of stress distribution for tube drawing by Hooker process with stationary dies and driven mandrel.

(Figure 20.12 labels:) $\frac{p}{\sigma_0'}$ $\frac{\sigma_x}{\sigma_0'}$ $f = 0.224$ $\frac{h_a}{h_b} = 0.7$ $\frac{R_1}{h_a} = 40$ vertical axis p and $\frac{\sigma_x}{\sigma_0'}$ horizontal axis $\frac{x}{h_a}$

are identical as far as the metal stresses are concerned. They differ, however, in that in tube drawing the mandrel is usually pulled in front of the tools, while in ironing the punch is pushed against the closed front end of the tubular part.

In tube drawing (and ironing) the frictional forces on the two tool surfaces act in opposite directions. Therefore, if the friction coefficients are identical at both metal surfaces, the solution is that for frictionless drawing, as discussed previously [see Eq. (20.4)] and shown in Fig. 20.13.

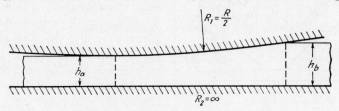

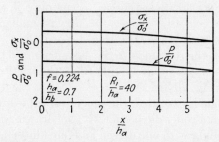

Fig. 20.13. Example of stress distribution for tube drawing and ironing with stationary dies and driven mandrel.

The limiting condition for this process is the same as for frictionless drawing of a strip through stationary dies. It is given again by the general limit for drawing processes, namely,

$$\frac{\sigma_{xa}}{\sigma_0'} = \frac{\sigma_0}{\sigma_0'} = 0.866$$

The longitudinal stress is, according to Eq. (20.4), independent of geometry and the friction coefficient; the forming limit is therefore

$$\ln \frac{h_a}{h_b} = -0.866 \qquad \frac{h_a}{h_b} = 0.425$$

or 57.5 per cent reduction in wall thickness.

20.11. Tube Drawing with Roller Dies and a Moving Mandrel

Another condition of drawing where the inner tool is moving is represented by tube drawing with a driven mandrel through roller dies. This process is identical with rolling a strip with one driven and one idle roll, the contour radii of which are twice that of the roller die for tube drawing.

Reductions within certain limits may therefore be performed in exactly the same manner as in rolling with one driven and one idle roll (Fig. 20.14). No front tension or draw stress acts on the metal, and the man-

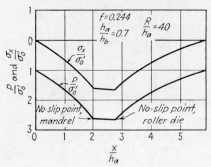

drel need contact the metal only under the roller die. The metal runs faster than the mandrel at the exit. Consequently, a tubular part would develop a cavity between the punch nose and the bottom of the part. The development of such cavities has actually been observed in drawing high-explosive shell bottles through roller dies. These equilibrium conditions, however, occur only if the roll angle at the entry is smaller than approximately 2.5 times the friction angle. In the case of rolling strip with one driven and one idle roll, the roll angle at the entrance must be less than one-half of this value, or approximately 1.25 times the friction angle, as discussed previously (see Fig. 20.3).

Fig. 20.14. Example of stress distribution for tube drawing with roller dies and driven mandrel.

If this roll angle is exceeded, the process of tube drawing with a moving mandrel through a roller die becomes a true drawing process. As already discussed for rolling with one driven and one idle roll, the application of a certain front tension will cause the no-slip point to move to the exit. In tube drawing with a stationary die, this particular value of front tension is automatically obtained because the speed of the mandrel and that of the metal leaving the die are kept the same (Fig. 20.13).

20.12. Tube Rolling with a Moving Idle Mandrel

Another condition of forming where the inner tool is moving is represented by the tube-reducing process in which a tube is rolled with the inner tool being a moving mandrel. This process is also identical with rolling a strip with one driven and one idle roll, the contour radii of which are twice that of the roll used in tube rolling (Fig. 20.15). The process is subject to the same limitations as tube drawing with roller dies and a moving mandrel.

Comparing Fig. 20.14 with Fig. 20.15, it can be seen that the no-slip point of the mandrel is closer to the entry in Fig. 20.15 than in Fig. 20.14. Consequently, the metal will run farther ahead of the mandrel when a moving mandrel is used with driven rolls than when a driven mandrel is used with an idle roll.

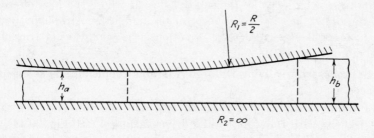

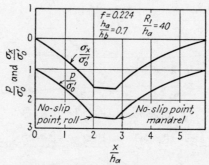

FIG. 20.15. Example of stress distribution for rolling tubing with moving mandrel.

20.13. Basic Relations for Forming with Different Friction Coefficients at the Two Contact Surfaces

For all processes previously discussed it was assumed that the coefficient of friction between the metal and the one tool was equal to that between the metal and the other tool. If it is assumed that the two friction coefficients f_1 and f_2 are different, the previously discussed processes can be again analyzed, introducing the notations

$$f' = \frac{f_1 + f_2}{2} \tag{20.10}$$

and

$$f'' = \frac{f_1 - f_2}{2} \tag{20.11}$$

Then, all boundary conditions in which only the sum of the two friction coefficients occurs yield solutions identical with those previously discussed. This applies to drawing strip through stationary dies (see Fig. 18.3), extruding strip through stationary dies (see Fig. 18.4), rolling strip (see Fig. 19.1), drawing tubing with stationary dies and a stationary mandrel (see Fig. 20.8), and the Hooker process for tube drawing (see Fig. 20.12).

However, if branches of the solutions occur where the frictions act in opposite directions, the solutions will be modified. Although the friction forces still act in opposite directions, the condition of frictionless forming no longer exists.

20.14. Processes Involving Different Friction Coefficients at the Contact Surfaces

For rolling strip with one driven and one idle roll (see Fig. 20.2), tube drawing with roller dies and a driven mandrel (see Fig. 20.14), and tube rolling with a moving mandrel (see Fig. 20.15), the central branch of the solutions will be changed only slightly.

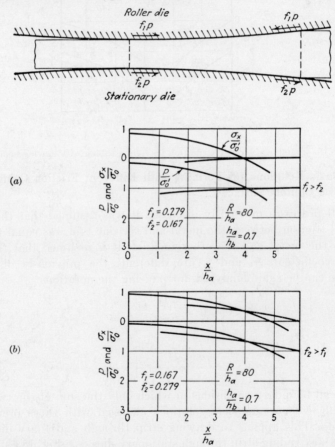

FIG. 20.16. Examples of stress distributions for drawing strip with roller die and stationary die.

In drawing strip with a roller die and a stationary die (see Fig. 20.5), if the values of the friction coefficient are different between the metal and the two dies, the solutions will be as shown in Fig. 20.16. The draw stress required when $f_1 = f_2$ (see Fig. 20.5) is greater than that required when $f_1 > f_2$, that is, when the friction on the roller die is greater than on the stationary die (see Fig. 20.16a), but it is slightly less than that required when $f_2 > f_1$ (see Fig. 20.16b). Therefore, a greater reduction in thickness can be made when $f_1 > f_2$ before the limit of drawing is reached.

The solution for tube drawing with roller dies and a stationary mandrel was previously shown to be identical with that for drawing strip with a roller die and a stationary die. Therefore, a greater reduction is again possible when the friction between the metal and the roller die is greater than the friction between the metal and the stationary die, and vice versa.

20.15. Forming with One Driven Tool and One Stationary Tool

The most interesting cases occur in rolling strip with a driven roll and a stationary die (see Fig. 20.5), including tube rolling with a stationary

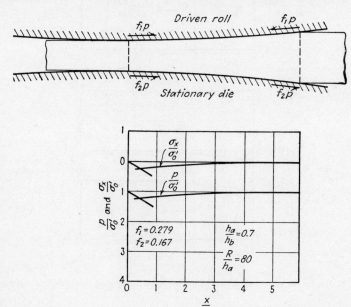

FIG. 20.17. Example of stress distribution for forming strip with one driven roll and one stationary die, $f_1 > f_2$.

mandrel (see Fig 20.10) and the closely related tube drawing with stationary dies and a driven mandrel (see Fig. 20.13).

In forming strip with a driven roll and a stationary die, no real solution is obtained (without front tension) when the friction coefficients are equal, as discussed previously. If, however, the friction coefficient f_1 between the roll and the metal is made sufficiently larger than the friction coef-

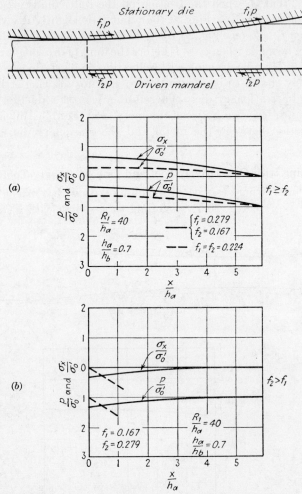

FIG. 20.18. Examples of stress distribution for drawing tubing with driven mandrel and stationary dies.

ficient f_2 between the metal and the stationary die, a solution is possible. This applies to the selected example (Fig 20.17), $f_1 = 0.279, f_2 = 0.167$.

Tube rolling with a stationary mandrel has been shown to have solutions identical with those for forming strip with a driven roll and a stationary die. Consequently, this process also becomes possible without applied front tension, if the friction between the driven roll and the metal is sufficiently greater than the friction between the metal and the mandrel.

Finally, in tube drawing with stationary dies and a driven mandrel, if the friction f_1 between the metal and the stationary dies is made larger than the friction f_2 between the metal and the mandrel, the solution becomes similar to that for drawing with a stationary mandrel. In the example shown (Fig. 20.18a), $f_1 = 0.279$, $f_2 = 0.167$, the solution is similar to that for $f_1 = f_2 = 0.224$, except that a larger draw stress is required.

However, if the friction f_2 between the metal and the mandrel is made sufficiently larger than the friction f_1 between the metal and the stationary dies the solution (Fig. 20.18b) may become similar to that for rolling strip with a driven roll and a stationary die where $f_1 > f_2$ (see Fig. 20.17). This solution is possible, however, only if a compression can be applied at the exit, as may be the case for drawing with a moving mandrel (see Fig. 20.11b) where the metal and mandrel are clamped in front of the die.

For the case of ironing (see Fig. 20.11c), no such compression can be realized; therefore, equilibrium is obtained only if the metal at the exit moves faster than the mandrel, reversing the direction of the friction near the exit. Then the solution becomes identical with that in Fig. 20.17, where a no-slip point occurs within the forming area and the tubular part will consequently run ahead of the mandrel.

REFERENCES

SACHS, G., and L. J. KLINGLER, The Flow of Metals through Tools of Circular Contour, *J. Applied Mechanics*, Vol. 14, pp. 88–98, 1947.

SIEBEL, E., Zur Theorie des Walzvorganges bei ungleich angetriebenen Walzen, *Arch. Eisenhuettenwesen*, Vol. 15, pp. 125–128, 1941–42.

CHAPTER 21

FORGING

21.1. Scope of Problem

Forming processes in which the metal is compressed or forged between two dies are of great practical importance. Prandtl's solution, discussed in Art. 11.6, gives a rigorous analysis applicable to the major portion of a wide plate of constant thickness compressed, in condition of plane strain, between two rough plates. Other problems, involving sliding friction, plates of variable thickness, and circular disks, will be treated in this chapter by approximate methods constructed after the fashion of the methods discussed in the preceding chapters of Part IV.

Compression or forging between dies is a nonsteady plastic-flow process during which the dimensions of the metal are continuously changing, and consequently the stress and strain at a given point of the space change also. The following analyses are to be understood to represent instantaneous conditions. Nevertheless, stress distributions thus obtained are in close relationship with those for the problem of sheet or strip rolling, which is a steady-flow process; and indeed the stresses for the latter problem can be derived, as a special case, from the more general case to be discussed in Art. 21.6.

21.2. Differential Equation of Forging of Plate of Constant Thickness in Condition of Plane Strain

Consider a volume element of unit width having the instantaneous thickness h and length dx (see Fig. 21.1). Assume that the width of the plate is maintained constant so that a condition of plane strain can be considered to exist. Assume, furthermore, that the longitudinal stress σ_x, constant over a plane normal to the x direction, and the pressure, $\sigma_y = -p$, acting on the metal-die interface, are the two principal stresses which enter in the distortion-energy condition of plasticity

$$\sigma_x - \sigma_y = \sigma_x + p = \frac{2}{\sqrt{3}} \sigma_0 = \sigma_0' \tag{21.1}$$

Because of symmetry, the metal flows away from the center plane in both directions, and it will be sufficient to analyze the conditions for one half of the plate. By introducing the shearing stresses τ_{xy}, acting on the

240

plate surfaces, the equilibrium of the x components of the forces acting on a volume element is expressed by

$$h \, d\sigma_x - 2\tau_{xy} \, dx = 0 \qquad (21.2)$$

On the other hand, by differentiating both sides of Eq. (21.1), one obtains

$$d\sigma_x = -dp$$

which, substituted into Eq. (21.2), yields, after simplifying,

$$dp + \frac{2\tau_{xy}}{h} \, dx = 0 \qquad (21.3)$$

This is the general differential equation of equilibrium which can be integrated after more specific assumptions are made concerning the shearing stresses τ_{xy}.

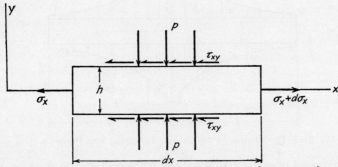

Fɪɢ. 21.1. Dimensions of volume element of plate in forging, and stresses acting on volume element.

21.3. Forging of Plate in Condition of Plane Strain with Coulomb Friction between Metal and Dies

Assuming the validity of Coulomb's law of sliding friction, expressed by the relation, $\tau_{xy} = fp$, Eq. (21.3) becomes

$$dp + \frac{2fp}{h} \, dx = 0$$

or, after separating the variables,

$$\frac{dp}{p} = -\frac{2f}{h} \, dx \qquad (21.4)$$

Integrating both sides, one obtains

$$\ln p = -\frac{2fx}{h} + C \qquad \text{or} \qquad p = C_1 e^{-2fx/h} \qquad (21.5)$$

where $C_1 = e^C$ is a new integration constant to be determined from the boundary condition at $x = L/2$ where $\sigma_x = 0$, and consequently $p = \sigma_0'$, from which one obtains

$$C_1 = \sigma_0' e^{fL/h}$$

With this value, Eq. (21.5) becomes, as Stone and Greenberger (1943) have shown,

$$\frac{p}{\sigma_0'} = e^{(2f/h)(L/2-x)} \tag{21.6}$$

The pressure-distribution diagram for the entire plate is made up of two symmetrical branches, each satisfying Eq. (21.6) (see Fig. 21.2).

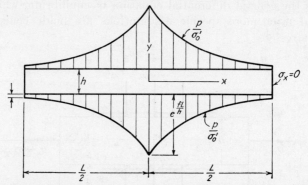

FIG. 21.2. Distribution of die pressure in forging with Coulomb friction.

The maximum pressure found for the plate center, $x = 0$, is

$$\left(\frac{p}{\sigma_0'}\right)_{\text{max}} = e^{fL/h} \tag{21.7}$$

21.4. Forging of Plate in Condition of Plane Strain with Sticking between Metal and Dies

Another possible assumption is that the die surfaces are rough enough to make the metal adhere perfectly to them. Then, as it was shown in Art. 11.4, the shearing stress τ_{xy} must be constant, equal to the shearing strength in plane strain, $\sigma_0'/2 = \sigma_0/\sqrt{3}$.

Substituting this value for τ_{xy} in Eq. (21.3), one has

$$dp + \frac{\sigma_0'}{h} dx = 0 \tag{21.8}$$

or, after separating the variables and integrating both sides,

$$\frac{p}{\sigma_0'} = -\frac{x}{h} + C \tag{21.9}$$

The integration constant C is determined again from the condition at the free end where

$$(p)_{x=L/2} = \sigma_0'$$

from which $C = 1 + L/2h$, and finally the pressure becomes

$$\frac{p}{\sigma_0'} = 1 + \frac{L/2 - x}{h} \tag{21.10}$$

It assumes its maximum value at center, where

$$\left(\frac{p}{\sigma_0'}\right)_{max} = 1 + \frac{L}{2h}$$

Figure 21.3 shows the pressure-distribution diagram and affords a comparison with the pressure distribution obtained by extending Prandtl's solution discussed in Art. 11.6 throughout the full length of the plate.

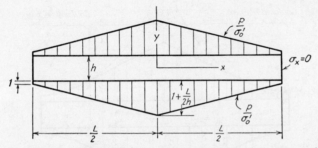

Fig. 21.3. Distribution of die pressure in forging with sticking between metal and dies.

It can be seen that the present approximate analysis yields two straight-line branches which are obtainable from the Prandtl solution by a parallel shifting by unit distance. The thinner the plate compared with its length, *i.e.*, the larger the L/h ratio, the more negligible is the difference between the two solutions.

21.5. Forging of Plate in Plane Strain with Mixed Frictional Conditions

The frictional force per unit surface fp cannot become larger than the shearing strength of the metal in plane strain $\sigma_0'/2$, because at this value of the shearing stress sliding occurs within the metal itself. Hence, the shearing stress, $\tau_{xy} = \sigma_0'/2$, can be considered as a threshold value, which characterizes the change-over from the condition of sliding friction to that of sticking. This occurs at the distance x from the origin where the frictional force per unit area calculated from Eq. (21.6) equals $\sigma_0'/2$, or

$$fp = f\sigma_0'e^{(2f/h)(L/2-x_1)} = \frac{\sigma_0'}{2}$$

from which

$$\ln \frac{1}{2f} = \frac{2f}{h}\left(\frac{L}{2} - x_1\right) \quad \text{or} \quad x_1 = \frac{L}{2} - \frac{h}{2f}\ln\frac{1}{2f} \qquad (21.11)$$

In the range $x_1 \leq x \leq L/2$, Coulomb's law of friction governs and hence the same equation (21.6) applies as for plates on which Coulomb friction is acting throughout. At the transition point, $x = x_1$, the pressure is given by

$$\left(\frac{p}{\sigma_0'}\right)_{x=x_1} = e^{(2f/h)(L/2-x_1)} = \frac{1}{2f} \qquad (21.12)$$

In the range $0 \leq x \leq x_1$, the shearing stress is constant and equal to $\sigma_0'/2$; hence, the general equation (21.9) applies, the integration constant

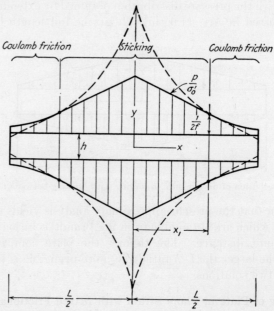

Fig. 21.4. Distribution of die pressure in forging with mixed frictional conditions.

C being determined from the condition that for $x = x_1$ the same expression [Eq. (21.12)] should be obtained from both Eqs. (21.6) and (21.9), or

$$-\frac{x_1}{h} + C = e^{(2f/h)(L/2-x_1)}$$

This yields

$$C = e^{(2f/h)(L/2-x_1)} + \frac{x_1}{h}$$

and the expression for the pressure becomes

$$\frac{p}{\sigma_0'} = \frac{L/2 - x}{h} + \frac{1}{2f}\left(1 - \ln\frac{1}{2f}\right) \qquad (21.13)$$

The resulting pressure-distribution diagram is composed of four branches and is shown in Fig. 21.4.

The forging problems discussed in the preceding articles 21.3 and 21.4 are now obtained as limiting cases.

(a) When $x_1 = 0$, Coulomb's law of friction and the corresponding equation (21.6) will govern for the full length of the plate, and from Eq. (21.11) it can be seen that this condition will exist when the plate dimensions satisfy the inequality

$$\frac{L}{h} \leq \frac{\ln(1/2f)}{f} \qquad (21.14)$$

(b) When $x_1 = L/2$, the metal will stick to the dies, and Eq. (21.10) will govern throughout. From Eq. (21.11) it follows that this condition will exist when the friction coefficient becomes

$$f \geq \tfrac{1}{2} \qquad (21.15)$$

21.6. Forging of Plate of Variable Thickness in Condition of Plane Strain

Consider a volume element of unit width having a length dx within which the thickness can be considered as varying with linear law from h

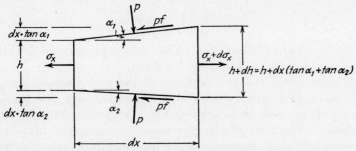

Fig. 21.5. Dimensions of volume element of plate of variable thickness in forging; and stresses acting on volume element.

to $h + dh$. The equilibrium of the element, shown in Fig. 21.5, furnishes the equation [see Eq. (20.6)]

$$h\,d\sigma_x + \sigma_x\,dh + p\,dx\,(\tan\alpha_1 + \tan\alpha_2 - 2f) = 0 \qquad (21.16)$$

By introducing the relationship $dh = dx\,(\tan\alpha_1 + \tan\alpha_2)$, this becomes

$$h\,d\sigma_x + \sigma_x\,dh - 2fp\,dx + p\,dh = 0 \qquad (21.17)$$

On the other hand, from the yield condition [Eq. (21.1)] one has

$$\sigma_x = \sigma_0' - p$$

and $d\sigma_x = -dp$, and with these expressions Eq. (21.17) becomes

$$-h \, dp + (\sigma_0' - p) \, dh + p \, dh - 2fp \, dx = 0$$

and, rearranging, one obtains the differential equation

$$\frac{d(p/\sigma_0')}{dx} - \frac{1}{h}\frac{dh}{dx} + \frac{2f}{h}\frac{p}{\sigma_0'} = 0 \qquad (21.18)$$

Whenever h is given as a function of x analytically, this equation may be integrated by known methods of the calculus. Forging of a plate of constant thickness (see Art. 21.3) and rolling of a strip (see Chap. 19) are examples of this type. For more irregular die contours a numerical step-by-step integration is entirely satisfactory, in view of the generally approximate character of the present analysis. The two branches of the p/σ_0' diagram are developed separately, starting the numerical integration from each free end and using the horizontal distances ξ_1 and ξ_2, from the left and right ends, respectively, as independent variables. Then, for the left branch the differential equation becomes

$$\frac{d(p/\sigma_0')}{d\xi_1} - \frac{1}{h}\frac{dh}{d\xi_1} - \frac{2f}{h}\frac{p}{\sigma_0'} = 0 \qquad (21.19)$$

and the initial condition

$$\left(\frac{p}{\sigma_0'}\right)_{\xi_1=0} = 1 \qquad (21.20)$$

A similar differential equation and a similar end condition are obtained for the right branch by replacing ξ_1 with ξ_2.

The point where the two branches of the p/σ_0' diagram meet is the no-slip point, from which the metal flows away in both directions.

As in rolling, each die is subjected to a longitudinal force, called the side thrust. This force can be determined by summation of the longitudinal components of the pressures and frictional forces acting on each die.

21.7. Forging of Solid Circular Disk of Constant Thickness

Consider a volume element of the disk, bounded by two concentric cylindrical surfaces of radius r and $r + dr$, respectively, and by two radial planes which include the angle θ. Owing to axial symmetry, the conditions on such a volume element can be considered to be representative of all volume elements located at the same radial distance.

It is reasonable to assume that at the mid-plane of the disk, the radial, tangential, and normal (z) directions are principal directions both for stress and strain; furthermore, that a state of generalized plane strain with $\dot{\epsilon}_z$ = constant, similar to that discussed in Art. 8.7, exists. Then, the following expressions can be written for the principal strain rates (see Art. 7.1):

$$\dot{\epsilon}_r = \frac{d\dot{u}_r}{dr} \qquad \dot{\epsilon}_\theta = \frac{\dot{u}_r}{r} \qquad \dot{\epsilon}_z = \frac{d\dot{u}_z}{dz} = \text{constant}$$

From the volume-constancy equation, $\dot{\epsilon}_r + \dot{\epsilon}_\theta + \dot{\epsilon}_z = 0$, one has the differential equation

$$\frac{d\dot{u}_r}{dr} + \frac{\dot{u}_r}{r} + \dot{\epsilon}_z = 0$$

the general solution of which is

$$\dot{u}_r = -\frac{\dot{\epsilon}_z r}{2} + \frac{C}{r}$$

The constant of integration must vanish in order to avoid infinitely large displacements at the center line; thus the solution becomes

$$\dot{u}_r = -\frac{\dot{\epsilon}_z r}{2}$$

from which

$$\dot{\epsilon}_r = \dot{\epsilon}_\theta = -\frac{\dot{\epsilon}_z}{2} \tag{21.21}$$

From Saint-Venant's plastic-flow relations it follows that $\sigma_z = \sigma_\theta$, and it can be concluded that a state of "cylindrical" stress exists,

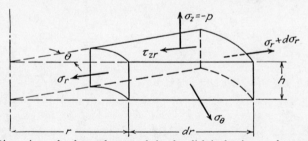

Fig. 21.6. Dimensions of volume element of circular disk in forging; and stresses acting on volume element.

for which both the maximum-shearing-stress condition and the distortion-energy condition of yielding furnish the same relation (see Art. 9.2)

$$\sigma_\theta - \sigma_z = \sigma_r - \sigma_z = \sigma_0$$

Assuming that the principal stress σ_z is equal to $-p$, the die pressure taken with negative sign, one has

$$\sigma_r = \sigma_\theta = \sigma_0 - p \tag{21.22}$$

The equilibrium equation for the radial components of the forces acting on the volume element, shown in Fig. 21.6, is written by assuming that σ_r and σ_θ at the mid-plane are the constant normal stresses throughout the disk thickness, obtaining

$$h\,d\sigma_r - 2\tau_{zr}\,dr = 0 \tag{21.23}$$

A comparison of this equation with Eq. (21.2) shows that the pressure distribution in a solid circular disk of diameter L is identical with that in a wide strip of the same length L, the only difference being that the distance x is to be replaced by the radial distance r, and the value σ_0' by σ_0. This identity holds for all previously discussed types of frictional forces between metal and dies.

REFERENCES

NÁDAI, A., The Forces Required For Rolling Steel Strip under Tension, *J. Applied Mechanics*, Vol. 6, pp. 54–62, 1939.

SACHS, G., Limits of Forging, *Modern Industrial Press*, March, 1941, pp. 9–10.

SCHROEDER, W., and D. A. WEBSTER, Press-forging Thin Sections: Effect of Friction, Area, and Thickness on Pressure Required, *J. Applied Mechanics*, Vol. 16, pp. 289–294, 1949.

STONE, M., and J. L. GREENBERGER, Rolling Pressures in Strip Mill, *Iron Steel Engr.*, Vol. 20, p. 61, 1943.

CHAPTER 22

FORMING OF THIN-WALLED SHELLS

22.1. Scope of Problem

In a number of forming processes a thin-walled metal shell of rotational symmetry is pulled or pushed by an axial force through a die opening, and undergoes a reduction in diameter. Figures 22.1a and 22.1b represent the sinking of a tube and the redrawing of a part; in both processes the diameter of a certain length is transformed into a smaller one by application of a pulling force. Both these processes are basically of the steady-flow type, annular elements of a certain initial diameter being

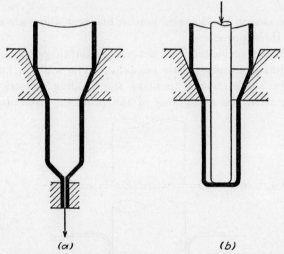

(a)   (b)

Fig. 22.1. Reducing of tube by pulling: (a) sinking; (b) redrawing.

reduced to another final diameter. However, deviations from the steady-flow condition may occur in redrawing, because of variations in either wall thickness or hardness of metal. Figure 22.2 shows reducing processes of the pushing type: (a) necking; (b) tapering; (c) nosing; and (d) closing. Of these, only the necking is a steady-flow process, while in the other processes the initial diameter of a given annular element is reduced to varying values during the process.

The deep-drawing process, shown in Fig. 22.3, transforms a circular

249

blank of constant thickness into a closed tubular part or cup; it belongs to the same group of processes as those shown in Figs. 22.1 and 22.2, with the only difference being that the annular elements of initially different diameters are reduced to the same diameter of the cup.

Expansion processes in which the shell diameter is increased by pulling or pushing over an internal tool or mandrel are basically similar to the

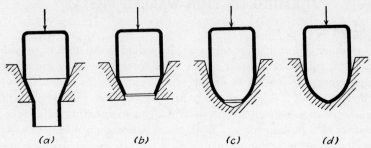

(a)   (b)   (c)   (d)

Fig. 22.2. Tube reducing processes of pushing type: (a) necking; (b) tapering; (c) nosing; (d) closing.

reducing processes to be discussed herein; however, there are no analyses available for these processes.

In the analyses presented here several assumptions will be made, in addition to that of ideally plastic behavior. The wall thickness will be assumed to be small enough to make the bending stresses negligible. Furthermore, with the exceptions of the problems presented in Arts.

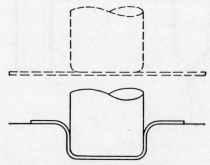

Fig. 22.3. Deep drawing.

22.7 and 22.8, the wall thickness will be assumed to remain constant along the path of a particle.

In all the processes discussed herein only the outer face of the metal shell is in contact with the die, and the die pressure, applied on one face of the wall, can be expected to taper off rapidly inside the wall. This circumstance, in conjunction with the fact, to be verified a posteriori, that the die pressures are negligibly small compared with the other stresses in the shell wall, justifies the assumption, to be made throughout this chapter, of a *plane-stress* condition with principal directions contained in the tangent plane.

22.2. Equilibrium Equations for Shells of Rotational Symmetry

Figure 22.4 shows a volume element of a shell of rotational symmetry bounded by two meridian planes making the dihedral angle $d\theta$ and by two planes normal both to the tangent plane and to the meridian plane and making the dihedral angle $d\alpha$. The mean radius of the parallel circle is r, the mean radius of curvature of the meridian, R_1, and the mean

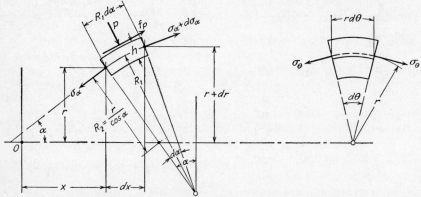

Fig. 22.4. Dimensions of volume element of shell of rotational symmetry, and stresses acting on volume element.

radius of curvature normal to the meridian, R_2. From Fig. 22.4 the following relationships can be established between these radii:

$$r = R_2 \cos \alpha \qquad (22.1)$$
$$dr = -R_1 \sin \alpha \, d\alpha \qquad (22.2)$$

where α is the angle between the meridian tangent and the shell axis.

The surface loads acting on the shell are the normal die pressure p and the frictional force intensity fp, acting, because of symmetry, in the direction of the meridian tangent. According to the assumptions made, the shell is in a state of plane stress (analogous to that assumed in the so-called "membrane theory" of shells), one of the two nonvanishing principal stresses being σ_θ in the direction normal to the meridian plane, and the other being σ_α in the direction of the meridian tangent.

Equilibrium equations for the volume element can be conveniently written with reference to (a) the normal to the tangent plane, (b) the meridian tangent, (c) the shell axis. All three equations will be developed here, though in any particular problem not more than two are needed to determine the stresses.   For the sake of generality, a continuous variation of the wall thickness h will be assumed.

(a) Equilibrium of the force components in the direction normal to the tangent plane is expressed by the equation

$$\sigma_\alpha h r \, d\alpha \, d\theta + \sigma_\theta h R_1 \cos \alpha \, d\alpha \, d\theta + p R_1 r \, d\alpha \, d\theta = 0$$

from which, by neglecting higher order terms and rearranging, one obtains

$$\frac{\sigma_\alpha}{R_1} + \frac{\sigma_\theta}{R_2} + \frac{p}{h} = 0 \tag{22.3}$$

(b) Equilibrium of the force components in the direction of the meridian tangent furnishes the equation

$$(\sigma_\alpha + d\sigma_\alpha)(h + dh)(r + dr) \, d\theta - \sigma_\alpha h r \, d\theta - \sigma_\theta h R_1 \sin \alpha \, d\alpha \, d\theta$$
$$+ f p R_1 r \, d\alpha \, d\theta = 0$$

or

$$\frac{d(\sigma_\alpha h r)}{dr} - \sigma_\theta h + \frac{f p r}{\sin \alpha} = 0 \tag{22.4}$$

(c) Equilibrium of the longitudinal force components gives

$$(\sigma_\alpha + d\sigma_\alpha)(h + dh)(r + dr) \cos (\alpha + d\alpha) \, d\theta - \sigma_\alpha h r \cos \alpha \, d\theta$$
$$+ p R_1 r \sin \alpha \, d\alpha \, d\theta + f p R_1 r \cos \alpha \, d\alpha \, d\theta = 0$$

or, by rearranging, and neglecting differentials of higher order,

$$\frac{d(\sigma_\alpha h r \cos \alpha)}{dr} + p r \left(1 + \frac{f}{\tan \alpha}\right) = 0 \tag{22.5}$$

22.3. Stresses in Tube Sinking with a Conical Die

The following analysis of the process of tube sinking with a conical die follows closely that given by Sachs and Baldwin (1946).   Figure 22.5

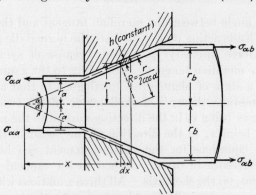

FIG. 22.5. Tube sinking with conical die.

shows the dimensions of the plastic shell during the forming process for which it is assumed that the wall thickness remains uniform.

It can be predicted, and verified later, that the meridian stresses are tensile stresses and the tangential stresses are compressive stresses, so that $\sigma_\theta < 0 < \sigma_\alpha$.

In the graphical representation of the state of stress by the method discussed in Art. 4.3, all points that correspond to states of stress in the shell are within the fourth quadrant of the $(\sigma_\alpha, \sigma_\theta)$ plane (see Fig. 22.6).

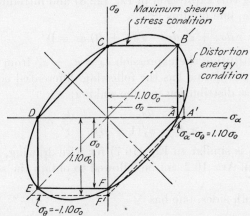

FIG. 22.6. Graphical representation of yield conditions for thin-walled shells.

This limitation permits the use of a simplified condition of plasticity which replaces the elliptic arc FA, corresponding to the distortion-energy condition, with a straight line parallel to the chord FA, corresponding to the maximum-shearing-stress condition, having the equation

$$\sigma_\alpha - \sigma_\theta = 1.10\sigma_0 = \sigma_0'' \qquad (22.6)$$

The dotted line $F'A'$ represents this modified plasticity condition, which should be used with caution without extending its validity to or beyond the σ_α and σ_θ axes.

The first equilibrium equation, Eq. (22.3), becomes, because for a conical shell $R_1 \to \infty$,

$$\frac{\sigma_\theta}{R_2} + \frac{p}{h} = 0$$

or, with the expression $R_2 = r/\cos \alpha$ obtained from Eq. (22.1),

$$\frac{\sigma_\theta \cos \alpha}{r} + \frac{p}{h} = 0 \qquad (22.7)$$

The second equilibrium equation, Eq. (22.5), referred to the shell axis, becomes in the present case, with constant h and α,

$$\frac{d(\sigma_\alpha r)}{dr} + pr\left(1 + \frac{f}{\tan \alpha}\right) = 0 \tag{22.8}$$

Solving Eq. (22.7) for p, one has

$$p = -\frac{h}{r} \sigma_\theta \cos \alpha$$

and, substituting this expression in Eq. (22.8) and introducing the notation $B = f/\tan \alpha$, one obtains

$$r\, d\sigma_\alpha + \sigma_\alpha\, dr - \sigma_\theta(1 + B)\, dr = 0 \tag{22.9}$$

Finally, by substituting the expression $\sigma_\theta = \sigma_\alpha - \sigma_0''$ from the plasticity condition [Eq. (22.6)], one has the following differential equation which governs the stress distribution in tube sinking:

$$\frac{d\sigma_\alpha}{\sigma_\alpha B - \sigma_0''(1 + B)} = \frac{dr}{r} \tag{22.10}$$

This equation is similar to Eq. (16.7) for wire drawing, and the same procedure used in Art. 16.2 can be followed to obtain the solution in the present case.

Integrating both sides, one has

$$\frac{1}{B} \ln\left[\sigma_\alpha B - \sigma_0''(1 + B)\right] = \ln r + C$$

or

$$\sigma_\alpha B - \sigma_0''(1 + B) = r^B e^{BC} = r^B C'$$

where C' is the integration constant. Solving for the stress ratio σ_α/σ_0'', one has

$$\frac{\sigma_\alpha}{\sigma_0''} = \frac{1 + B}{B} + C' \frac{r^B}{\sigma_0'' B} \tag{22.11}$$

The constant C' is determined from the condition that at the entry section, where $r = r_b$, the meridian stress is equal to the (elastic or applied) backpull stress σ_{ab} or

$$\frac{\sigma_{ab}}{\sigma_0''} = \frac{1 + B}{B} + \frac{C' r_b{}^B}{\sigma_0'' B}$$

from which

$$C' = \left(\sigma_{ab} - \sigma_0'' \frac{1 + B}{B}\right) \frac{B}{r_b{}^B}$$

Substituting in Eqs. (22.11) and (22.6), the following expressions are obtained:

For the meridian stress:

$$\frac{\sigma_\alpha}{\sigma_0''} = \frac{1+B}{B}\left[1 - \left(\frac{r}{r_b}\right)^B\right] + \frac{\sigma_{ab}}{\sigma_0''}\left(\frac{r}{r_b}\right)^B \tag{22.12}$$

For the tangential stress:

$$\frac{\sigma_\theta}{\sigma_0''} = \frac{1}{B} - \left[\frac{1+B}{B} - \frac{\sigma_{ab}}{\sigma_0''}\right]\left(\frac{r}{r_b}\right)^B \tag{22.13}$$

and similarly from Eq. (22.7) one has for the die pressure

$$\frac{p}{\sigma_0''} = -\frac{\sigma_\theta}{\sigma_0''}\frac{h\cos\alpha}{r} \tag{22.14}$$

The draw stress, defined as the longitudinal stress in the tube at the exit section, is equal to the meridian stress at the same point and is expressed by

$$\frac{\sigma_{\alpha a}}{\sigma_0''} = \left(\frac{\sigma_\alpha}{\sigma_0''}\right)_{r=r_a} = \frac{1+B}{B}\left[1 - \left(\frac{r_a}{r_b}\right)^B\right] + \frac{\sigma_{ab}}{\sigma_0''}\left(\frac{r_a}{r_b}\right)^B \tag{22.15}$$

Comparison with the analogous expression [Eq. (16.9)] given in Art. 16.2 for the draw stress in wire drawing is made easier by introducing the approximate expression for the cross-sectional area of the tube

$$A \approx 2\pi rh$$

from which

$$\frac{r_a}{r_b} \approx \frac{A_a}{A_b}$$

With such an expression, Eq. (22.15) becomes

$$\frac{\sigma_{\alpha a}}{\sigma_0''} = \frac{1+B}{B}\left[1 - \left(\frac{A_a}{A_b}\right)^B\right] + \frac{\sigma_{ab}}{\sigma_0''}\left(\frac{A_a}{A_b}\right)^B \tag{22.16}$$

This expression is identical with Eq. (16.9) for wire drawing, where

$$\frac{A_a}{A_b} = \frac{D_a{}^2}{D_b{}^2}$$

except for the fact that in Eq. (22.16) $\sigma_0'' = 1.10\sigma_0$ replaces the value σ_0 appearing in Eq. (16.9). The term B has the same significance in both cases. One can conclude that, as confirmed by experiments, the draw stress in tube sinking is about 10 per cent higher than the draw stress in wire drawing, if the tube-wall thickness is small, provided that reduction in area, die geometry, and die-metal friction are the same in both processes.

22.4. Stresses in Tube Reducing with a Conical Die

Among the various processes of tube reducing, the necking of a tube (see Fig. 22.2a) is most closely related to the tube-sinking process. Both operations involve a steady plastic flow and can be analyzed in a similar manner. Tapering and nosing, however, are nonsteady plastic-flow processes in which the stresses, while depending upon the same types of equations as in the necking process, depend also upon the instant position of the front end. This position can be readily obtained from the volume-constancy condition if a constant and uniform wall thickness is assumed, as will be done in the present analysis.

Tube reducing is characterized by large tangential compressive stresses σ_θ and by comparatively smaller meridian compressive stresses σ_α, that is,

$$\sigma_\theta < \sigma_\alpha < 0$$

The points in the $(\sigma_\alpha, \sigma_\theta)$ plane which represent possible states of stress are within the sixth octant, counted from the positive σ_α axis (see Fig. 22.6), and within this range of stress states a modified plasticity condition will be adopted, similar to that used in the preceding article. The elliptic arc EF, corresponding to the distortion-energy condition of plasticity, will be replaced by a straight line parallel to the chord EF and having the equation

$$\sigma_\theta = -1.10\sigma_0 = -\sigma_0'' \qquad (22.17)$$

Equation (22.9),

$$r \, d\sigma_\alpha + \sigma_\alpha \, dr - \sigma_\theta(1 + B) \, dr = 0$$

which was derived from the equilibrium equations (22.3) and (22.5), applies here as before, but now it is to be combined with the simplified plasticity condition [Eq. (22.17)] to obtain

$$\frac{d\sigma_\alpha}{\sigma_\alpha + \sigma_0''(1 + B)} = -\frac{dr}{r} \qquad (22.18)$$

The solution of this differential equation is

$$\frac{\sigma_\alpha}{\sigma_0''} = -(1 + B) + \frac{C}{r}$$

where the integration constant C is determined from the assumption of a negligible resistance at the exit section, that is, $(\sigma_\alpha/\sigma_0'')_{r=r_a} = 0$. One obtains $C = r_a(1 + B)$ and finally the following expressions:

For the meridian stress:

$$\frac{\sigma_\alpha}{\sigma_0''} = -(1 + B)\left(1 - \frac{r_a}{r}\right) \qquad (22.19)$$

For the tangential stress:

$$\frac{\sigma_\theta}{\sigma_0''} = -1 \tag{22.20}$$

For the die pressure:

$$\frac{p}{\sigma_0''} = -\frac{h\cos\alpha}{r} \tag{22.21}$$

The compressive stress σ_{ab}, required to perform the reduction process, is

$$\frac{\sigma_{aa}}{\sigma_0''} = \left(\frac{\sigma_\alpha}{\sigma_0''}\right)_{r=r_a} = -(1+B)\left(1 - \frac{r_a}{r_b}\right) \tag{22.22}$$

22.5. Alternate Solution for Stresses in Nosing with a Conical Die

Nádai (1944) gave the following solution of the problem of tapering or nosing with a conical die, basing it on the distortion-energy condition of plasticity rather than on the approximate condition [Eq. (22.17)] used in the preceding article; the other basic assumptions are the same for both solutions.

Equation (22.9), which governs both tube sinking and reducing with conical dies, can be rewritten as follows:

$$k\frac{d(\sigma_\alpha r)}{dr} - \sigma_\theta = 0 \tag{22.23}$$

where

$$k = \frac{1}{1+B} \tag{22.24}$$

The distortion-energy condition of plasticity is expressed in the present case by the equation

$$\sigma_\alpha^2 - \sigma_\alpha\sigma_\theta + \sigma_\theta^2 = \sigma_0^2 \tag{22.25}$$

Equations (22.23) and (22.25) contain the two dependent variables σ_α and σ_θ and the independent variable r. The solution here discussed is obtained by introducing the new independent variable

$$\xi = \ln\frac{r}{r_a} \tag{22.26}$$

and the new single dependent variable η, such that σ_α and σ_θ can be expressed in terms of it as

$$\sigma_\alpha = -\frac{2}{\sqrt{3}}\sigma_0\sin(\eta + \eta_0) \tag{22.27}$$

$$\sigma_\theta = \frac{2}{\sqrt{3}}\sigma_0\sin\left(\eta + \eta_0 + \frac{2\pi}{3}\right) \tag{22.28}$$

These expressions satisfy identically the plasticity condition [Eq. (22.25)]. With these new variables, the differential equation of the problem, Eq. (22.23), assumes the form

$$\frac{d\eta}{d\xi} = \frac{c_0 \sin \eta}{k \cos (\eta + \eta_0)} \tag{22.29}$$

and the constants η_0 and c_0 satisfy the relations

$$\tan \left(\eta_0 - \frac{\pi}{3} \right) = \frac{\sqrt{3}k}{2 - k} \quad \text{and} \quad c_0 = \sqrt{k^2 - k + 1} \tag{22.30}$$

The solution has to satisfy the boundary condition at the lower end

$$(\sigma_\alpha)_{r=r_a} = (\sigma_\alpha)_{\xi=0} = 0$$

and it is obtained as

$$\frac{r}{r_a} = \left[\frac{\sin \eta}{\sin \eta_0} \right]^{k/c_0} e^{k/c_0 [\pi - \sin \eta_0 (\eta - \eta_0)]} \tag{22.31}$$

The stresses corresponding to this solution differ only slightly from the solution given in the preceding article 22.4. The greatest differences are found in the values of the tangential stresses, which are functions of r in the present solution, while in the solution of Art. 22.4 they are assumed to be constant, $\sigma_\theta = \sigma_0''$.

When the meridian compressive stress σ_α becomes numerically larger than the tangential compressive stress σ_θ, the physical significance of any solution becomes questionable, inasmuch as the limit of nosing is reached when $\sigma_\alpha = \sigma_\theta = \sigma_0''$.

22.6. Stresses in Nosing with a Die of Circular Contour

Another important problem arises in connection with forming by pressing of a torus-shaped nose at the end of a tubular part, the inner and outer surfaces being generated by concentric circles tangential to the tubular shell. The solution of this problem, due to Nádai (1944), is based on the same assumptions as the preceding analyses of this chapter, *i.e.*, ideally plastic material and negligible changes in wall thickness. In this presentation the modified plasticity condition [Eq. (22.17)] will be used, while Nádai's original presentation made use of the maximum-shearing-stress condition of plasticity, which furnishes a similar expression except for the value on the right side being σ_0 instead of σ_0''. In the present case the mean radius of curvature of the meridian R_1 is constant; the mean radius of the parallel circle r is expressed by

$$r = r_b - R_1(1 - \cos \alpha) \tag{22.32}$$

and the mean radius of curvature normal to the meridian is (see Fig. 22.7)

$$R_2 = \frac{r}{\cos \alpha} \qquad (22.33)$$

The equilibrium equation (22.3) can be solved for p, after substituting the expression from Eq. (22.33) for R, to obtain

$$p = -h\left(\frac{\sigma_\alpha}{R_1} + \frac{\sigma_\theta \cos \alpha}{r}\right) \qquad (22.34)$$

The equilibrium equation (22.5) becomes, by substituting the expression for dr from Eq. (22.2) and by considering that a constant wall thickness h is being assumed,

$$h\frac{d(\sigma_\alpha r \cos \alpha)}{d\alpha} - prR_1\frac{\sin(\alpha + \varphi)}{\cos \varphi} = 0 \qquad (22.35)$$

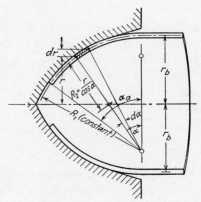

FIG. 22.7. Nosing with die of circular contour.

where the notation $\varphi = \tan^{-1} f$ is introduced for the so-called angle of friction.

With the approximate plasticity condition [Eq. (22.17)]

$$\sigma_\theta = -\sigma_0''$$

and with the expression of p given by Eq. (22.34), one obtains the differential equation

$$\frac{d[(\sigma_\alpha r/R_1) \cos \alpha]}{d\alpha} + \frac{\sin(\alpha + \varphi)}{\cos \varphi}\left(\frac{\sigma_\alpha r}{R_1} - \sigma_0'' \cos \alpha\right) = 0 \quad (22.36)$$

In this equation the term $\sigma_\alpha r/R_1$ can be considered as a single independent variable, so that it can be rearranged as follows:

$$\frac{d(\sigma_\alpha r/R_1)}{d\alpha} + \left(\frac{\sigma_\alpha r}{R_1}\right)\tan \varphi - \sigma_0''\frac{\sin(\alpha + \varphi)}{\cos \varphi} = 0 \qquad (22.37)$$

At the shell nose, where $\alpha = \alpha_a$, $\sigma_\alpha = 0$, this condition is satisfied by the solution

$$\frac{\sigma_\alpha r}{R_1} = \sigma_0''[e^{f(\alpha_a - \alpha)} \cos(\alpha_a + 2\varphi) - \cos(\alpha + 2\varphi)] \qquad (22.38)$$

22.7. Stresses and Strains in Frictionless Sinking and Reducing

If the friction is assumed to be zero, $f = 0$, and, as previously, the changes in wall thickness are neglected, the stresses both in sinking and in reducing of tubular parts become simple functions of the radius and independent of the contour of the die used in the forming operation. To prove this assertion, consider the equilibrium equation (22.4) which under the assumptions stated above becomes, both for sinking and reducing,

$$\frac{d\sigma_\alpha}{dr} + \frac{\sigma_\alpha - \sigma_\theta}{r} = 0 \qquad (22.39)$$

From this point on, the two processes must be discussed separately because of the different expressions assumed by the plasticity condition for the two processes.

(a) *Tube Sinking.* In this case the plasticity condition [Eq. (22.6)] applies and on substitution into Eq. (22.39) furnishes the differential equation

$$\frac{d\sigma_\alpha}{dr} + \frac{\sigma_0''}{r} = 0 \qquad (22.40)$$

The solution of this equation, under the condition of zero meridian stress at the entry section, $(\sigma_\alpha/\sigma_0'')_{r=r_b} = 0$, furnishes the following expressions for the stresses:

$$\frac{\sigma_\alpha}{\sigma_0''} = \ln \frac{r_b}{r} \qquad (22.41)$$

$$\frac{\sigma_\theta}{\sigma_0''} = \ln \frac{r_b}{r} - 1 \qquad (22.42)$$

(b) *Tube Reducing.* The plasticity condition in this case is $\sigma_\theta = -\sigma_0''$ Eq. (22.17)], and the differential equation becomes

$$\frac{d\sigma_\alpha}{dr} + \frac{\sigma_\alpha + \sigma_0''}{r} = 0 \qquad (22.43)$$

The solution which satisfies the condition of zero meridian stress at the exit section, $(\sigma_\alpha/\sigma_0'')_{r=r_a} = 0$, gives the following expressions for the stresses:

$$\frac{\sigma_\alpha}{\sigma_0''} = \frac{r_a}{r} - 1 \qquad (22.44)$$

$$\frac{\sigma_\theta}{\sigma_0''} = -1 \qquad (22.45)$$

It should be pointed out that these simple relationships are predicated upon the assumption of constant wall thickness. The alternate method of the next chapter, due to Swift (1949), dispenses with such assumption and furnishes both strains and stresses.

22.8. Frictionless Sinking and Reducing with Variable Wall Thickness

The equilibrium equation (22.4) assumes the following form for frictionless processes with variable wall thickness:

$$\frac{d(\sigma_\alpha h r)}{dr} - \sigma_\theta h = 0 \tag{22.46}$$

(a) *Tube Sinking.* In conjunction with the plasticity condition, $\sigma_\alpha - \sigma_\theta = \sigma_0''$, Eq. (22.46) becomes

$$\frac{d\sigma_\alpha}{dr} + \frac{\sigma_\alpha}{h}\frac{dh}{dr} + \frac{\sigma_0''}{r} = 0 \tag{22.47}$$

or, with reference to the definition of logarithmic strain, $d\bar{\epsilon}_h = dh/h$, $d\bar{\epsilon}_\theta = dr/r$,

$$\frac{d(\sigma_\alpha/\sigma_0'')}{d\bar{\epsilon}_h} + \frac{\sigma_\alpha}{\sigma_0''} + \frac{d\bar{\epsilon}_\theta}{d\bar{\epsilon}_h} = 0 \tag{22.48}$$

From Saint-Venant's plastic-flow relations [Eq. (5.23)], it follows that

$$\frac{d\bar{\epsilon}_\theta}{d\bar{\epsilon}_h} = \frac{\sigma_\alpha - 2\sigma_\theta}{\sigma_\alpha + \sigma_\theta}$$

or, by substituting $\sigma_\theta = \sigma_\alpha - \sigma_0''$ from the plasticity condition,

$$\frac{d\bar{\epsilon}_\theta}{d\bar{\epsilon}_h} = \frac{2 - \sigma_\alpha/\sigma_0''}{2\sigma_\alpha/\sigma_0'' - 1} \tag{22.49}$$

With this expression Eq. (22.48) becomes

$$\frac{d(\sigma_\alpha/\sigma_0'')}{d\bar{\epsilon}_h} + 2\frac{(\sigma_\alpha/\sigma_0'')^2 - \sigma_\alpha/\sigma_0'' + 1}{2\sigma_\alpha/\sigma_0'' - 1} = 0 \tag{22.50}$$

the solution of which, with the initial condition $\sigma_\alpha/\sigma_0'' = 0$ for $\bar{\epsilon}_h = 0$, is as follows:

$$\bar{\epsilon}_h = \ln\frac{h}{h_b} = -\frac{1}{2}\ln\left[1 - \frac{\sigma_\alpha}{\sigma_0''} + \left(\frac{\sigma_\alpha}{\sigma_0''}\right)^2\right] \tag{22.51}$$

To determine $\bar{\epsilon}_\theta$, Eq. (22.48) can be rewritten as follows:

$$\frac{d(\sigma_\alpha/\sigma_0'')}{d\bar{\epsilon}_\theta} + \frac{\sigma_\alpha}{\sigma_0''}\frac{d\bar{\epsilon}_h}{d\bar{\epsilon}_\theta} + 1 = 0 \tag{22.52}$$

and one obtains, with reference to Eq. (22.49), the differential equation

$$\frac{d(\sigma_\alpha/\sigma_0'')}{d\bar{\epsilon}_\theta} + \frac{4\sigma_\alpha/\sigma_0'' - (\sigma_\alpha/\sigma_0'')^2 - 1}{2\sigma_\alpha/\sigma_0'' - 1} = 0 \tag{22.53}$$

The solution which satisfies the condition $\sigma_\alpha / \sigma_0'' = 0$ for $\bar{\epsilon}_\theta = 0$ is the following:

$$\bar{\epsilon}_\alpha = \ln \frac{r}{r_b} = \frac{1}{4} \ln \left[1 - \frac{\sigma_\alpha}{\sigma_0''} + \left(\frac{\sigma_\alpha}{\sigma_0''} \right)^2 \right] - \frac{\sqrt{3}}{2} \tan^{-1} \left[\frac{\sqrt{3}(\sigma_\alpha / \sigma_0'')}{2 - (\sigma_\alpha / \sigma_0'')} \right]$$

(22.54)

Finally, from the volume-constancy relation, $\bar{\epsilon}_\alpha + \bar{\epsilon}_\theta + \bar{\epsilon}_h = 0$, one obtains the logarithmic strain in the meridian direction

$$\bar{\epsilon}_\alpha = \frac{1}{4} \ln \left[1 - \frac{\sigma_\alpha}{\sigma_0''} + \left(\frac{\sigma_\alpha}{\sigma_0''} \right)^2 \right] + \frac{\sqrt{3}}{2} \tan^{-1} \left[\frac{\sqrt{3} \, (\sigma_\alpha / \sigma_0'')}{2 - (\sigma_\alpha / \sigma_0'')} \right] \quad (22.55)$$

(b) *Tube Reducing.* The developments given above can be repeated for this case with the sole difference that the plasticity condition becomes $\sigma_\theta = -\sigma_0''$. Then, the differential equation corresponding to Eq. (22.47) assumes the form

$$\frac{d\sigma_\alpha}{dr} + \sigma_\alpha \left(\frac{1}{h} \frac{dh}{dr} + \frac{1}{r} \right) + \frac{\sigma_0''}{r} = 0 \quad (22.56)$$

and the final solution consists of the following expressions:

$$\ln \frac{h}{h_\alpha} = - \frac{1}{4} \ln \left[1 + \frac{\sigma_\alpha}{\sigma_0''} + \left(\frac{\sigma_\alpha}{\sigma_0''} \right)^2 \right] + \frac{\sqrt{3}}{2} \tan^{-1} \left[\frac{\sqrt{3} \, (\sigma_\alpha / \sigma_0'')}{2 + \sigma_\alpha / \sigma_0''} \right] \quad (22.57)$$

$$\ln \frac{r}{r_\alpha} = - \frac{1}{4} \ln \left[1 + \frac{\sigma_\alpha}{\sigma_0''} + \left(\frac{\sigma_\alpha}{\sigma_0''} \right)^2 \right] - \frac{\sqrt{3}}{2} \tan^{-1} \left[\frac{\sqrt{3}(\sigma_\alpha / \sigma_0'')}{2 + (\sigma_\alpha / \sigma_0'')} \right] \quad (22.58)$$

The complete solution of a specific problem by this method requires, first, that from Eq. (22.54) or (22.58) the meridian stresses for several values of the radius r be determined; then the wall thicknesses at the same points are determined from Eq. (22.51) or (22.57).

22.9. Stresses and Strains in Frictionless Deep Drawing

Deep drawing of a cup from a circular plane blank is closely related to the process of tube sinking and is governed by similar fundamental equations, with the important difference, however, that deep drawing is a nonsteady process during which the outer radius of the blank decreases continuously. Furthermore, the initial phases of the process are not clearly defined, and only after the cup begins to emerge at the exit of the die does the inside radius become constant and equal to the die radius at the exit. Then it becomes possible to analyze the stresses as functions of the instantaneous blank radius; to make the solution complete, this outer radius should be correlated with some independent parameter of the process, such as the stroke of the punch. This can be obtained by using simple geometrical relationships in conjunction with the assumption of constant wall thickness.

When friction between the die and the metal is neglected (in addition to the changes in wall thickness), results of the analysis of tube sinking apply with the proviso that the boundary condition of zero meridian stress, $\sigma_\alpha = 0$, is prescribed at the variable outer radius of the blank b

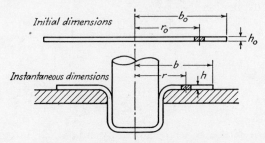

FIG. 22.8. Dimensions in deep drawing.

(see Fig. 22.8). The expressions for stresses then become, for the meridian stress

$$\frac{\sigma_\alpha}{\sigma_0''} = \ln \frac{b}{r} \qquad (22.59)$$

and for the tangential stress

$$\frac{\sigma_\theta}{\sigma_0''} = \ln \frac{b}{r} - 1 \qquad (22.60)$$

The draw stress at the exit section is

$$\left(\frac{\sigma_\alpha}{\sigma_0''}\right)_{r=r_a} = \ln \frac{b}{r_a} \qquad (22.61)$$

Thus the stresses appear to be independent of the die contour, in analogy to what was found in the preceding analyses for tube sinking and reducing.

The first step in the analysis of strains in the deep-drawing process is similar to that for strains in tube sinking. From Saint-Venant's plastic-flow relations one has first

$$\frac{d\bar{\epsilon}_\theta}{d\bar{\epsilon}_h} = \frac{\sigma_\alpha - 2\sigma_\theta}{\sigma_\alpha + \sigma_\theta}$$

and this equation combined with the plasticity condition, $\sigma_\theta - \sigma_\alpha = \sigma_0''$, yields Eq. (22.49),

$$\frac{d\bar{\epsilon}_\theta}{d\bar{\epsilon}_h} = \frac{2 - \sigma_\alpha/\sigma_0''}{2(\sigma_\alpha/\sigma_0'') - 1} \qquad (22.62)$$

At this point the assumption is introduced that Eq. (22.59), based on $h = $ constant, is still valid for the radial stresses, although the blank thickness is changing along the path of a particle. Substituting in Eq. (22.62) the expression from Eq. (22.59), one has

$$\frac{d\bar{\epsilon}_\theta}{d\bar{\epsilon}_h} = \frac{2 - \ln (b/r)}{2 \ln (b/r) - 1} \tag{22.63}$$

On the other hand, the definition of the logarithmic strain increment furnishes the expression

$$d\bar{\epsilon}_\theta = \frac{dr}{r} = d\left(\ln \frac{r}{r_0}\right)$$

and with this, solving for $d\bar{\epsilon}_h$, one has

$$d\bar{\epsilon}_h = d\left(\ln \frac{r}{r_0}\right) \frac{2 \ln (b/r)}{2 - \ln b/r) - 1} \tag{22.64}$$

The transverse strain $\bar{\epsilon}_h$ is obtained by numerical integration of this equation along the path of a particle, the initial radius of which is r_0, when the outer blank radius is b_0. Such a procedure requires that the ratios r/r_0 and r/b be expressed as functions of two parameters, for example, b/b_0, which characterizes the straining process, and r_0/b_0, which represents the initial location of the particle. Hill (1950) suggested that a correlation between the quantities r, r_0, b, and b_0 be derived from the assumption that at any instant the wall thickness is uniform between the outer blank radius b and the particle radius r. Then, the constancy of the annular volume comprised between these two radii is expressed by

$$\pi(b^2 - r^2)h = \pi(b_0^2 - r_0^2)h_0 \tag{22.65}$$

On the other hand, it is known that the particles on the blank rim are in a state of uniaxial stress, because $(\sigma_\alpha)_b = 0$, and that consequently the state of strain in the incompressible plastic material must be such that

$$\bar{\epsilon}_h = \bar{\epsilon}_\alpha = -\frac{\bar{\epsilon}_\theta}{2}$$

Introducing the definitions of the logarithmic strains, $\bar{\epsilon}_\theta = \ln (b/b_0)$ and $\bar{\epsilon}_h = \ln (h/h_0)$, one obtains the relation

$$\frac{h_0}{h} = \sqrt{\frac{b}{b_0}} \tag{22.66}$$

Substituting this relationship in Eq. (22.65) and rearranging, one has the equation

$$b^2 - r^2 = \sqrt{\frac{b}{b_0}} (b_0^2 - r_0^2) \tag{22.67}$$

which can be solved for the two required ratios to obtain

$$\left(\frac{r}{r_0}\right)^2 = \sqrt{\frac{b}{b_0}} - \left(\frac{b_0}{b}\right)^2 \left[\sqrt{\frac{b}{b_0}} - \left(\frac{b}{b_0}\right)^2\right] \tag{22.68}$$

$$\left(\frac{r}{b}\right)^2 = 1 - \left(\frac{b_0}{b}\right)^3 \left[1 - \left(\frac{r_0}{b_0}\right)^2\right] \tag{22.69}$$

Sachs (1930) determined the strain distribution in deep drawing experimentally and also numerically from Eq. (22.64); see also Swift's work (1943).

REFERENCES

CARLSON, R. K., "An Experimental Investigation of the Nosing of Shells," *ASME Symposium on Forging of Steel Shells*, 1944.

HILL, R., "The Mathematical Theory of Plasticity," pp. 282–287, Oxford University Press, New York, 1950.

NÁDAI, A., "Plastic State of Stress in Curved Shells: The Forces Required for Forging of the Nose of High-Explosive Shells," *ASME Symposium on Forging of Steel Shells*, 1944.

NÁDAI, A., The Flow of Metals under Various Stress Conditions, *Inst. Mech. Engrs. (London), J. & Proc.*, Vol. 157, pp. 121–160, 1947.

SACHS, G., "Spanlose Formung," pp. 11–38, Springer-Verlag, Berlin, 1930.

SACHS, G., and W. M. BALDWIN, JR., Stress Analysis of Tube Sinking, *Trans. ASME*, Vol. 68, pp. 655–662, 1946.

SWIFT, H. W., Two-Stage Drawing of Cylindrical Cups, *Trans. Inst. Engrs. Shipbuilders Scot.*, Vol. 195, 1943.

SWIFT, H. W., Stresses and Strains in Tube-drawing, *Phil. Mag.*, Series 7, Vol. 40, pp. 883–902, September, 1949.

CHAPTER 23

BENDING OF PLATES

23.1. Scope of Problem

In Art. 10.2 the bending of beams with narrow rectangular cross section was analyzed under the assumption of a material possessing incompressible elastic behavior up to the yield limit and ideally plastic behavior beyond the yield limit. It was found that simple relations can be obtained by assuming that the deformations of the beam are small compared with the beam dimensions and that the persistence of an elastic nucleus can be expected within such limits of deformation. In the present chapter, still assuming ideally plastic behavior, it will be assumed that large deformations take place and that the extension of the elastic region becomes negligible.

In the range of large strains, the problem of the beam of narrow rectangular cross section, *i.e.*, the plane-stress problem, is not susceptible of a direct analytical treatment because of the large changes in the width of the cross section. Lubahn and Sachs (1950) indicated a method of successive numerical approximation by which such a problem can be handled. The following analysis deals with the problem of bending stresses in a plate under the assumption of plane-strain condition, which presumably represents correctly the behavior of the central portion of a wide plate, *i.e.*, of a beam of very wide rectangular cross section. The problem has its importance in connection with metal-forming processes and with an often-used technological testing method.

23.2. Differential Equation of Equilibrium

Consider a plate deformed by two equal and opposite end couples into a hollow circular cylinder, with inner radius a and outer radius b, while its transverse dimensions (in the direction of the generators of the cylindrical surfaces) remain unchanged. A condition of plane strain exists, and from symmetry it can be concluded that the radial and tangential directions are principal directions of stress, with principal stresses σ_r and σ_θ, and the z direction, parallel to the generators of the cylindrical surfaces, is a principal direction also, with the principal stress

$$\sigma_z = \frac{\sigma_r + \sigma_\theta}{2}$$

(see Fig. 23.1).

266

The distortion-energy condition of plasticity is expressed, as shown in Art. 11.2 by

$$\sigma_r - \sigma_\theta = \pm \frac{2}{\sqrt{3}} \sigma_0 = \pm \sigma_0' \qquad (23.1)$$

For the volume element shown in Fig. 23.1 the equilibrium equation of the radial forces, derived in Art. 8.2, is

$$\frac{d\sigma_r}{dr} = \frac{\sigma_\theta - \sigma_r}{r} \qquad (23.2)$$

or, substituting from Eq. (23.1),

$$\frac{d\sigma_r}{dr} = \pm \frac{\sigma_0'}{r} \qquad (23.3)$$

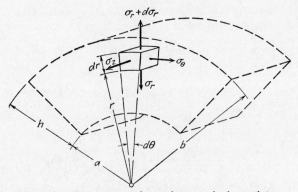

Fig. 23.1. Stresses on volume element of a bent plate.

23.3. Stresses in a Wide Plate Subjected to Bending

The general solution of Eq. (23.3) is obtained, as shown in Art. 8.5, by separating the variables as follows:

$$\frac{\sigma_r}{\sigma_0'} = \pm \ln r + C \qquad (23.4)$$

In the region of tensile tangential stresses, the radial compressive stresses vary from zero at the convex free surface, of radius b, to a maximum at the surface of zero tangential stress or the so-called "neutral surface," of radius r_n. In this region the positive sign applies to the right side of Eq. (23.4), and the constant of integration C is determined from the condition of vanishing radial stress at the outer surface, $r = b$. One obtains $C = -\ln b$ and the stresses

$$\frac{\sigma_r}{\sigma_0'} = \ln \frac{r}{b} \qquad (23.5)$$

$$\frac{\sigma_\theta}{\sigma_0'} = \ln \frac{r}{b} + 1 \qquad (23.6)$$

In the region of compressive tangential stresses, the radial compressive stresses always have smaller absolute values than the tangential stresses, as can be verified later; hence, the negative sign is to be used on the right side of Eq. (23.4), and the following expressions are obtained for the stresses:

$$\frac{\sigma_r}{\sigma_0'} = \ln \frac{a}{r} \qquad (23.7)$$

$$\frac{\sigma_\theta}{\sigma_0'} = \ln \frac{a}{r} - 1 \qquad (23.8)$$

The radius of the instantaneous neutral surface r_n is determined from the condition that for this value of r the two expressions (23.5) and (23.7) furnish identical values of σ_r/σ_0', or

$$\ln \frac{r_n}{b} = \ln \frac{a}{r_n}$$

from which

$$r_n = \sqrt{ab} \qquad (23.9)$$

The distribution of radial, tangential, and transverse stresses is shown in Fig. 23.2 for an example with the particular value of the ratio

$$\frac{h}{a} = \frac{b - a}{a} = 1 \qquad \text{or} \qquad \frac{b}{a} = 2$$

It can be noted that the stress distribution in the outer portion of the plate, between the neutral surface and the convex surface, is the same as that in a fully plastic thick-walled tube subjected to the internal pressure $-(\sigma_\theta)_{r=r_n}$; while the inner portion is subjected to the same stresses as a fully plastic thick-walled tube subjected to the same inward-directed pressure $-(\sigma_\theta)_{r=r_n}$ applied to its outer surface. In other words, the plate in bending can be considered as subjected to the same stresses as two thick-walled tubes, one shrunk onto the other, so as to produce full plasticity in both tubes.

The above analysis was given by Lubahn and Sachs (1950) and, independently, by Hill (1950). Hill has shown also that the stresses on a cross section of the plate yield zero resultant, in consistence with the pure bending condition,

$$\int_a^b \sigma_\theta \, dr = \sigma_0' \left[\int_a^{\sqrt{ab}} \left(\ln \frac{a}{r} - 1 \right) dr + \int_{\sqrt{ab}}^b \left(\ln \frac{r}{b} + 1 \right) dr \right] = 0 \quad (23.10)$$

and that their resultant couple per unit width has the moment

$$M = \int_a^b \sigma_\theta r \, dr = \sigma_0' \left[\int_a^{\sqrt{ab}} \left(\ln \frac{a}{r} - 1 \right) r \, dr + \int_{\sqrt{ab}}^b \left(\ln \frac{r}{b} + 1 \right) dr \right]$$

$$= \sigma_0' \frac{(b - a)^2}{4} = \frac{\sigma_0' h^2}{4} \tag{23.11}$$

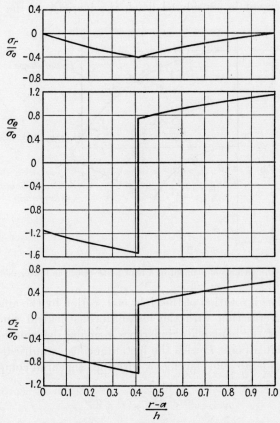

FIG. 23.2. Example of stress distribution in bent plate; $h/a = 1$.

23.4. Strains in a Wide Plate in Bending

The solution for stresses obtained in the preceding article is not complete unless the dimensions of the deformed plate are known. The following analysis of strains is similar to that given by Hill (1950) and permits establishing relationships between the initial and the deformed dimensions of the plate.

Figure 23.3 shows an element of the plate of unit width, initially bounded by two plane cross sections. The initial length of the plate is L_0, and its original thickness h_0. After deformation the plate element becomes an annular sector, with inner radius a, outer radius b, and the two end faces making the angle α. During an additional deformation of the plate, the inner radius changes to $a + da$, the outer radius to $b + db$, and the angle α changes into $\alpha + d\alpha$. If, for example, the left face of the plate element is considered fixed, the increase in the angle α can

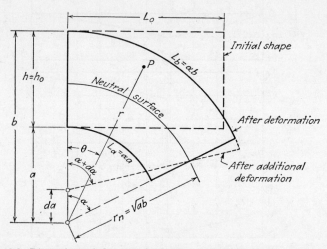

FIG. 23.3. Dimensions of element of a bent plate before and after deformation.

be visualized as a rotation of the right end section by the angle $d\alpha$ about its line of intersection with the instantaneous neutral surface. Since every sector of the bent plate undergoes a similar deformation, it can be concluded that a point P with the instantaneous cylindrical coordinates r and θ will undergo a displacement, with the tangential component

$$u_\theta = (r - r_n)\frac{\theta}{\alpha}\,d\alpha \qquad (23.12)$$

and with the radial component u_r, a function of the radial coordinate r only. Then the logarithmic strain increments are obtained from the equations

$$d\bar{\epsilon}_r = \frac{du_r}{dr} \qquad (23.13)$$

and

$$d\bar{\epsilon}_\theta = \frac{u_r}{r} + \frac{1}{r}\frac{\partial u_\theta}{\partial \theta} \qquad (23.14)$$

In the latter equation, u_r/r is the tangential strain due to the radial displacement, and $\frac{1}{r}\frac{\partial u_\theta}{\partial \theta}$ is due to the tangential displacement.

The volume-constancy equation, for the plane-strain condition assumed here, is $d\bar{\epsilon}_r + d\bar{\epsilon}_\theta = 0$, or by substituting the expressions from Eqs. (23.13) and (23.14),

$$\frac{du_r}{dr} + \frac{u_r}{r} + \frac{1}{r}\frac{\partial u_\theta}{\partial \theta} = 0 \tag{23.15}$$

From Eq. (23.12) one has by partial differentiation

$$\frac{\partial u_\theta}{\partial \theta} = (r - r_n)\frac{d\alpha}{\alpha}$$

which, substituted in Eq. (23.15), yields the differential equation

$$\frac{du_r}{dr} + \frac{u_r}{r} + \left(1 - \frac{r_n}{r}\right)\frac{d\alpha}{\alpha} = 0 \tag{23.16}$$

The general integral of this equation is

$$u_r = \frac{C}{r} - \frac{d\alpha}{\alpha}\left(\frac{r}{2} - r_n\right) \tag{23.17}$$

from which

$$\frac{du_r}{dr} = -\frac{C}{r^2} - \frac{d\alpha}{2\alpha} = d\bar{\epsilon}_r = -d\bar{\epsilon}_\theta \tag{23.18}$$

The integration constant C is determined from the condition that

$$(d\bar{\epsilon}_\theta)_{r=r_n}$$

from which

$$C = -\frac{r_n^2}{2\alpha}$$

and

$$d\bar{\epsilon}_\theta = -d\bar{\epsilon}_r = \frac{d\alpha}{2\alpha}\left(1 - \frac{r_n^2}{r^2}\right) \tag{23.19}$$

The change in plate thickness dh is obtained from the integral

$$dh = \int_a^b d\bar{\epsilon}_r\, dr = \frac{d\alpha}{2\alpha}\int_a^b \left(\frac{ab}{r^2} - 1\right) dr = 0 \tag{23.20}$$

i.e., the plate thickness remains unchanged, $h = h_0$, during the bending deformation.

The relationship between the initial length L_0, the final length of the inner fiber L_a, and that of the outer fiber L_b, is obtained by expressing the volume constancy of the entire plate element shown in Fig. 23.3.

$$L_0 h_0 = \frac{L_a + L_b}{2} h_0 \qquad \text{or} \qquad L_0 = \frac{L_a + L_b}{2} \tag{23.21}$$

Substituting $L_a = \alpha a$ and $L_b = \alpha b$, one has

$$L_0 = \frac{\alpha}{2} (a + b) \tag{23.22}$$

Finally, the conventional strain of the inner and outer fibers ϵ_a and ϵ_b is obtained from

$$\epsilon_a = -\epsilon_b = \frac{L_a}{L_0} - 1 = -\frac{1}{1 + 2a/h} \tag{23.23}$$

REFERENCES

HILL, R., "The Mathematical Theory of Plasticity," pp. 287–292, Oxford University Press, New York, 1950.

LUBAHN, J. D., and G. SACHS, Bending of an Ideal Plastic Metal, *Trans. ASME*, Vol. 72, pp. 201–208, 1950.

INDEX

A

B

C

D

E

273